CHILDREN IN COLLECTIVES

CHILDREN IN COLLECTIVES

Child-rearing Aims and Practices in the Kibbutz

Edited by

PETER B. NEUBAUER, M.D.
Director, Child Development Center
New York, New York

CHARLES C THOMAS · PUBLISHER
Springfield · Illinois · U.S.A.

Published and Distributed Throughout the World by
CHARLES C THOMAS • PUBLISHER
BANNERSTONE HOUSE
301-327 East Lawrence Avenue, Springfield, Illinois, U.S.A.
NATCHEZ PLANTATION HOUSE
735 North Atlantic Boulevard, Fort Lauderdale, Florida, U.S.A.

With THOMAS BOOKS careful attention is given to all details of manufacturing and design. It is the Publisher's desire to present books that are satisfactory as to their physical qualities and artistic possibilities and appropriate for their particular use. THOMAS BOOKS will be true to those laws of quality that assure a good name and good will.

Printed in the United States of America
N-1

PARTICIPANTS - ISRAELI INSTITUTE

MONI ALON
Teacher
Board of Education
Hasorea, Israel

EDITH ALT
Director, Division of Community Resources
Health Insurance Plan of Greater New York
New York, New York

HERSCHEL ALT
Executive Vice-President
Jewish Board of Guardians
New York, New York

E. JAMES ANTHONY, M.D.
Blanche F. Ittleson Professor of Child Psychiatry
Director, Division of Child Psychiatry
Washington University School of Medicine
St. Louis, Missouri

MOSHE AYALON
Special Teacher
Oranim Child Guidance Clinic
Kiryat-Tivon, Israel

NOOMI BEN ISRAEL
Educator
Board of Education
Beit-Alpha, Israel

VIOLA W. BERNARD, M.D.
Clinical Professor of Psychiatry
Director, Division of Community Psychiatry
Columbia Univeristy
New York, New York

BARBARA BIBER, Ph.D.
Distinguished Research Scholar
Bank Street College of Education
New York, New York

v

LEON EISENBERG, M.D.
Professor of Child Psychiatry
The Johns Hopkins University School of Medicine
Psychiatrist-in-Charge
Children's Psychiatric Service
Children's Medical and Surgical Center
Johns Hopkins Hospital
Baltimore, Maryland

MENAHEM GERSON, Ph.D.
Board of Directors
Oranim
Kiryat-Tivon, Israel

JUDIT GILAN, Ph.D.
Clinical Psychologist
Oranim Child Guidance Clinic
Kiryat-Tivon, Israel

MARIANNE GOLDBERGER, M.D.
Psychiatrist
Children's Hospital of the District of Columbia
Washington, D.C.

HILDE T. HIMMELWEIT, Ph.D.
Reader in Social Psychology
Head of Psychology Department
London School of Economics & Political Science
University of London
London, England

EMI HURWITZ
Director
Child Guidance Clinic
Ichud Hakibbuzim, Israel

ELI ILAN, M.A.
Child Psychologist
Ministry of Health
Jerusalem, Israel

ELIZABETH E. IRVINE, M.A., A.A.P.S.W.
Senior Psychiatric Social Worker
Department for Children and Parents
Tavistock Clinic
Senior Tutor
Advanced Casework Course
Tavistock Institute for Human Relations
London, England

MORDECHAI KAFFMANN, M.D.
Child Psychiatrist
Oranim Child Guidance Clinic
Kiryat-Tivon, Israel

MARIETTA KARPE, M.S.S.
Psychiatric Social Worker
Child Guidance Clinic
New Britain, Connecticut

RICHARD KARPE, M.D.
Assistant Clinical Professor
Yale Medical School
New Haven, Connecticut
Consulting Psychiatrist
Connecticut Valley Hospital
Middletown, Connecticut

ERIKA KNOLLER, M.A.
Child Psychologist
Oranim Child Guidance Clinic
Kiryat-Tivon, Israel

MARIANNE KRIS, M.D.
Psychiatrist
Faculty, The New York Psychoanalytic Institute
New York, New York

PROFESSOR SHLOMOH KUGELMASS
Department of Psychology
Hebrew University
Jerusalem, Israel

NECHAMA LEVI
Educator
Board of Education
Ramat Jochanan, Israel

GIDEON LEWIN
Lecturer on Child Psychology
Board of Directors
Oranim
Kiryat-Tivon, Israel

AVIVA MANDEL
Nursery Teacher
Ma'agan Michael, Israel

RACHEL MANOR, M.A.
Psychiatric Social Worker
Oranim Child Guidance Clinic
Kiryat-Tivon, Israel

GUSTI MELZER, M.A.
Psychiatric Social Worker
Oranim Child Guidance Clinic
Kiryat-Tivon, Israel

JEHUDA MESSINGER
Board of Directors
Oranim
Kiryat-Tivon, Israel

SHMUEL NAGLER, Ph.D.
Psychologist-Director
Oranim Child Guidance Clinic
Kiryat-Tivon, Israel

PETER B. NEUBAUER, M.D.
Director, Child Development Center
New York, New York
Associate Clinical Professor
Division of Psychoanalytic Education
Downstate Medical Center
State University of New York
Brooklyn, New York

FRITZ REDL, Ph.D.
Distinguished Professor of Behavioral Sciences
Wayne State University
Detroit, Michigan

MIRYAM ROT, M.A.
Teacher of Pedagogic
Oranim
Kiryat-Tivon, Israel

J. A. M. SCHOUTEN, M.D.
Psychiatrist Psychiatric Department
University of Utrecht
Utrecht, Holland

MORDECHAI SEGAL
Director
Oranim
Kiryat-Tivon, Israel

CHAVAH SHAMIR
Teacher
Board of Education
Shaar Hagolan, Israel

SHIMON STERN
Teacher
Board of Education
Kfar Szold, Israel

THELMA M. WILLIAMS, Ed.D.
Assistant Superintendent
Children's Institutions
Department of Welfare
New York, New York

PROFESSOR HEINRICH ZVI WINNIK
Psychiatrist
Associate Professor of Psychiatry
Hebrew University Medical School
Jerusalem, Israel

CHARLOTTE B. WINSOR, M.A.
Director, Division of Teacher Education
Bank Street College of Education
New York, New York

HELEN L. WITMER, Ph.D.
Director, Division of Research
U. S. Children's Bureau
Washington, D.C.

ANNA KRIS WOLFF, M.D.
Assistant in Psychiatry
Beth Israel Hospital
Harvard Medical School
Cambridge, Massachusetts
Staff, James Jackson Putnam Children's Center
Roxbury, Massachusetts

INVITED GUESTS - ISRAELI INSTITUTE

SARAH FAIANS-GLUECK, Ph.D.
Head, Department of Nursery Teachers
Ministry of Education
Jerusalem, Israel

HAIM GILAN, Ph.D.
Clinical Psychologist
Oranim Child Guidance Clinic
Kiryat-Tivon, Israel

STEPHEN GOLDSTON, Ed.D.
Training Specialist
Training and Manpower Resources Branch
National Institute of Mental Health
Bethesda, Maryland

ADA HAGARI, M.A.
Clinical Psychologist
Oranim Child Guidance Clinic
Kiryat-Tivon, Israel

NATASHA JOSEFOWITZ
Former Research Assistant
Child Development Center;
Member, Management Committee
Child Development Center
New York, New York

ALLEN E. MARANS, M.D.
Child Psychiatrist—Pediatrician
Research Associate
Department of Psychiatry
Children's Hospital of the District of Columbia
Washington, D. C.

EDITH MARKS
Former President
Management Committee
Child Development Center
New York, New York

MICHAEL NATAN, M.A.
Psychologist
Board of Education
Beit Keshet, Israel

HELEN B. REDL, Ed.D.
Former Visiting Professor and Research Consultant
Detroit, Michigan

RIVKA RIKLESS
Board of Education
Ashdot Yaakov, Israel

GLORIA ROSS
Vice-Chairman
Management Committee
Child Development Center
New York, New York

J. W. SCHOUTEN-VAN SETERS
Psychologist
Child Guidance Clinic
Research in Early Development
Holland

MARTIN WOLINS, D.S.W.
Associate Professor
School of Social Welfare
University of California
Berkeley, California

PREFACE

HERE IS A SOCIETY CREATED by modern man to find new ways of reaching fulfillment for the individual, with equal consideration for all, by a sharp change in its traditions and institutions: the kibbutz.

In order to understand its aims, one does not need to search through a clouded past expressed in myth. In order to understand the personality characteristics of its adults, one must not only study its mode of child-rearing, but also listen to the founders of the kibbutz and to their well-defined reasons for the changes they have initiated with regard to their own background, in order to attain this new child-care and educational program. The integration of economic, cultural and political forces into a planned unity of social fabric is what makes the kibbutz so unique. No wonder it has received so much attention from social scientists and practitioners all over the world! The number of people living in the kibbutzim may be small, yet great is the significance of this unity of planning, this courage in building a new social image and a new social model, by turning away from tradition.

The one-week Institute held in Israel during the Summer of 1963 provided specialists with a rare opportunity to study and to learn from the kibbutz. There is already an extensive literature on kibbutz education and child development; but this is only a beginning, for long-term, systematic studies have yet to be undertaken.

It is for this reason that we have decided to publish the proceedings of this Institute. Its overall topic was child development; its aim, to make possible an exchange of questions and findings between those directly engaged in kibbutz life and visi-

xiv CHILDREN IN COLLECTIVES

tors "from the outside world." Position papers were the platform for a dialogue designed to sharpen the issues and carry the participants, if not to agreement, then to a fuller understanding than that with which they came.

The generous contributions of The Grant Foundation, Inc.; The Aaron E. Norman Fund, Inc.; the Oversea Foundation, Inc. (Mr. Raphael Recanati) and Mr. and Mrs. Arthur Ross made this Institute and the publication of its proceedings possible.

The Institute was prepared under the auspices of Oranim (the Teachers' College in Israel) and the Child Development Center, New York. Special credit must be given to the Directors of Oranim; to Dr. Gideon Lewin, for his collaboration in the planning of the program, and to Natasha Josefowitz, for her tireless effort as Project Assistant. Finally, we are especially grateful to Harold Collins, our Editorial Assistant, for his excellent work on the preparation of this document.

PETER B. NEUBAUER, M.D.
Director, Child Development Center

INTRODUCTION

T HE INSTITUTE ON "Child Development in Kibbutzim" brought together for discussion kibbutz representatives whose field is the psychology of education and scientists from abroad. Research workers in education and psychology have a quite understandable desire to study the influence of collective life on educational methods and on the personality of the child. They are in danger, however, of starting from a narrow professional view, which does not take into account the wider social processes. Kibbutz representatives, on the other hand, being as close as they are to the subject, are in equal danger of being strongly biased.

During the course of these discussions, it seemed that the "two sides" had overcome these pitfalls and the material that follows proves this. Now we must ask what special interest the Israel kvutzah had in holding such discussions. One of our purposes was to bring before the wider public reliable material on the progress in communal education, and its psychological, pedagogical and social implications. Articles are published all over the world about these things, on the basis of information gained at second or third hand. Sometimes these are mere impressions, but often they are the results of a scientific, social or political prejudice. The kibbutz therefore has a vital interest in putting the facts in their proper light and in presenting them in their connection with the kibbutz society.

Furthermore, our intention was to examine educational and psychological conceptions from both the theoretical and the practical points of view. The question of infant care is not to be answered solely in terms of scientific truths, which often serve social aims at the same time that they give expression to them. Consider, for example, the status of woman in society and in the family, or the task of the family, in a society which guides child care and gives it a higher meaning. Psychological and pedagogical conceptions that have become axiomatic in Western scientific literature, such as separation, maternal repression, fear of strangers, group dynamics, and many others, change their meaning under different circumstances, and may even cease to be axioms.

It is the difficult task of communal educators to examine conceptions derived from different social conditions and to try to adapt them to communal education — or, if this is not possible, to discard them. This can only be done by serious discussion and a friendly exchange of views with scientists who combine their knowledge of education, psychology, medicine, anthropology and sociology with a tolerant and enlightened view of life in its different shades. It is just such a discussion that is presented to us in this publication.

A wide latitude of expression was given to the scientific authority of the participants — with, however, one limitation. Academically derived scientific conceptions often came face to face with ideological and psychological conceptions that had their roots in everyday reality. At such times, stringent scientific authority was felt to clash with the experience of the collective way of life, which no longer requires scientific "confirmation."

We welcome the presentation of these findings to the public, in the hope that they will help deepen the understanding of the educational problems of children and youth, wherever these may occur. We would like to believe that this account of the development of the child in the kibbutz reveals the facts about communal education and kibbutz life, primarily by putting them in their correct light.

Thanks are due to all who participated in this symposium — to the Israelis from the kibbutzim as well as to our guests from afar.

GIDEON LEWIN
SHIMON STERN
NECHAMA LEVI

★ ★ ★

The following are introductory messages delivered to the Institute by Dr. S. Faians-Glueck, Mr. Gideon Lewin, and Dr. Peter Neubauer.

DR. FAIANS-GLUECK:

Distinguished Guests:

I bring you the greetings of the Ministry of Education and Culture, as well as my own hopes for a successful conference. We welcome the guests who have come from the U.S.A., Europe and Israel to participate in it.

We regard this international conference on child development in communal education as a very important event. During the fifty years of their existence, the communal settlements have succeeded in bringing up thousands of children to follow their ideals and their modes of life. These include: strong ties to the land, pride in labor, and the readiness to share one's life with one's fellow man. Since its inception, the communal settlement has gone through many changes, and so has its educational system. In spite of these changes, the great majority of the settlement's children continue in the footsteps of the founding fathers, hoping to approach the age-old goal of the greater part of humanity — the creation of a constructive and peaceful world.

The studies that have been made of communal education indicate that it answers the needs of a communal society. Good will and friendship are outstanding in this children's society, even among the very young age groups. To this day, there is no record of juvenile delinquency or crime among children of the communal settlements. Yet, in spite of these achievements of communal education, there still remain unresolved problems and difficulties. A methodical study of the system as a whole — knowledge of the reasons for its successes and the sources of its difficulties — will contribute to a better understanding, not only of this particular system of education, but of education in general, in Israel and elsewhere.

★ ★ ★

GIDEON LEWIN:

Much has been written about kibbutz life and kibbutz education. Most of the researchers have regarded the kibbutz as a sort of experiment — a social, educational and human experiment. As such, it has been measured according to values that often do not fit our kibbutz society. This has given rise to many misunderstandings.

We are not an experiment; we are *living* a certain way of life. We are eager to learn how that way of life influences our children's development, and we wonder whether we can contribute to the understanding of child development in general. To quote the late David Rapaport: "The scientific problem is not whether collective education is good or bad. Even if that were the question, we would have to ask further: good or bad *for whom* and *for what?*"

If one really wants to understand child development in the kibbutzim, one has to rid oneself of certain traditional misapprehensions, and to take care not to turn concepts into prejudices. With that sort of openmindedness, one may be able to gain insight and understanding, difficult as this often is to achieve.

We are happy to have you with us. This is the first time that a whole group of outstanding scholars in education, psychology and psychiatry from different countries have come to us to study, to learn and to teach. We hope that this will be an informal meeting of free discussions, questions and answers, intensive work and mutual understanding.

This Institute has aroused a good deal of interest in our country. We had decided to limit participation to kibbutz members only, with a very few exceptions — for example, Professor Winnik, Dr. Faians-Glueck of the Ministry of Education, Mr. Eli Ilan of the Ministry of Health. We made this restriction in order to keep the group within the limits of effective work. Israeli scientists who are eager to study child development in collective education, we thought, can do so the whole year round.

During the fifty years of kibbutz life, many things have changed. Today we already have a second and third generation of kibbutzniks. Thousands of our sons and daughters are already adults and parents; they have finished their military service and joined their kibbutzim. We may say, with the greatest modesty, that it was the kibbutz and its educational system that provided the proper conditions for their social and educational development, and endowed them as completely as possible for their way of life.

Finally, allow me to thank Dr. Peter Neubauer, without whose efforts and initiative this Institute would never have taken place. And to all of you, thank you for being with us. Let this be a week of cooperation and learning!

★   ★   ★

Dr. Peter Neubauer:

It is a privilege for those of us who have come from outside the collective to have this opportunity to meet with our colleagues from the kibbutz, in order to exchange experiences and to discuss our common professional interests. In the past, researchers have often studied kibbutz life and kibbutz children, employing methods applicable to other conditions, but without enjoying the collaboration of professional workers from the kibbutz itself. Whatever our theories, whatever insight we have derived from the numerous writings on kibbutz education, we are indeed fortunate to be able to gain the reactions of those who are or have been direct participants in kibbutz life. This is a unique opportunity.

We all realize, I am certain, that one week's deliberations are not a substitute for research, nor can such an Institute hope to arrive at final conclusions on the basis of data presented here for discussion.

Let us restate the aims of this Institute. We from the outside do not look upon ourselves as "consultants," nor as authorities on specific problems of kibbutz education and child care. We have come here to share with you our questions, including problems that we find in our own work, and to learn from you about those aspects of kibbutz child-rearing that may be applicable to our own. We do not claim to have discovered the best child-rearing procedures; an examination of how children fare under different circumstances will enable us to check on our practices and our theoretical formulations. We have little doubt, from past experience, that such an exchange of thought, the opportunity to think with others about similar interests, can be quite productive. Even though we may come to no conclusions, we should arrive at a new approach to old questions, perhaps at a new set of questions on matters that we have routinely accepted thus far.

Our expectation of what we can learn from this meeting is not altogether unfocused; our previous knowledge of the conditions of collective life was certain to have elicited in us some rather specific questions. Many here, particularly from America, have come with certain topics in mind, on which our inquiries will have a direct bearing. I mention these few, but not as our proposal for an agenda:

1. GROUP LIVING OF VERY YOUNG CHILDREN. There is a trend among us towards the establishment of more nursery schools for children, and the question has arisen as to what is the most appropriate starting age for group experiences among children. Three has been generally considered the earliest age for nursery attendance; but does the total care of the child before that age *have to be individual?* Or is it possible to have groups of children at an earlier age? What should be the format of such groups? their size? the ratio of adults to children? There are many children in America for whom, because of the absence of both parents, or because of other circumstances that have made care by members of the family impossible, the community has to establish child-care programs. Institutional care has fallen into disrepute, while individual care, by way of foster-home placement, has raised many questions. Day care of such children has become an alternative and, with it, the possibility of bringing groups of children together, even during their first years of life. In spite of the very different social conditions in which the group care of children takes place in a kibbutz, we hope to learn from your experience in this respect.

2. MULTIPLE MOTHERING. There is a long history of other people assisting mothers in their child-care responsibilities. The upper classes and even the middle class have made extensive use of this over the centuries, and the procedure has rarely been questioned as it has been when the poor and underprivileged are forced to seek similar assistance. The question that we in the United States today must face is that of the responsibility of the state to step in when the most minimal care for the development of children is absent. Since the deprived child often falls within the province of the community's child-welfare program, the issue arises of how to care for infants and young children in the absence of, or in collaboration with, the mother. The kibbutz example, naturally, would give us the greatest insight into the latter problem — not of substitute care, but of *coordinated* care. How can we set up a *collaborative system* between the nurse and the mother, so that the care of the child does not become unduly fragmented?

3. MENTAL HEALTH PLANNING FOR THE COMMUNITY. The trend in our society is towards the establishment of comprehensive community services. By their very nature, they must be regional; furthermore, they should include not only those in

need of help, but also those who are healthy. The kibbutz is a unique "region," in which a comprehensive mental health program can be outlined with greater likelihood of success. The fact that it is a geographic entity, the stability of the population, the mutual interests and aims of all its members — these should permit the establishment of comprehensive programs under especially favorable circumstances. When are disturbed members of the kibbutz separated from the community and assigned to special facilities? How many such problems can be absorbed and managed within this society? How can education, health, and social planning be integrated so that each can make its contribution to the individual in trouble?

There have been many who desired to take part in this conference. We wish that this could have been possible, but proceedings designed for an exchange of thoughts and for the exploration of new questions and new ideas must be limited as to the number of participants. Furthermore, various professional positions are represented here. We are quite happy to have succeeded in bringing together educators, psychologists, child-rearing personnel, sociologists, therapists and psychiatrists from outside the kibbutz, as well as from the kibbutzim. Collectives that base themselves on different ideological positions are represented here, giving us a chance to see how different programs influence patterns of child care, and how these, in turn, affect development.

No limits will be imposed on any participant as to where his imagination may lead him, or what connections he chooses to establish between the data presented and those stemming from his own experiences. This conference is set up, rather, as an open-end discussion, in which we are all invited to learn and to think, without the responsibility for final formulations.

This is a new experiment in international institutes. Such meetings will take place more and more often, and we shall all have to learn how to make the most of them. Some of the international meetings follow the pattern of national conferences; they are usually of shorter duration than this one, though some are longer. It may be important to the participants, as well as to many others, just how we proceed here and how successful our format proves to be. After the first day's discussion, which will outline the general frame of reference of the collective society, and the place of child-rearing within it, we shall have an opportunity to spend a day in a collective — in order to see what we are talking about, but more than that, in order to give us a chance to exercise our faculty of observation.

What will be the impressions of skilled observers? What will be our reactions to direct exposure? How much uniformity or diversity of opinion will we collect and bring back? How generalizable will our impressions be? The reactions of our Israeli colleagues to our reports will permit us to obtain a measure of the correctness of our observational data. After this, we shall divide into groups, each to take up a particular topic. Following this period of exploration, the high points of the discussions will be presented to the total group. This, then, is the general outline of our program. A free and open spirit will surely make this a most valuable undertaking.

CONTENTS

CHILDREN IN COLLECTIVES

Chapter I

FUNDAMENTAL CONCEPTS

THEORY AND AIMS OF KIBBUTZ EDUCATION
Mordechai Segal

It would be well for us to keep in mind that kibbutz education is a *planned system,* not a "tradition." It has been thought
out, by its founders, at least as far as its aims and its lines of
structure are concerned. I do not mean, of course, that we started
from nothing; on the contrary, we have had a very rich heritage.
We inherited the fruits of our national educational history, which
is very old and very rich. The Jewish people had a democratic
system of education for boys as early as the beginning of the
Christian era, and its history shows its long-standing consciousness of the role of education. It has provided a welcome atmosphere for education and established a more or less spiritual relationship between teacher and student.

There is also the socialist inheritance — by which I do not
mean only the socialist ideology (that is, of course, the central
theme of kibbutz education), but the main ideas on education
derived from socialist thought, such as the societal aspect of education and the linking of study with productive manual labor. Last,
but not least, kibbutz education has organic links with the new
education — "progressive" education in modern society. There
have also been special influences in different quarters of the kibbutz movement: the Central European influence, the influence of
the youth movements, and the Eastern European influences.

We have conducted our education in line with our kibbutz
aims: first of all, to raise a kibbutz type of man, who will be — as
the result of his education — fit to go on with kibbutz life. The
founders of the kibbutz, as well as the people who now make it
up, are very obstinately intent on remaining in history. We have
always been conscious of those communes that sprang up in differ-

ent parts of the world and, after one generation, disappeared. We intend to remain, and we find the key to that aspiration in education — which has been and still is the central thought for the kibbutz.

There now exist a second and third generation of people fit to continue our way of living. Kibbutz members are much more equal in the field of education than in any others. The first step toward the equalization of opportunities — emotional, social and cultural opportunities — for both sexes has seemed to us to be to relieve the mother of her daily child-rearing tasks. Finally, we must mention the rationalization and modernization of the educational process that has been characteristic of the kibbutz community — which is not a monastic commune. On the contrary, the kibbutz is very much interested in the scientific, social, cultural, and artistic developments of modern society, and of course in education.

What are our psychopedagogical assets in education? First, a new socializing factor: the children's home, which is intended to possess rich activities and rich contents — work activities, social activities, study and play activities, etc. It should be, in that way, a feeding-ground for the society — not only for kibbutz society in particular, but for society in general.

Our second asset has been the integration of the educational environments: filling the gaps between organized education and home, and between school and society. We are not, of course, closed up within walls; there takes place a certain filtering of influences from the outside, as they rush into the children's homes.

Thirdly, we believe that the "multiple mothering" involved in shared child-rearing between a family and the children's home, should bring about a healthier child life. These are our basic ideals and our educational assets, as we have gone on with our practice.

This is one side of the picture; the other side has to do with the problems of realization. Perhaps our first aim — to educate the new generation for kibbutz life — can be considered to have been achieved to a very great extent. More than 90 per cent of our sons and daughters have stayed in the kibbutz so far, and the third generation from the older kibbutzim is now coming on.

Those who leave do so mainly for reasons that are not central to the kibbutz educational situation. Children who have felt frustrated — mainly owing to their family relations and their own life history — may drop out after military service, which gives an opportunity to our young people to know better and more clearly the world outside of the kibbutz.

Another reason for leaving has been the striving for an academic or artistic career. Although the kibbutz is providing for these more and more, our young people may have easier and better opportunities in those directions outside the kibbutz, and some of them leave for that very reason. The question of fully equal educational opportunities implies, of course, differentiation. There is still too much uniformity in secondary education in the kibbutzim; providing as much differentiation as we would like to have is not easy in small schools. So far as the equality between the sexes are concerned, women have come into full social rights in the kibbutz, yet the education of girls is still lagging.

As to the modernization of education, very large numbers of prepared workers are required. These include not only school teachers and kindergarten teachers, but also, and mainly, the nurses and metaplot and those who keep the children's homes. Previously, many of the metaplot went through a very short training period. Next year we are starting, for the first time, a full year's course for them, but it will still take a long time before most of all metaplot go through the full course.

DISCUSSION

What Is Fundamental?

DR. REDL: There seems to be some anxiety among you about characterizing issues as other than "ideological" or "value" issues, or issues of "faith" and "belief." Once they fall into those categories, we cannot, of course, be specific about them any longer. The attitude appears to be something like this: "What good will it do to tell those nice people about some of our problems? They couldn't do anything about them, anyway; in fact, they might even come up with something unpleasant and challenging, which we really couldn't make use of, because it would contradict our basic goals."

Up to a point, you may be quite right. It is obvious that in a planned society, there *are* certain value issues involved, which go beyond any speculation about "technique," and lie outside the realm of "Mental Health and Child Development." On the other hand, in the process of daily work and daily living, one comes to realize that not everything that sails under the flag of "value issue" actually *is* one, nor is it necessarily tied in with basic items of "faith." Sometimes you run into problems that are created — and can be solved — by certain *procedures;* not all of these are "basic" to your fundamental beliefs.

Nevertheless, it is also clear that some of the procedures that we may regard as positive or negative, in terms of *our* overall concept of mental health, may be so intrinsically interwoven with our value system, that you do have the right to say to us: "We regard what we do as basic and we do not want to change it. We would like you to point out to us the problems we may be creating. Then we will have to decide on our own how to mitigate them; or else we may have to consider them as among the prices we must pay for the philosophy we will live by."

What I propose, therefore, is this: Let's delineate more sharply which of the problems that concern us here belong in the category of "basic beliefs," and which can actually be resolved into issues of technique, or of secondary goals, lying well within the range of modification. For instance, the question of the *size of the subgroup* for kids of varying ages would seem to fit in here. The kind of healthy adult you want is for you to define. But if we are able to show that smaller groups in the toddler age are *better designed to attain that sort of adult* than "mass herding," then that is obviously a question on which you ought to be as flexible as you can, without regarding whatever steps you do take as problems of overall philosophy.

In short, I think there are a number of issues than can be separated from the overall "value" and "basic belief" categories, and freely explored. This may also be applicable, in fact, to issues of teaching and instruction. Obviously, you want your school system to have a certain flavor, a certain design and motivational basis, attuned to your basic philosophy of life. Your wider convictions on educational issues remain impregnable, of course.

However, I have no doubt that within that scope will emerge a wide range of issues providing ample and legitimate room for questioning, experimentation, and tryout. An important task, if we only had the time to carry it out, would be to define which issue falls into which category, and then to discuss in ample detail the various alternatives of method — after which we could speculate on the anticipated results, as well as on the price that might have to be paid in each case. With this as our focus, our discussions in this area will become much more specific.

DR. HIMMELWEIT: We outsiders have, I am sure, accepted your value system as our working basis. Our concern is with ways and means of dealing with what I might describe as "secondary questions."

While some of the ways in which child-rearing is handled here may seem to those who view them "from the inside" to represent *essential elements* of the value-system, to us they may appear to be of secondary significance, and thus capable of being changed, with no fundamental loss. We might follow the practice of looking at the debit side and at the credit side of each mode of operation. In order to do this, however, we must be clear about our assumptions.

JEHUDA MESSINGER: The kibbutzim began on the basis of a faith — something that cannot be scientifically proven and stated. We have made statements about equality, for instance, or about cooperation being better than competition, more scientific. But the case could probably have been proven the other way around, as well, for all the scientific data we had.

What we started with, therefore, were some basic concepts, precepts, articles of faith. These still have to be taken, by those who deal with us, as something that *cannot* be changed. One of our articles of faith is the possibility of the "rationalization" of social life, yet we rationalize our *faith*, in that very expression. This probably accounts for the fact that, in the long run, we cannot ask you to help us very much. There is only one way for you to do this: psychiatrists and psychologists would have to *live in the kibbutz*. As a society based on articles of faith, we want to perpetuate our social structure. However, there is the ever-present danger that, in the very effort to perpetuate itself, this society will instead kill itself. We will use science, whenever it fits our basic articles of faith, and wherever it will allow us what we have called "acculturation," as against "assimilation." We are always in danger of assimilating to the general culture around us, which has exerted tremendous pressure on kibbutz culture, and will continue to do so. We cannot, therefore, accept all the values or all the latest research of science, i.e., outside science. We must attempt to take as much of it as will allow us to live within the framework of a foreign culture, and still retain our identity. We must try continuously to adjust a little, and to slowly modify our systems and our techniques of work, and of education, in order to overcome the negative and destructive influence (from our point of view) of the outside society.

This is where we probably can get some help from you; but only if both sides see very well what is needed: *your* understanding that we *will not change* these basic *articles of faith,* and *our* understanding that we *have to accept* certain changes in *details.*

MR. ALT: Over and over again, in discussing any problem, we will have to come back, I am certain, to the fact that you Israelis do have a system of social relations, and of interpersonal relations which is different from ours. We from the outside can only evaluate these experiences from a totally different viewpoint. There is a risk — of which I'm sure everyone here is aware — of our too readily transferring our own experience to your needs. The most you can do, it seems to me, is to react to what we say, incorporate our conclusions and suggestions as you see fit to incorporate them — but always stop and say: Is this really transferable to our experience?

What Is Modifiable?

MRS. WINSOR: Would I be presumptuous in suggesting that the basic tenet of kibbutz philosophy is faith in the value of the pioneering life? Well, then, I have a question: pioneering for *what?*

Suppose we were a group of economists who had come here to talk with you. Have you not very profoundly rationalized your socialist-economic articles of faith? Is it not "for the building of a better life?" The question then becomes: What do you allow yourselves to *cut away* from these basic articles of faith without cutting out their heart? I would also ask how you deal with a changing world that demands a *different expression* of that basic tenet of pioneering.

In the forty or fifty years during which the kibbutz movement has flowered, there has been a congruence between kibbutz philosophy and the social-technological-political scene. At this time, it may be necessary to engage in some philosophical rationalization — not opportunism, but a sober consideration of the significance of contemporaneous change. When we hear about the work of the hand and the soil as a tenet of faith, I am sharply reminded of the fact that I could count on the fingers of my two hands the numbers of people I have actually seen here working on the soil! But tractors are commonplace, and so are refrigerating plants and milk-pasteurization facilities, and I dare say many more mechanized agricultural facilities. All this mechanization may be no more than an extension of the love of the land, and the grand conception of the life of toil. However, it does require new techniques, and with new techniques for production comes the necessity to re-examine the faith that is so deeply grounded in that aspect of life.

We are not economists, however. We are in a much more sensitive area when we are talking about your children and ours — an area in which articles of faith have a far deeper grounding. Therefore, we all need to see that we are *not* abusing your articles of faith when we strive for philosophical questioning; instead, you can view change as part of a continuum, and we can perhaps pose a probing question or two. Would we not then really be moving in *new directions of pioneering,* in a more adult fashion?

My question still remains: pioneering for *what?* The pioneering spirit of this group has had our profoundest admiration; it is that which makes us dare ask: what needs to be done *to move on from here, in the same pioneering spirit?*

NECHAMA LEVI: I am glad to hear questions about our life being brought up here, among the people who came to us from outside. I am very proud of our lives. Still, I get the feeling that we sometimes fail to draw the line between the ideological thinking and the living of our children. We don't sufficiently distinguish their beliefs from their lives. We are so deeply involved in our beliefs that we expect our children to be as deeply involved too, without taking into consideration the fact that *they have their own lives,* as children, and as adolescents.

Throughout the world, in books on psychology and education and research, one deals with children's lives as *lives;* they are connected with family life, with surrounding life, with technical problems and many others. Other people, of course, don't have our kind of problem — building a life that also has ideological and political roots. It is important for us, as psychologists and as educators, to deal with children; yet sometimes *I don't find the child* in all this. We talk about what we can do to strengthen the kibbutz ideal and how to deal with children when they want to leave the kibbutz; but *what about the children themselves?*

As a mother, and as a member of the kibbutz for many years (I hope to stay here till the end of my life, and I hope that my children will stay), the question that occurs to me is how far we can *change our means* from time to time — not so as to *break* our ideological patterns, but in order to *fit* them to the children's needs. Maybe, as we sit here together, we can find the answers. I want us to examine closely the different opinions in our movement, because we are now sitting with people who have come to us from very far and have a perspective. Let us open up the problems, and then perhaps together we will find the strength to change some things, to recognize that some basic ideals we have had may not be altogether basic for this or that age.

I would be the last to want my own children, or anyone else's, to leave our kibbutz, and I think that if we can be flexible in our thinking, our children will be able to find their place within our kibbutzim. But when we are rigid about something, when we say: "No, this is political; this we can't change," it means that *the child* cannot be political — in his mind, perhaps, but not in his emotions, or in his desires.

MRS. WINSOR: You man never come to know the definitive answers to some questions, but you should look with a truly open mind at some of the processes of development in your unique community. To do this, you need to divest yourself, even when you are only going about the business of finding out, of every theory and belief and dogma and article of faith. This must be done quite consciously; you must hammer at precisely those points which you believe are quite well taken care of, because it is likely that these are the very ones that need the most thoughtful reappraisal.

Dr. EISENBERG: An interesting study on values in the kibbutz has been carried out by two Americans who are with the Hebrew University. In it a comparison was made between first- and second-generation kibbutzim. The results showed, briefly, that the second-generation kibbutz revealed much more strength in many of the "values of the kibbutz" than did the first-generation. This would seem to indicate that the educational system has been effective — but primarily with regard to the specific values of the kibbutz. When it came to the broader social values touching on the rest of the world, there were no particular differences between generations.

When you attempt to build a society based on planning, there is a conscious effort to arrange things. Some of the conflicts that then arise look very specific, simply because they have been made explicit. In an unplanned society — which is true of most, or a good part, of the rest of the world — one finds (particularly when the society is a relatively affluent one), a wide tolerance of individual differences because, within that range, the society is still able to perpetuate itself. The less rich the society is, the less flexible can its demands afford to be, and the less choice there is for the individual.

In our society we have an apparent "freedom of choice" (it is, in fact, differentially available to different segments of the population); on the other hand, some of the differences that appear on the surface are less real than they appear to be, mainly because we do not make our planning explicit. That is to say, if we find that there is a shortage of teachers, for example, as we have found in recent years, and if our values are shifting because it is now apparent that we need more engineers, then we raise the salaries for teachers so as to recruit more people into the teaching profession. This is somewhat successful, although there still remains, of course, a tremendous dislocation: it takes a generation to make up for the loss that existed before. Finally you begin to get the desired ratio — probably at a time when the needs have already become different, and you have to shift once more, to another direction.

This kind of unplanned or after-the-fact solution, of course, has as its one virtue the fact that the individual within the society enjoys a good deal of (sometimes only apparent) freedom. When we do start to plan, and make a mistake — then, as a former mayor of New York City used to say, "It's a beaut!" We can throw our society into confusion in a much more far-reaching way than you can. On the other hand, when you make the right decision, you save your society a great deal of difficulty. The problem in offering advice is that we frequently have to make explicit decisions at a time when the information necessary for a careful and complete scientific judgment is not yet available. I should like to emphasize that when you listen to what we have to say, you must bear in mind that we can relate ourselves directly to only one kind of experience, aside from any reading we may have done about another kind of society.

There have been societies in which "freedom of choice" was far more restricted than it is in the kibbutz. What is called "classical Chinese society" — I am speaking now of the society of the upper classes in China, not of the hundreds of millions of peasants — had no room for adolescent rebellion. One did not become a man in ancient classical Chinese society until one was more than forty years old; the period between twenty and forty was called "the green years." In that society, the child did not belong to the mother, but to the grandmother. The anthropologists tell us, for example, that the mother living in the grandmother's house would wait until the grandmother said "My grandchild is crying; go to him!" and then she would go to him.

Now *that* society did preserve itself, up to the point where there was a cataclysm; apparently, it worked for a long period of time. Unfortunately, we have no scientific data about *the cost to young people* of living in such a society.

MR. ALT: It has been said here that the function of education is to *perpetuate* the existing culture. In my view, this is not enough: education must also develop human beings, members of our society who can assume its constant *re-making* and *re-formation,* in the light of added knowledge and experience; otherwise, we have in store for us that which happened to Chinese society. Accordingly, one of the central tasks of education is to develop individuals with the initiative and the imagination to continuously *re-form* — *re-shape* — the social order, in the light of their accumulated knowledge and experience.

What Goals for Education?

MENAHEM GERSON: I regard the following as kibbutz objectives: building the agricultural foundation for the Jewish national home in Israel; the creation and management of a classless society, with equality of manual and intellectual workers, and a high esteem for manual work; safeguarding the needs of the individual, in accordance with the community's tasks and its economic capacity. I think we have to bear these objectives in mind, if we wish to understand the mainstream of kibbutz education. The questions just asked (we are always being asked such questions) do not touch on the central problems we are facing. We have a great thirst here for knowledge in general, but the kibbutz also needs many specialized workers. In the kibbutz itself — both in agriculture and in industry (which is now becoming very strong in the kibbutz economy) — managerial skills are needed for the fulfillment of certain tasks. You need teachers, metaplot. The kibbutz life needs cultural activity as well.

What we must bear in mind are these two things: (1) The problem of the individual career is not the same in our society as it appears to be in American society. (2) We need a lot of talent in order to be able to fulfill our kibbutz tasks. Nevertheless, we have a problem.

Things have changed during the last thirty years. A kibbutz that is just starting has to use its manpower for the tasks of sheer existence, for work, for security; but the kibbutz today is on the verge of a new development, as is the whole of Israel. Specialists are becoming more and more important, and as our children, during their military service, meet other youths from outside the kibbutz, they come to feel the desire to study new things. This is more urgent today than it was twenty years ago, and we feel that we must provide for it. We will have to make provisions for those youngsters who wish to continue study.

DR. EISENBERG: I do not see how, within the kibbutz framework, it would ever be possible to educate people in the areas of higher learning — as physicists, for example. How can a small group of 500 people ever become able to afford even two physicists? Higher education is really an urban function.

MORDECHAI SEGAL: We are not in fact able to provide higher education within the kibbutz — except for teachers' seminaries.

DR. EISENBERG: After someone has completed his training outside, can he then come back to the kibbutz?

MORDECHAI SEGAL: That depends on what he has studied. If he has studied teaching, or medicine, he can come back. The same thing holds for engineering; even artists can find their place in kibbutz life. As far and physicists or philosophers are concerned, they can go on working as kibbutz members — but outside of the kibbutz.

MR. ALT: What are the feelings of your young people about the present limits of education?

MORDECHAI SEGAL: They are not happy with uniform study and demands; they are pushing us in the direction of differentiation.

RACHEL MANOR: Outside the kibbutz, people strive for academic careers; but that is not the general feeling of kibbutz members. It is not the ideal of every one of our youngsters to go to the University; on the contrary, the ideal is to be a tractor-driver, or the organizer of an agricultural branch, etc. Anyone who has special talents will get his special education — *after* secondary school. However, only the *very* talented really put up a fight for it.

EMI HURWITZ: The problem of choice is greater for girls than for boys. Today, the youth are far more eager to study than they were ten to twenty years ago, and some experiments are being made with regard to differentiation in the secondary schools — particularly where technical studies are concerned. Until now, however, these efforts have been important only in the case of boys. The division of work in the kibbutz has changed, so that women are, in fact, excluded from many professions and occupations.

DR. HIMMELWEIT: But how do you deal with the very real differences in intellectual ability that you undoubtedly encounter among the children? How do you avoid a sense of failure on the part of the duller child who is constantly in contact with children better able than he to grasp the various forms of instructions? I realize that the objective — and it is one with which I heartily agree — is to widen the diversity of forms of work from which the child can derive a sense of purpose and self-esteem. But how does this procedure work in practice?

SHMUEL NAGLER: Kibbutz youngsters often become disappointed by the fact that their kibbutz is not ready to handle their special talents and desires for vocational training. This is often true, also, with less gifted children who are unable to keep up with the rest of the class in the theoretical curriculum. We are told that these youngsters are helped a great deal in their studies; in spite of that, they are dragged from grade to grade, suffering from the feeling of being a failure. These children finally come to us as problem students, even though they could have enjoyed the satisfaction of accomplishment in another kind of school curriculum — for instance, in trade schools. Other youngsters who, after completing their kibbutz secondary education, have been eager to further their studies at the high-school levels, are not permitted to do so, except in those rare cases where their professional choice meets specific kibbutz needs. This lack of opportunity for professional decision and training represents an unfilled need of self-realization in professional fields.

There are in the kibbutz great possibilities for self-realization in the arts, and in other cultural activities — especially social and political life. However, in our society, the choice of a profession may be a very important step in the direction of finding one's identity. On the other hand, the greatest advantage that adolescents have in the kibbutz is the fact that they do not live in a "no-man's-land," or in some "not quite" stage. They live in their own society, and have their own definite rights and duties, appreciated and encouraged by the adult society. The psychological reaction of the "marginal man" — feelings of frustration, insecurity, aggression against parents and authority, as their defense against insecurity — are found much less frequently in the kibbutz than in other societies.

Evaluation: Role and Methods

MR. ALT: There is among us a great deal of awareness of concepts of human behavior. There are all sorts of psychological concepts that really stem from other kinds of societies or have their applicability to other kinds of societies. If we were seeking something approaching final answers to the questions that will be raised in our discussions (we'll never get *final* ones, but relatively more final answers), then it seems to me that the kibbutz movement would have to examine its own psychological climate and the elements *within it,* the impact of that climate on the human beings in it, and how they, in turn, sustain or modify it.

DR. HIMMELWEIT: Many problems could be tackled by research — if the different movements could devise ways of carrying out a joint research program. It would be disastrous — and I use that word advisedly — if differences in the political and social orientations of these movements were to stand in the way of such joint research. Without a research operation that cuts *across* the movements, the relative value of different child-rearing techniques cannot really be examined.

Examples of such research problems might include:

1. Sleeping arrangements: How does the sexual map of the adolescent who sleeps in mixed dormitories differ from that of boys and girls whose sleeping arrangements are separate after the onset of puberty?

2. The high school: What are the advantages and what are the disadvantages of having the high school restricted to one kibbutz, as compared with those that would follow from having a joint high school, which provided wider opportunities, as far as the teaching is concerned, *plus* the first experience of living with young people outside of the initial primary group? What sort of children, for example, find it easier to adapt to army life? Which ones are more stimulated intellectually? How do their attitudes toward their family, or their own kibbutz, differ?

3. The educators seem to be very much concerned with the bad consequences of academic failure. But what about failures in social relations, in leadership? May not these also be experiences with a profound effect? What, in fact, are the compensatory factors

available to a child who sees himself a failure in those very fields in which he is far less protected — e.g., in his relations with others?

You have produced so many theories, and yet so little in the way of fact-finding. The balance should now shift: first allow the facts to speak, and then see how far your theories need to be adjusted to fit what is really happening — or how far the actual situations need to be modified, in order to fulfill the purposes of the theory designed for them.

MOSHE AYALON: I would like to hear some discussion about the role of the therapeutic worker in the kibbutz, as well as about the research worker's role. In the future, we must assign a good deal of time and manpower for research work. I am sure that someone from the outside can do it very well — but not without running into problems. A *chaver* from outside can do it — very likely much better — but then there are other problems. It is like what faces a kibbutz member who is trying to do therapeutic work in his kibbutz; in most cases, he will fail. In Oranim, it took years before we were emotionally able to take money from our *chaverim* for treatment. Even now we are not free of this; we work in very close relations, but it is very hard. I am sure that the solution will be along the lines of a Kibbutz team, rather than by inviting in an outsider.

DR. KRIS: We have to be very careful not to overvalue one or the other single factor, and then, on the basis of that evaluation, either perpetuate or do away with the total structure. This admonition not to be prejudiced, or to use one or the other element to "prove one's point," goes for all of us — no matter on which side our present convictions lie.

I remember reading in the literature that was sent to us that mothers react too strongly in the feeding situation — for instance, when a mother is deeply hurt because her cooking has not been accepted by the child. This explanation struck me as somewhat strange. In our area, the "feeding problem" seems to have practically disappeared; the idea that pressure on the child for food intake might have adverse consequences in various areas of development, has been widely accepted, even by mothers. Thus, this example seems a little outmoded to us, and we may hope that other such knowledge as we have acquired and are still acquiring can be similarly conveyed to a wide population. Except for the very neurotic parent, new understanding acquired through group discussions seems to be reassuring and helpful: it helps the parent to avoid mistakes — e.g., to expect too much or too little from the three-year-old, etc.

DR. EISENBERG: One theoretical question to which it is not yet possible to give a definitive answer is that of basic instinctual forces or "human nature" — something biologically inherent in the human being, which is true of all people and is therefore reflected in certain stages of development that are dependent, basically, on the internal constitution and only in some ways on the cultural milieu.

There is one group of people who believe that very little is biologically given in human existence, and that there is a wide variety of socially enforceable solutions. Some people will go to the point of denying almost *any kind* of biological limitation. Remember, this is still in dispute; none of us here can speak as though we were talking about the laws of physics. Our psychological principles, no matter how avidly we believe them, are at present open to considerable discussion. The best we can do is to reflect our own points of view, without presenting them as final scientific statements of the truth.

MORDECHAI KAFFMAN: I want to speak in support of what Dr. Eisenberg has said about the problem of our emotional involvement with some particular psychological approach, so that we tend to interpret whatever we see in the light of that approach. We have to be very cautious about this. I, myself, do a lot of play therapy, for example, and, while I do not have an orthodox Freudian approach, *I* have not seen, for instance, the fantasy of the primal scene, nor the "reconstitution" of an actually unexperienced family life.

DR. BERNARD: I should like to address myself to the question of the importance of the *appropriate* approach when it comes to attempts at psychological fact-finding, on the one hand, and, on the other hand, psychological assistance to groups within the kibbutz society. I shall do this from the standpoint of two principles.

The first has to do with the problem of the balance between

distance and closeness — on the part of the investigator or worker within the kibbutz society who is trying to carry on either fact-finding or helping. The problem arises, let us say, when the person doing the fact-finding and the interpretation of these facts tries to evaluate a procedure that has been instituted in the kibbutz. A change has been made, such as the establishment of age mixtures from, say, three to six, when previously, children of the same age were kept together. This change has been based both on theoretical grounds and on experience; one wants to evaluate, after a while, whether one's original hypotheses have been substantiated, and whether the change has proven to be effective or not. By that point, one has to have decided what *is* effectiveness and what are the *criteria of effectiveness*, in terms of the value system, and so on.

Now, is it advantageous for the person who is doing this to be *close to* the society, to have a basic understanding of the reality of the society in which the investigation is being pursued? Can he in that way establish rapport with the members of that society, and thus a greater confidence on the part of his respondents, since they know that they will be understood? As against those advantages, there are the possible advantages of "distance," with its resultant detachment and minimizing of bias.

In such a very small, intimate or familiar society as the kibbutz, in which every member has multiple roles, if the fact-finding person, or the person leading a group of parents in parent education is *too* close, it seems to me that this very closeness might entail the stimulation of additional complex interactions within the society, unrelated to the immediate purpose of the investigation or the assistance. On the other hand, someone from outside could conceivably be regarded as simply a nuisance, since he has no basis in the value system of the group, does not really understand its actualities, and so on.

There has been mention of inter-kibbutz efforts, joint efforts on the part of the three organizations, employing someone who would be equipped both as a kibbutz member and as a member of some professional institution. . . . I don't know how to balance these two aspects, but surely it must be done, because otherwise, the very investigation or the attempt to help might have the effect, instead, of altering the facts — which sometimes happens in psychological matters.

The other principle is this: in carrying on psychological investigation or assistance, I would advocate a greater use, than I have thus far heard mention, of psychologically-trained clinicians. These sorts of psychological endeavor do call for a level of scientific sophistication that only the clinicians in the psychological sciences — social work, psychiatry, clinical psychology — have really developed. It has been traditional, in many countries, for there to be first the acceptance of clinicians for work with obviously very sick people; and only later and gradually, is some of their clinical understanding put at the service of the intricate problems of health.

DR. NEUBAUER: During our interchange of ideas and experiences, we have made a number of statements, which I would like to summarize briefly: (1) The participants in this Institute came together not just to express their findings, but to learn from each other. (2) We visitors are rather hesitant to apply what we know from our own conditions of life to conditions that differ so greatly. (3) We nevertheless cannot help comparing the experiences of others, stemming as they do from different conditions, with those we know, and noting what the nature of these differences is. While we do not want to rush into conclusions, neither are we able to refrain from putting forward propositions based on our experiences prior to and since coming here. (4) Material based on psychoanalytic investigation is limited, for there were too few who had been analyzed for us to be able to make culturally valid generalizations. Nevertheless, those who believe in the usefulness of psychoanalysis will continue to prefer their propositions, even if they cannot offer supporting data of a quantitative character.

As is usual with regard to a theory, one tends to select the data according to one's theoretical propositions.

Chapter II

VISITS TO THE KIBBUTZIM

REPORTS ON THE VISITS

Mr. Alt: What we saw, particularly with regard to the children's sense of assurance, of security, was absolutely overwhelming. I must, at this point, observe that we did not get together as a group to discuss our impressions, so that what I shall be saying will be strictly personal, filtered through my own particular experiences, predilections and interests.

The children's appearance was quite remarkable — and this held true for children of all ages, starting with those we saw in the baby home and the kindergarten, and including those we saw in the school, and later on in the swimming pool. I was struck by their animation, their evident good health and intelligence, and their unusual poise. Nor did I encounter any signs of affect-hunger, of the kind usually manifested by children in all the group care situations which I have observed in my professional experience. There was neither rushing nor clinging to the adult, at any time. The children seemed to be quite self-contained as they went about their affairs. While friendly and normally outgoing, each maintained his own identity.

I shall not, at this time, discuss what we learned about child-care patterns and methods, or our impressions of child-care personnel, but I will say that I was very much struck by the degree of identification of the children with their parents.

It is important for us to recognize that the arrangements for child nurture and child-rearing are so closely interwoven with total kibbutz life that there is a danger lest anyone involved in a study or assessment should tend to look at some piece of this total mosaic, instead of taking care to relate that piece to the totality. If we look at only one piece, there is a great risk of focusing on something incomplete; thus, our view is bound to be distorted, because so many elements and dimensions may be missing. We have here a *complex* of human relationships, the principal participants in which are the mothers and fathers, the teachers, the other parents, the siblings and the members of the group. No study ever can afford to lose sight of this totality, this network of interpersonal relationships.

This leads me to two detailed problems which are part of this total pattern. One is the place of women in this picture, both as mothers and as workers, and the question of their self-realization. There seemed to be little question that women did not like to be assigned to the kitchen — at least, many of them did not. There is also little question that women's work is not accorded the prestige or recognition that men's work receives. (It should be said that the leaders with whom we discussed this problem recognized its importance and the need to do something about it.)

The problem of higher education for girls comes very close to that of the role of women. What we learned — and this may not be completely accurate — is that there is an extraordinarily long period of preparation for the girl who wishes to proceed to higher professional education. We were told that after she has served in the army, she has to return to the kibbutz for a time, to make up her absence, and it is only after that, that she is free to leave the kibbutz and go to the University. By that time, she is likely to be in her early twenties, at least.

There is one other problem to which I should like to draw your attention. It has to do with the relations between the generations. We discovered some of the factors that may have a bearing on this. One is that positive identification is promoted by the fact that the youngsters work alongside their fathers or other adults, at tasks useful to the community. Closely related is the unusual degree of closeness and mutual trust between parents and young people. They spend a lot of time with each other, discussing concrete problems of kibbutz life, and this extends to relationships of confidence and trust between girls and their mothers. On the other hand, we were also told of a good deal of ambivalence on the part of the younger generation toward their parents, which stems from some rather unusual factors in the kibbutz situation.

I can only conclude by saying that the visit was extraordinarily stimulating and thought-provoking, and may cause me to revise some of the views I have previously held about kibbutz life.

Dr. Anthony: Four of us were treated yesterday to an almost complete picture of kibbutz life. Nothing could have succeeded so well in bringing to life the fascinating blend of tough manual demands and monotonous work routines with enthusiastic scholarship on the part of the teaching group, and above all the pervasive idealism about the brotherhood of man. It seemed to us a far cry from conditions with which we were only too familiar.

The kibbutz we visited is described in the guide books as "a well-to-do kibbutz," and our first impression was of a well-organized and productive settlement, a model of what can be achieved through this way of life. The idea that it was unusual, as far as settlements went, could very well have been induced by the patriotism of our guides, who were members of it; only later did we come to realize that such extraordinary pride in one's kibbutz is common to kibbutz members anywhere in Israel. This *esprit de corps* was so infectious that it has become difficult for any of us to speak of our visit in a detached, impartial, and uninvolved manner. Our interchange with visitors to other kibbutzim revealed our plainly partisan feelings, in that we found ourselves talking of "our kibbutz."

"Our kibbutz" had better farms, of course, more industry, finer schools, more varied cultural opportunities, and more constructive group activity than any of the others we heard about. "Our kibbutz" had built its own swimming pool; extra special about it was a piece of sculpture set in the middle of the children's pool — a giant mermaid that provided the naked little bodies with a wonderful water slide (and possibly a wonderful shower of fantasies as well). We learned later that almost every kibbutz prides itself on something "extra special."

We did detect a general inclination to make the life of the community as self-contained as possible, so that it would be unnecessary for anyone to leave the settlement, even momentarily, in search of cultural or social satisfaction. If anyone developed a hobby which had no place, as yet, in the general activities, he could apply to the appropriate committee to have his particular interest considered. If it was approved — and there was every likelihood of its being approved, unless it was regarded as detrimental to community life — the member was granted permission to obtain the necessary equipment.

During the course of the day, we experienced for ourselves the different facets of kibbutz organization. We were first introduced to the babies and observed the caretaking activities of the nurse and her assistant. We were present when the mothers came in from the fields to feed their infants, and watched the "taking over" and "giving back" procedures; it seemed rather "matter-of-fact."

We then moved on to the toddlers' home, where the children entertained us with some spontaneous dancing and singing. Like any other nursery group, they did "warm up" to the visitors after a while; but here as elsewhere, the barrier of language kept us apart. At the kindergarten home, we were treated with similar reserve; one little boy had an acute "stranger reaction," which was not altogether uncalled-for, since we were interrupting their mealtime. After lunching in the main dining room of the kibbutz, we made a grand tour of the kitchens, and learned about the planning required to feed five hundred hard-working people at every mealtime. The noise in the dining room was much less than is usual in communal settings; but camaraderie was everywhere in evidence, both between adult and adult, and between child and adult. It bore the marks of long familiarity and complete acceptance.

In the afternoon, we visited the schools, the cultural center, the library, and the record room. In the last building, a small quiet room held the mementos of dead members. These were miscellaneous collections of photographs, drawings, schoolbooks, etc., coupled with a short biography; they emphasized for us, almost more than anything else, the strong bonds that are forged in kibbutz life. Still later in the afternoon, we went down to the swimming pool, where the parents and children were congregating. Although the children mixed well with one another, they seemed to feel that this was a special family hour and were therefore never very far away from their parents. At this time, we observed several older children (about seven or eight years old) vigorously sucking their thumbs, but nobody paid any attention to them. No one appeared surprised to see us and everyone was ready to talk to us. The simple, yet beautiful, word "Shalom" functioned like an "open sesame" throughout the kibbutz.

The group of teachers who guided us on our tour through the kibbutz were tireless in answering our questions. They had also set aside several hours to cover some of the problem areas involved in communal living. The areas (this was all we could manage in the time) comprised firstly, the relationship between the sexes; secondly, the clarification ritual that took place at the age of seventeen, and thirdly (this will be commented on separately by Dr. Eisenberg), some crucial education problems and their implications for the progress of the kibbutz system.

Because of the group upbringing of the children, sexual development and concomitant interests are handled differently in the kibbutz from the way they are usually dealt with in a familial setting. Children of both sexes have lived intimately with one another since infancy, and consequently have come to look upon one another as siblings. As is the case with real siblings, the ordinary intimacies of growing up involve a certain amount of exploration and experimentation that is treated tolerantly by the caretakers. Moreover, as our guides pointed out to us, there were more "sublimations" available in kibbutz life than in the more constricted environment of the Western family.

During adolescence, when biological sexuality intervenes, exploratory play between real siblings in family life diminishes in frequency. This is partly due to the fact that sibling contacts of this nature are implicitly condemned by the culture, but also because the amount of physical contact and response has generally been greatly reduced by this age. By contrast, we were confronted with the sharing of bedrooms by boys and girls up to the age of eighteen, an arrangement which ran contrary to all our Western ideas on the subject. Under such conditions, in our own country, we would have been lead to anticipate the emergence of an unhealthy promiscuity, with venereal disease and illegitimate pregnancies among its expected consequences.

We were, therefore, curious as to what effect this unusual arrangement had on both the current and future sexual functioning of the kibbutz adolescent. We were told that our concern was understandable, and that the question was not handled dogmatically by the kibbutz movement as a whole. Each section, and sometimes each kibbutz, made its own arrangements by the decision of the respective general assemblies, but even now, in each separate kibbutz, the matter was still being hotly debated.

Our guides were, therefore, not surprised that their visitors had rather strong feelings on this question, but they approached our concerns with the same rationality that they applied to questions about almost any other branch of kibbutz functioning. In its simplest form, this might be expressed as a behavioral law: if you make it your aim to keep young people of the two sexes apart, they will inevitably come together promiscuously; if, on the contrary, you keep them excessively close together, they will stay apart. A second behavioral law might read as follows: individuals who have undergone a group upbringing are more sensitive and responsive to group pressures and group prohibitions than are "familistic" children, and more likely to conform to implicit and explicit community mandates. If it was therefore not considered the "right thing" to have serious sexual relationships with another member of your own group of "sociological siblings," because it interfered with overall group functioning, the group in effect saw to it that any intimacies did not go beyond group expectations. These two "laws" together create an inhibition that has functioned more effectively as a control than some authoritarian precept. (Adult asceticism was not, in fact, a feature of kibbutz life; divorce and remarriage seemed to be as common in the kibbutz as elsewhere, and trial relationships were not infrequent.)

In addition, the setting of the kibbutz militated against clandestine arrangements. This was very much an open system, with — at least as far as the children were concerned — a minimum of privacy: everybody knew where everybody else was and what they were doing. A great deal was also offered in the way of "doing something else"; in fact, there was a somewhat overloaded program from morning to night, so that a child with his schedule of school, work and cultural activity really had little "secret" time to himself. A third law governing relationships in the kibbutz might therefore read: "Keep them as busy as can be — and always in the public eye!"

This intimacy *sans* intimacy had long-term effects on sexual functioning, chiefly in the direction of serious inhibition. This we learned from the clinician who accompanied us. In cases presented at the clinic for psychotherapy, sexual inhibition was frequently a prominent symptom. From what we were told, it seemed very likely that some sort of artificial "incest barrier" had been set up. This would certainly seem to support Westermarck's theory of the role of overfamiliarity in the genesis of incest taboos!

The adolescents themselves supported the rooming arrangement. The girls felt that they gained from the presence of the boys by the "serious conversation" that was carried on; the boys were in favor of it because the girls made the rooms "more homelike and attractive." During times of menstruation, the girls had to be especially careful, and a few of them cited this as their reason for wanting to be separated from the boys. The rooms that we saw were four-bedded; they usually contained two boys and two girls, although three girls and a boy might share it — but not three boys and a girl. (It is always interesting to find out where the limits of any system are reached; we were curious about this last embargo, but could discover nothing but what appeared to be an instinctual aversion to it!)

Some of our group were a little dismayed to hear of the clarification or "purification" ritual that took place in the kibbutz at the age of seventeen, for they had had previous experience with initiation rites both in Europe and America. On a certain day, in an atmosphere heavy with significance and foreboding, the boys and girls met together very solemnly for a profound discussion. This sometimes happened when the group was out for a walk and came upon a clearing in the forest, or when they felt that they were by themselves and that the time and place were appropriate. With them was a leader from an older generation.

The way in which the leader handled the group at this particular time made a great deal of difference as to whether it was merely a trite experience; or a progressive step in the development of each individual, as he saw himself honestly, in terms of his past and present record, in relation to his future as a kibbutz member; or, finally, a traumatic episode. Each member of the group talked very freely about himself, sometimes for an hour or more, and they could apparently have as much time as they required. They gave voice to their previous doubts and failures; they clarified their present attitudes and future intentions; finally, they confirmed their loyalties to the kibbutz.

In general, our guides felt that the group derived a great deal of strength and self-knowledge from the meeting. Not only did they understand themselves better, they also understood one another more, and this served to cement group ties. Once again, we sought for clinical comment and learned that, in certain sensitive children, already on the road to neurosis, the meeting was likely to be recalled as a highly traumatic experience, especially when rejection was involved, as was sometimes the case. (Certain of the teenagers might be considered to be not "ready" on this occasion, and would accordingly be "deferred.") For individuals brought up in a group setting, any rejection by the group would obviously constitute a severe trauma. Even this could be handled by a sensible and sensitive leader (in age not too far removed from the group) ; the situation, nevertheless, in the minds of the visitors, contained a real hazard.

Of the various age groups that we saw on our visit, the one which seemed to be the least satisfactory from the point of view of emotional support and stimulation was the toddlers. The child in this group seemed to be more at loose ends, less settled, more "expectant" and less lively; not quite ready for group experience, and therefore unable to avail himself of group support, while at the same time missing the individual care for which he seemed to be hungering. The toddler period is a vulnerable transitional period for any child during its development; it seemed to be especially so in the development of the kibbutz child.

We were not surprised to learn that the child's vulnerability was well known to the clinic, in the form of various "adjustment" disturbances. The toddler seemed to suffer particularly from being separated during the sleeping hours from the parents. In many kibbutzim this was recognized, and children were allowed to sleep during that period in the parents' house. In our kibbutz however, the losses were felt to be more than balanced by the gains derived from separating the children. Our guides pointed out that *not* sleeping in the vicinity of their parents made the children less liable to exposure to the primal scene and therefore less stimulated sexually by such exposure; that, theoretically, they were thus less prone to certain forms of neurosis. However, one of the clinicians who accompanied us remarked that this was not necessarily the case — that, in play therapy with kibbutz children, primal scene material was often very much in evidence, fantasy once again proving as powerful as fact.

The third and final area which was discussed with our teacher guides involved secondary education. During our tour we were shown the high school and the excellent facilities it possessed, and we were frequently assured that the children, although oriented toward farming, were not at all averse to studying. We were told of some exceptional children who had made some interesting field studies in the natural sciences. There was some reason for our concern, for scholastic pursuits are not usually encouraged in pioneer settlements, where the plough and the sword are more in demand than the pen. Was there, in the kibbutz culture as it stood today, any aura of pride and prestige surrounding the things of the mind? To what extent could children brought up under such circumstances become the scientists and scholars of the future? The boast that kibbutz children are the best read farm-children in the world may well be true; but is this enough? (Dr. Eisenberg has an extended comment to offer on this.)

DR. EISENBERG: I am somewhat concerned (although this may not be a concern shared by the kibbutzniks, who have perhaps a different set of values) that there may be an insufficient emphasis on intellectual achievement. This is not true in terms of the *amount* studied in the secondary school, which seems quite exemplary (in fact, the children seem motivated to study harder than even the teachers sometimes want them to do) ; nevertheless, one gathers that even among the girls, for whom there is insufficient opportunity within the kibbutz for the more prestigious jobs, it is not easy to persuade them — in spite of the fact that funds or positions are available — to go on to university life.

Therefore, one of the questions for the educational system is "Where does it lead the youngsters in terms of professional and technical studies?" As I see the future, agriculture will play a diminishing role, so far as places and opportunities are concerned. It will become increasingly more technical, mechanized, etc., and unless you have a viable system to turn out people oriented towards scholarly study beyond the high school level — not just adult self-education, but rigorous courses of study directed toward specialization — the movement itself may have some difficulties.

I should like to speak briefly on the tremendous degree to which we were impressed by the people, the achievement, the spirit, and the feeling in this kibbutz. These are truly things that no paper can convey. Papers merely report the number of hours, the number of children, etc.; one doesn't get from them the feeling and presence of the people — namely, the extent to which they *care*, the fact that they're *involved*, that this *means something* for them. While it may be that the five people who met with us were of leadership caliber, and not ordinary members of the collective, they were most impressive people, indeed.

DR. GOLDSTON: Our group had Dr. Gerson as our very gracious host. My comments will focus on the content of our discussions, but will also include some of our impressions and observations.

Our discussion dealt with some educational problems. We were told that there are no academic failures among the children; children are not "left back" in school. Although a child may be academically slow, his peer group and other members of the kibbutz society have so many opportunities to observe him in a variety of non-academic activities that he may develop a sense of achievement by excelling in areas such as sports, work, or other sectors of kibbutz life.

We also spoke of problems of toilet-training. When we observed that the toddlers were not wearing diapers, we were told that this was based on the desire to prevent discomfort for the babies, as the result of the summer heat, and also to spare additional work for the metapelet. We observed a male child about two years old who, upon indicating his desire to urinate, was handed a pan by the metapelet, into which the child performed quite adequately. When we asked the metapelet whether the child was rewarded in any way for this behavior, we were told, "Yes, the child is told while he is urinating, 'Wonderful'."

We spent a great deal of time talking about sexual behavior. We were told that masturbation is not interfered with in young children; there is no prohibition until a child is about nine years old, at which point he is told that, if he wishes to masturbate, he is to do so in private. We then learned of a six-year-old boy who was quite aggressive in reaching out to female genitalia. This problem was handled satisfactorily by simply telling the child to "explore his own body."

Our hosts spoke of their discontent with sex education practices. A physician is brought into the kibbutz to talk to the teenagers about the physiology of sex, and an adult from another kibbutz is brought in to talk in a "chum-like" manner to the adolescents about sexual behavior. Sexual intercourse is frowned upon before adolescents have finished school; but we were informed that contraceptive devices are freely available to adolescents, and that girls, upon request, are fitted with diaphragms prior to going into the Army. However, there appeared to be some confusion as to what constitutes "freely available," and just how the contraceptives are obtained.

We were told with pride that there were many places in a kibbutz where adolescents could enjoy heterosexual behavior. Therefore, there was no need to have any sense of shame or to hide relationships between the sexes. A boy who had finished school and wished to bring a girl to live with him in the kibbutz could do so freely, without evoking any negative reactions from others.

Another area dealt with was the role of religion in the kibbutz. We were told that the Bible is studied as history; that atheistic beliefs prevail in this kibbutz; that formerly religious rituals around such areas as birth, *bar mitzvah,* and death have been replaced by new rituals. Religious festivals such as Passover are apparently observed; however, "We don't know quite what to do with Yom Kippur." Nonetheless, children are taught to respect the religious beliefs of others. There seemed to be a rather clear differentiation between the Jewish people as a nation and the Jewish religion as such.

The children we observed appeared to be healthy, happy, and not at all distracted by our presence. We saw a mother playing with her infant; both appeared quite delighted with each other, and we were interested to see what the child's reaction would be upon the mother's departure. The metapelet went to the child, physically stimulated him a bit, cuddled him, and gave him some toys; there wasn't any whimpering whatsoever. The motor development of the young infants appeared, to some of us, to be above normal.

We were impressed by the thinking of kibbutz members about the children of the second generation, who are referred to, with great pride, as "the daughters and sons of the kibbutz." Finally, we were impressed by the recognition on the part of the leaders of the kibbutz that there was much yet to be done and many unsolved problems. This awareness was coupled with a very great sense of pride — deserved pride, we felt — in what they have accomplished.

Mrs. Karpe: I should like to add something. Some of us went back to the children's house at the time when the parents come to call for their children, because we thought that this would be an interesting situation to observe. We got there a few minutes early and spoke briefly to the metapelet.

There were six children, varying in age from fifteen months to two years, playing in a relaxed way. The first three mothers appeared near the same time and picked up their three children. As soon as this happened, the children who were now left, and who had been playing quietly before, started to talk; in spite of my very limited Hebrew, I recognized the recurring words "aba" and "ima," meaning father and mother. These three very young children became restless when they saw that their playmates' mothers had arrived, while their own mothers or fathers had not yet come. This restlessness stimulated the children's speech as well as their activities; they got up, held on to the gate which enclosed their play area and started to shake it. The metapelet was sitting there rather passively, it seemed. All this happened within a very short time — maybe five or seven minutes — but as the children's tension seemed to increase, they *took each other's hands* and started to dance and sing.

Now this is something very unusual for children of that age, I think — especially the fact that they turned towards each other rather than to the metapelet at this moment of tension. Two sets of parents appeared just after that, the father in one set walking a little behind the mother. Their child, a girl, called out "aba, aba," even though the father was somewhat farther away. She stretched out her hands to "aba" and, since mother held a cigarette in her hand and was obviously not ready to pick up the child at that moment, it was actually the father who did so. This family, and the next set of parents with their child, left quickly; the last child had to wait a few minutes. This child became extremely restless, but he still did not go to the metapelet; instead, he shook the gate until the very young and very attractive mother appeared to call for her child.

Then I observed that every mother first picked up her child and then went inside, carrying the child, to get clothing and diapers. It was probably inconvenient to have the child in one hand while having to search through drawers with the other; but they all did it that way. I do not know whether they were *asked* to do it that way, or whether this was an expression of their own sensitivity, but each made sure to *pick up the child first*.

DR. HIMMELWEIT: When we first arrived at this conference, we were — perhaps appropriately, for psychologists and psychiatrists — filled with concern about the effect on young children of their not being sufficiently with the parents, especially their mothers. Further, because most of us had spent some time reading about "the kibbutz theory," and had not yet had an opportunity to see how theory is reflected in practice, we were not prepared for the enormous amount of spontaneous love and affection that we saw poured onto the children.

Very striking to me was the fact that of the group of toddlers I was personally observing, two were missing; they had just gone to visit their mothers at work! They were very small, but they found their way around — something which, I think, would be quite beyond a child brought up in our society — and they came back, quite happily, twenty minutes later. Also, the toddlers generally were very much interested in the visitors. However, their interest lasted for no more than about five minutes, and then they became busy playing once again.

We must also keep in mind the role of the extended family. In a sense, the entire kibbutz is the child's family. Very soon he knows everyone, and everyone talks to him as he wanders along the paths; he has no fear of being lost. This extended family must, I feel sure, add an important ingredient to the growth of trust and confidence on the part of the child.

In this particular kibbutz, the children were put to bed by the parents — which seemed an excellent arrangement. If one considers how little an average town child, especially of middle-class background, sees of his father, it is more than likely that the kibbutz child has, in fact, more contact with his father. In this kibbutz, the children saw their parents from five to eight every night, and nearly all day at *shabbat*.

In the light of what we have seen, the way in which we use the term "separation" in our society, and the effects assigned to it, have no parallel in kibbutz society. True, for certain periods the children are separated from their mothers, but this is under known and fixed conditions; access to the mother is possible at most other times, and of course there are the daily periods of being together. During these periods, the parents devote themselves, not to their own affairs, as it so often necessary outside the kibbutz, but wholly to the children. These children are in no sense "deprived"; they are warmly and affectionately handled. The society in which they live I would describe as essentially child-centered.

I would like to indicate a number of questions that arose among us for further discussion.

1. We know, so far, from discussion as well as from our experiences as visitors to the different kibbutzim, how much variation in child training and educational practice there is from kibbutz to kibbutz, and more particularly among kibbutzim belonging to different movements.

Such variations are quite major: in some kibbutzim parents put their children to bed, in others the metapelet does; in some, boys and girls, after puberty, sleep in the same room, in others they are free to choose, and in still others the arrangement has grown up, by tradition and/or by design, for mixed sleeping to cease once puberty has been reached.

In education, one of the most striking differences is that between the regional high school and the single kibbutz school. In the former, the adolescent attends a boarding school during the week, along with young people from different kibbutzim. As a result, his original age group becomes extended, he encounters new teachers, and he is able to use a wider range of educational facilities, e.g., libraries and laboratories, than are possible within a single kibbutz.

What astonished me was that the effects of these different practices were not examined by the kibbutzim educators themselves, using proper research techniques. Surely, a community as child-centered as this, and at the same time so full of theorizing, should want to find out *which implementations of a given theory produce what consequences:* (1) for the child, and (2) for the community.

The explanation for given practices is often put forward in terms of some *a priori* theory of personality development, but here are ready-made opportunities for carrying out comparative studies, and they should be grasped with eagerness. In the field of agricultural production, there are both planned and unplanned variations in method; these are examined minutely, so that the most effective method can be adopted. It is unlikely that for child training and educational practices, there is *one* optimal course; what is more likely is that each brings its own particular debit-and-credit account, and these are what should be charted.

2. The second question concerns the kibbutzim's attitude toward education. There is clearly a great emphasis on the worthwhileness of knowledge and on intellectual pursuits. Everyone seems to recognize the need to develop young people who question, who have a wide range of cultural interests, and who are informed on a variety of subjects. Yet, when I asked whether the children sat for matriculation, I was told that this was not done because it would introduce an element of competition and impose an undesirable rigidity on education. Coming from an educational system in England which is paying dearly for its restric-

tive system of entry into higher education, even going so far as to have school curricula subordinated to examination requirements, I have some sympathy with that point of view. However, I can see no reason why the young people should not work for an examination *devised by the movement itself.*

The kibbutz educators are not averse to singling out individuals of special ability; for example, I was told, with justified pride, that four of the children in "our" kibbutz had taken part in an International Competition and had returned with Gold Medals. There are, therefore, spheres of activity, important and relevant to young people, in which the singling out of certain individuals is permitted; why not, then, in the intellectual sphere? I suspect that this is a reaction against the previous overvaluation of intellectual success on the part of the older generation, and they fear the repercussions of such a system on the child who may be less successful. But why do they not also fear this for the child who is a poor swimmer?

I should have thought that the introduction of some means of evaluating scholastic performance, including the use of examinations, could (provided it is carefully handled) *increase motivation,* without having any undesirable side effects. After all, if kibbutz education has been successful, then achievements in the intellectual sphere should carry no special weight, any more than achievements in the arts, where the singling out of individuals has long been the rule.

3. I am curious about the way in which young kibbutzniks see moral and social issues; some comparative study would be invaluable here. What moral and social issues excite them? To what extent does their map of society differ from that of other people of their age? How far do they see themselves as members of the society of Israel; how far as members of the kibbutz? What do they see as their tasks? What are their aspirations? What, for them, would constitute failure? What self-image do they have? Asked to write an essay on looking back over their lives as old men and women, by what would they most like to be remembered?

4. I was struck by the amount of theorizing that seems to go

on. I understand there is a meeting every week about the children. For me, coming from England where serious discussion about children (unless they are acute problem cases) is to be found only in the progressive schools, I find this quite strange, though far from unpleasing. Yet, I have a feeling that it may be carried too far. I wonder how many warmhearted, but not very verbal meta-plot might simply become confused; also, how many people teaching the children do, in fact, "work with" a whole theoretical superstructure, before which they bow in admiration, but which in practice they ignore.

5. I was not as much impressed with the ingenuity shown in organizing kitchens, laundries and clothes distribution centers as with that shown in streamlining work on the farm or in the animal houses. I think far more could be done to achieve a saving in man- — or rather, woman-hours. I should like to see someone examine the way the work is organized, in order to devise a system whereby the workload is reduced without adding to the monotony or fatigue of the task. I am sure it can be done.

6. Finally, you bring up children in an almost paradise-like situation: their individuality is encouraged, and their talents responded to, probably far more than is possible in the academic rat-race that is characteristic of our educational system. You introduce children to work, through the school farm, at a time when a good attitude toward work has a maximal chance of development. All this is admirable. However, once he is educated in this fashion, the individual's range of opportunity is then severely reduced. Is the curtailment really quite as necessary as you suggest?

Not only is the diversity of work tasks offered somewhat limited; more important, so are the opportunities for young people to effect change. The very success of your educational system lies in developing young people with a concern for others, with a wish to *improve* society. But what genuine, non-patronizing opportunities do you offer? How far can the kibbutz accommodate change?

DR. REDL: I think it would be exciting to dwell on what Dr. Himmelweit has just said and to have a good discussion on that now. However, since it is my turn to report on our visit, let me describe first some of the feelings within me — perhaps within all of us, in part at least — while we were exposed to this experience.

This is the sequence, as I remember it:

1. At first, I felt a terrific amount of involvement, a feeling of deep excitement and affection for those whom we met, and a tremendous amount of *admiration:* "How can people be that selfless, that sacrificing?" Especially when one realizes what they had to go through in order to build all this. Living with that much restraint, as far as egotistic demands for privacy, and so forth.

2. Then the next phase of my feelings took over; I might describe it as "anger at the saint." I felt like saying: "There must be something wrong somewhere; it just isn't normal to be that good and that self-restrained. If they want to be that way, that's up to them. But what's all that got to do with me. . . .?"

3. Once that irrational feeling was out of the way, I finally discovered that they were so nice, they wouldn't even mind if I didn't think I had to be that good myself. (Besides, I'm too old for that, anyway.) I can be a friendly outsider, without having to make the same sacrifices they do. Now I can relax again.

Now, to the observations themselves and my comments on them. First of all, let me comment on the much younger group, the one we started out with, and about which we were shown most. One thing about this younger group that all of us have commented on so uniformly, and expressed so much enthusiasm about, is the relaxedness and affection they are surrounded with. I need not add to that. I would like to focus on the question of controls, and the handling of behavior, as I observed it.

First, as to controls in general. In spite of the fact that they appeared to be rather unobtrusive, controls in many situations were most forceful, indeed. As far as the children are concerned, I was most interested in your mixture of permissiveness and intervention. The first has already been referred to; the second — namely, behavioral intervention — seemed to me to be passed over, or even, at times, openly denied. So I kept an especially watchful eye out for that, and I think your metaplot did beautifully on that score, too. For instance, even in the short time —

fifteen minutes — during which I observed one of your toddler groups, five different ways became readily visible in which the metapelet as well as the parents managed some form of intervention in child behavior, without losing any of their warmth or rapport. All of these are well-known techniques, but they were beautifully demonstrated, even within that short stretch of time:

1. *Prop-diversion.* The kids want to drink out of their can of water, which also has sand in it. Obviously, the adult tries, quite benignly, to take the water away from them aud pour it out; and of course the kid, in turn, just waits until the adult turns around and drinks it anyway. He does get away with it, but the message that this behavior *needs* limiting has been clearly established.

2. *Personal seduction.* The youngster is excited or angry about something. The adult then offers him a special inducement toward involvement with her, or some special affection; this means to the kid: "Well, if I can get that much affection by stopping, to heck with that other stuff . . .," and he stops doing whatever he shouldn't be doing.

3. Another technique was the offering *of substitute gratifications to other group members in cases of special involvement with one.* For example, a mother would come to take one of the children away for a short time. The others were quite obviously also at the gate and watching. Rather than simply grabbing her child with a "to heck with the rest of the group" attitude, the mother, as well as the metapelet, would be quite sensitive about the other kids' predicament. Both would take their time; the mother would make sure that she established some fringe-relationship with the other children while in the process of taking her own out for a stroll. The metapelet, too, would be quite aware that the other kids needed an extra dose of affection at this very moment, in order to cope with their potential upset. It was all beautifully handled, and again showed how well potentially "upsetting" experiences can be coped with by a group of children — provided they get the support at the moment that they need it.

4. Another technique I saw skillfully used several times during this short period of observation was *appeasement of potential envy in the rest of the group by extra tokens.* When the mother

I just referred to came back from her stroll with her child, the child was carrying a cookie in her hand. However, mother had an extra cookie for everybody else, implying the message to the others: "You, too, are important to me." Whether all this happens spontaneously or by training, I wouldn't know — and, frankly, I don't care. At the moment when this happened, it was a well-coordinated move on both sides. Metapelet and mother, at that moment, did not have to communicate with each other about it; they played the scene with perfect coordination and naturalness.

Of course, the biggest asset — and I want to underline it especially — is the *incredibly small size of the group*. One adult, plus others available on the scene, for about four children, is simply wonderful. It is not only that one can give children more "affection" that way, but because one could not otherwise offer them the support they need for coping with frustrating and anxiety-producing experiences. It is in this respect that *numbers* become very important, indeed.

I assume that those concerned with the economic problems of a kibbutz have a problem similar to the one that "money managers" have in our country — namely, they may be worried whether such a high expenditure for staff coverage really "pays." In the United States, we are constantly running into the idea that such a high staff ratio cannot be afforded, because it "does not pay." This, of course, is idiotic. It is the *one* thing that is surest to pay.

No matter how much you love your kids, or how skillful you are as a teacher or parent, the moment you have to deal with eight instead of four — in a situation of anxiety, envy, confusion, anger, depression or excitement — you can no longer offer the ego-support that the individuals and the whole group need, in order to cope with their experiences in a non-detrimental way. You would invariably have to require the kids to cope by themselves with moments of tension beyond what they can manage by themselves — which means a real mess, either visibly now or internally later. In short, it is quite clear that high staff ratios do pay off handsomely in the end.

I wish you would let us know how one can make this clear

to people in charge of administrative and economic affairs, who are so often not aware of the fact that adults, after all, have only one body and, therefore, can only be at one place at a time, no matter how well trained, affectionate or self-sacrificing they may be. The very smallness of your groups is, in itself, an asset beyond anything I have ever seen. It speaks more loudly than anything else of the tremendous sincerity with which you approach the mental health needs of your youngsters.

It also implies real respect for the factor of *timing*. If it takes a little while for a youngster to settle down, or to react to an adult demand to let go of a toy, or divert his play, or break off a beginning struggle with another kid — so what? We can watch how he is doing, and eventually he will respond; or I can just observe what happens, and then go over, in case he needs a repeat-intervention signal or more support. The metapelet I observed was never in a hurry, never impatiently hasty — and she could afford that because of the smallness of the group. She could also afford it *internally*, because she knew that kids have their own rhythm, and that doing violence to it invariably ends in disaster, or in post-situational bad effects.

I was deeply impressed by all this, while watching your young children's groups; but, from our discussions, I have begun to wonder whether it is equally true for your work with the older children. I have not had enough opportunity to observe them, but from what has been said in these meetings, it seems to me that your older children are about as over-scheduled and over-pressured as the kids in one of the suburban areas near New York, or in any of the larger towns in the USA. That worries me.

There may, of course, be reasons for it; maybe you are not able to implement what the older kids need as well as you can the needs of the younger children. But let us remember that the basic need is equally strong, even though the reasons may be somewhat different. Of course, the older children do not need as much coddling and body-related mothering as the little ones do; yet they, too, need ego support when they are hit by overwhelming feelings of anger, fear, distrust, depression, excitement, etc., and they need as much respect for their own natural rhythm of timing as do children of any other age. They may not need quite as much as the little ones; but somehow I have the impression that they get a lot less than they need, or that the appropriateness of small-group leeway is less clearly recognized for the older kids.

Here are some other concerns I have, beyond the issue I just mentioned:

1. There must be some *group rituals* which the groups themselves set up for the limitation of potential deviant behavior. Since so much of your children's living happens in groups, some individually deviant behavior is bound to make the others envious or angry. What does a group do — and what does it expect the "malefactor" to do or not to do — if one of the individual members, for instance, takes too many privileges, shirks some work or job assignment, or deviates too widely from what the rest of them consider appropriate? What are the built-in group rituals for behavioral control? Are there penalties? If so, what penalties? Or do the kids rely primarily on shame, embarrassment, ostracism of a milder or less overt sort, etc.?

2. What *group restitutional rituals* do your children's groups employ? (Or your adults, for that matter?) It is not enough to make a deviant feel embarrassed or guilty, or to have rituals that group members can expect to occur when they have trespassed. Groups also need rituals by which they *reinstitute* the culprit into the graces of the group. In short, what would I as a kid have to do, if I have fallen "out of line" with group or adult expectations, so as to get the group to "forgive and forget," and to make it possible for me to forget too, so that we all know "This one is over with; let's start from scratch again." All groups develop such "restitutional rituals"; my question is: What are they here? Which of them are cultivated by the adults in charge of the children, and which of them are introduced by the peer groups on their own? What do they really look and feel like, for all involved?

3. One of the big issues that emerged from our discussions is the question: *What defenses do individuals have against dependence,* on adults and on the terrifically loving "group" of which they are so intensely a part, at all moments of their lives? There

is no question in my mind that the whole group — the "over-group," as I would like to call it; the collective as such — is basically *loving*. The love a kid gets doesn't come only from the specific parent or metapelet or teacher involved; it is experienced by him as coming *through* those people *from the collective as such*. The question then, is this: If one feels out of line with adult or collective expectations, or harbors desires in a different direction, and knows that the collective wouldn't like it if they knew — what defenses does one develop to cope with such internal conflict? I mean constructive as well as destructive, adaptive as well as maladaptive defenses. It seems to me we assume that such defenses would be the same as any individual would develop against dependence on his parent or teacher, anywhere else; but I suspect that there may be vast differences. Only you who live in this atmosphere can really tell us if this is so, and what the differences are.

Mrs. Irvine: Our party, too was very much impressed with the warm, informal atmosphere, the tremendous devotion and enthusiasm of the educators, and the spontaneous, relaxed, un-clinging affection between children and parents. Every now and then, we would suddenly notice that some child was keeping near one of the adults in our party, and one would sense that this meant a member of our party had met one of her own children. The children would join us for a little while, staying close to the parents, and then they would go off to their own affairs; later on, we might see them again.

In the babies' home we visited, the metapelet was the wife of the headmaster. Assisting her, and holding a baby in a very charming, warm fashion was a young adolescent girl. In fact, she was holding this baby so charmingly that for a moment I wondered whether this was a very young mother. Later, we learned that this was the daughter of the metapelet and the headmaster. Although she is still in school, she is spending her working time assisting her mother in this apprenticeship role, looking after the babies.

We developed a very strong liking for the group of educators who were our hosts. I think it is, perhaps, because we felt so friendly with them that we were able to raise with them a great many points that would have sounded like attacks, had they come from outside the framework of our relationship.

This kibbutz has instituted a new type of kindergarten, which is something of a deviation from the standard pattern of the traditional kibbutz. It is a relatively large kindergarten, with some twenty-eight children of mixed age-groups, ranging from three to seven. The children still live elsewhere in their little groups of eight. They come in the morning to the kindergarten, a large, open-plan building with a number of rooms and a variety of equipment, and they spend some hours there. The older children remain for an extra half hour or so for a reading lesson, and if any of the younger children are interested in this, they stay and participate too. Then they go back to their own houses for their meals and their afternoon rest, and spend the rest of the day in their small groups of eight.

Although the large mixed-age kindergarten is characteristic of this whole group of kibbutzim, it is only in this kibbutz that the children go home for their midday meal and rest. There have been some discussions about this arrangement with the Central Committee of the group, where the experiment is not wholly approved; nevertheless, there has been no attempt to override the desires of the kibbutz to experiment in this way.

We began by asking *why* they had decided to separate the children's house from the kindergarten for this group of children. For the primary-school children, they have retained the traditional system, in which the children's house has its schoolroom as part of the home. The reasons given were not very clear to us. We also had some discussion about the advantages of the mixed-age group, and how gathering children from various groups together in the kindergarten permits a greater continuity for the metapelet in the children's home. Since the children don't need someone who is trained as a kindergarten teacher to *live* with, they can continue with the metapelet they had earlier. Various points were made about the advantages for the child of being in a mixed-age group, such as would be true of a family, rather than of the much more limited age-range of peers.

I think that in asking this question about the separation of home and kindergarten, we had hoped to arrive — from one side, as it were — at the issue which we then raised. Some of us were concerned about the integration of home and school, which was a characteristic of kibbutzim in general, and the practice in this kibbutz from kindergarten-age onwards. We therefore asked, more directly: Is the child condemned to remain all the time in one group, in which any failure in some important area, such as school work, will depress his general status? He seems to have no way to escape to another group which will know him in some other role. The answer was that even though the group is the same, he still maintains his various roles, so that "what he may lose on the swings, he can gain on the roundabouts." Success in sports, play or work will counterbalance a relative failure at some other activity. In addition, because there is so little emphasis in the kibbutz on competitive success, the fact that a child is not so quick at learning as his fellows are, proves to be far less noticeable than it is in a Western school.

We were also told that although the child spends a great deal of time in his small group of eight, he cannot be said to be "confined" to it, even during the time he doesn't spend with his parents. There is also the school community, where he can mingle with children of any age in various activities which include work on the children's farm, excursions, and certain weekly meetings where they discuss their affairs and make decisions and rules for their conduct.

We heard a good deal about this decision-making process: how the children make rules about all sorts of matters, and with a minimum of adult intervention. For instance, they make the rules about the conditions for going to the sea: young children may go only with an adult, and older ones in a group — provided an adult has been notified; still older ones may go alone, and the oldest even at night. If the children were to propose a degree of freedom that might be dangerous for too young an age-group, the adults would intervene in the interests of physical safety; but, in fact, the children themselves seem to be well aware of the dangers and they make responsible decisions.

Some of the children had received presents of bicycles, with the result that some now had bicycles while others didn't. At one time, it had been accepted that these bicycles were private property; since this created problems, the children's group decided that all bicycles would become common property. Another problem arose when some of the parents got bicycles for their children, who claimed the right to ride them. The group then decided, against the advice of their educators, to allow the lucky children this privilege; later, they pronounced this decision unsatisfactory and reversed it.

Somebody voiced his impression that although the kindergarten was tremendously well-supplied with toys and with every kind of play material, the children's house — in which we assumed they spent the other part of the day — really didn't seem very well equipped with toys. We were told that there is a deliberate differentiation between kindergarten and home; they don't want the children's house to compete with the kindergarten. Further, the children do not spend the entire other part of the day in the children's house; they go for walks, and use the external natural environment for their activities. Finally, when they visit their parents in the afternoon, there are toys in the parents' house. It seems that the children's house is not intended as a place for play activity.

A question was raised about the provisions for the pre-kindergarten child (one to three years) which is, perhaps, the weak point in child care for the kibbutz as a whole. These children may be quite limited in their activity; sometimes there seems to be little play material, and few opportunities for manipulation. The equipment is also sometimes rather old and battered, as if it has been there so long that it has surely lost its interest and stimulus value. Somehow we felt that there was less sensitivity to the needs of this particular age group.

When we asked how the educators in the kibbutz looked at the needs of children of this age, the answer seemed rather theoretical — that this is the period when the child should be structuring his ego and establishing sublimations. There didn't seem to be very much awareness of the value of activities — the use of toys and materials — in sublimations.

Soon afterward Dr. Biber asked the educators to give us an account of a day in the life of a kibbutz child. This was done by one of the teachers in charge of a group of thirteen-year-old children. We got the impression that there is a very full program of learning and work (including work on the children's farm and also on the kibbutz farm), sports and music. We became keenly aware of the fact that some of the teachers are also parents, when one of the younger women teachers present told us, quite frankly, that she felt that this program was too full, and that she, as a mother, resents it. Although the timetable includes periods for sport, for instance, practice periods clash, once a week, with the visit to the parents' home. She said that her children share her resentment. They don't want to miss the sports practice, since they are important members of the team, but they are angry because their attendance at practice must be at the expense of the visit to the parents. She also felt that there was too little really free time; in particular, some children would like much more time for reading than they have, and she felt it was wrong that the opportunities were so limited.

We spent quite a lot of time on teaching methods. Each group, it seems, has a weekly timetable which is divided into periods of the sort we are familiar with in our own countries. In response to questions about whether this weekly timetable did not involve an artificial breaking of interests, the staff defended it quite energetically. We were told something about a method of teaching called the "process method."* We gathered that there is considerable integration of various subjects around a central theme each year. In one year, for instance, the central theme would be "Primitive Peoples," and there would be lessons on the lives of these people, including their handwork and painting and various other subjects.

Someone has spoken about the children identifying with the teacher, and clearly this is so, in certain respects; yet when it comes to vocational choice, the boys don't seem to identify with the male teachers they have had. For example, there was a very fine head teacher, and we asked why the boys didn't choose to

---

*See Appendix C, p. 343.

follow in the footsteps of such a teacher. It was suggested that
this may have something to do with the value system of the kibbutz, which is so much concerned with the direct conquest of
nature — the battle with the elements and with the soil — that
even though learning and teaching are demonstrably related to
this, they seem to lack the prestige of the actual battle with
nature. Then we were told that the teachers can't dramatize themselves as heroes, in the same way as they can present the heroes
of technology and agriculture as models for imitation. Finally, it
emerged that young men seem to regard teaching as an essentially
feminine function, and they resist the invitation to train as
teachers out of reluctance to deprive women of one of the most
interesting jobs available to them.

I shall mention only two further points that were discussed.
One was why there is little or no homosexuality. Can this be because the intensity of the oedipal problem is reduced by the
living arrangements? We have already been told that the relationship with parents is strong. However, one hasn't sufficiently
characterized the relationship of a child with his parents when
one says merely that it is strong or weak, because its nature and
its quality can cover a wide range. One would have to decide this
in terms of what *needs* the parents and the child reciprocally
satisfy.

The final point was: Why is there so little adolescent rebellion? Such rebellion as there was, we were told, was manifested
mainly in withdrawal. It seemed that there was far less opportunity for disillusionment in the kibbutz than there is with us in
the West, and that those who do leave the kibbutz don't throw
it off as something unworthy. Instead, they tend to leave it quite
apologetically, explaining that one can also be quite socially useful elsewhere. We had some discussion about whether adolescent
rebellion is equally necessary in all societies, as a means of establishing identity. When we say that it is valuable, are we perhaps
making a virtue of necessity? It may be that in the kibbutz, the
adolescent has less difficulty finding his identity and for that
reason has less need to assert himself in a rebellious way.

DR. BIBER: Before I make any comments as an observer or

educator or psychologist, I would like to talk subjectively for a few minutes about what the experience of visiting a kibbutz meant for me. I found myself sharing Dr. Redl's feeling of admiration for the "sainthood" of people who have been able to live the kibbutz way of life; at the same time, I found myself involved in something more complex, emotionally. It has to do with the degree to which the values, the ideals that any of us as individuals hold dear, are in tune or in conflict with the values of the society within which we act out our roles as people, as parents, as professionals. In that respect, kibbutz life presents a rare human circumstance: each individual moves, ethically, within a society that *implements* his ideals of how man should live with man. This, I want to say plainly, arouses in me a feeling of envy.

In a Western democracy, such as ours in the United States, where pluralism is a prime principle, coming to maturity involves *constructing* a system of values, through conscious intellectual activity as well as unconscious identification processes. For those whose systems are embedded in humanist or socialist ideals, there is a lifelong process of adaptation or resistance — or a dynamic blend of both — to be made with regard to those social forces that run counter to our images of social progress and well-being. A great deal of life energy is invested by each of us in trying to arrive at a balance which will be psychologically healthy and socially constructive. When we think of our children — our own, or the ones we influence as teachers (or as teachers of teachers) — the problem becomes more difficult: how to create a life of learning through which these ideals will be transmitted (or rather, regenerated) , and how to develop the kind of ego strength that can deal creatively with the impact of negative, often hostile, forces in the life environment.

I do not only admire, I also envy, the freedom from the necessity for this draining process. It occurs to me that the things we have found here — the pervasive feeling of warmth of people towards each other, the loving concern of *all* the adults for *all* the children, the intimacy with nature — all these may be rooted in the basic congruence between how one lives and how one thinks life ought to be lived. Yet I do not feel that I am in the presence of a human idyll, free from all blemishes, problems or conflicts. I know you don't think so either, or we would not be here.

We are on common ground, in *general* terms, as we engage in this common inquiry: how to nourish and support the development of the individual toward his own fulfillment, when fulfillment includes the concept of contributing outward, beyond the bounds of self-realization, toward some form of enriching human endeavor. Yet the differences in our systems of thought lead me to raise specific questions that may not seem to you to be the essential ones. Still, these are the ones we know how to think about. (We did not always understand each other while we were talking under the trees, but we seemed to be communicating, and certainly to enjoy talking to each other — although, without Dr. Neubauer's experience and expertise in acting as intermediate communicator, we would have remained at a much more superficial level.)

The first question I would like to raise has to do with the problem of individualization, and some assumptions about what experiences in childhood contribute to the optimal integration of each child's qualities and capacities, and his uniqueness. Mrs. Irvine has mentioned our interest in the relative presence or absence of toys in the settings for the very young children. We look on toys as materials for play, and we look upon play as the vital experience for learning and growth. Through play in the preschool years, especially in its dramatic forms, we see the child developing his own idiomatic ways of understanding and reacting to his life experience.

Using play as an educational tool requires skill and training: how to create for the child the freedom to construct a highly fantastic world, rich in symbolic meanings to him as an individual, and then gradually to support his natural tendency, in later preschool years, to engage in play about real events, the real relationships of his world; above all, how to do this in a way that leaves the child with the inner feeling that he can *make his own sense out of life* — without, however, encouraging solipsistic tendencies. Is early play life seen in these terms? Are teachers, nurses, metaplot being trained in such educational techniques? Is the development of the individual idiom an important goal for kibbutz life?

There is another question that several of us have been asking: How much time does a child have, in order to be alone — in the middle years of childhood? In adolescence? These questions arise in the context of the goal that we set for this period of maturation. Recognizing the drives that lead children to find safety and pleasure in their peer relations, in merging themselves with the group aims and mores, we still consider it important that children be helped to develop a kind of self-constancy, to build strength within themselves as individuals, while they are experiencing the strength that comes from being one of a group. For this, they need to know themselves, to have satisfying ways of being alone, to feel strong enough at times to think and act counter to the group.

This is an issue that *we* have become worried about in recent years, in our own experimentation in education: Have we over-accentuated — especially with regard to some children — the values and even the imperatives of group life? As Mrs. Irvine has already reported, we took a personal interest in hearing about the way children in "our kibbutz" move from one peer group to another, in the round of their varied activities. But how dominant is the expectation that the child will be functioning in one or another peer group almost all the time?

There are so many areas in which one can look for evidences of the individualizing process. How many avenues of expression are being opened up for the children? How are they utilized by them? We noted the wide-open, empty walls in the children's house, without pictures or murals or any other products of a burgeoning creative growth. Not that these same children do not engage in creative activities; but they seemed to be of the kind that involve children in a formalized, structured, and therefore not too spontaneous kind of work.

For example, the children had made mosaics out of the pieces of ancient tiles that they had picked up on the ground! (I don't think the people in the kibbutz could have been nearly as excited about this as I was. I could not keep my attention on talk of

individuality and creativity while I was absorbing the curious
reality of a child picking up bits of ancient history, remaking
them into a design, and having a thing of his own.) How much
in this unique fact of living right in the midst of past times and
lives being absorbed into the educational process? The study of
history could be so meaningfully personal and dramatic to these
children. Is it? Is the science of archaeology likely to have a
special attraction for them? But, then, would that fit in with the
goals of kibbutz education?

It is time to turn to a second question: Where is authority
vested? Since Dr. Redl has already raised this question, there is no
need to pursue it in general terms. But the facts about resistance
to authority in adolescence have particular interest. If I understand correctly, resistance often takes the form of passivity and
lack of interest, and among the boys, a sort of ridiculing of the
girls for their more compliant acceptance of what this society
expects of them. In contrast to what we are familiar with, this
resistance to authority seems to be pointed directly against the
society's demands — not, as with us, against the parent as the
agent of society (except, of course, where the adolescent's anger
takes the path of delinquency). How is this resistance dealt with?
How is it resolved?

There are two more points I would like to make, briefly. I
must confess to some doubt as to how, logically speaking, we can
talk together about methods of education and child-rearing, in
specific terms, if there are substantial differences in our social-
philosophical outlooks. In our society, we hold an image of the
well-developed individual as one who can "adapt," yet at the
same time be a moving force in changing his world. Here, I have
heard the dictum that the kibbutz form of enacting socialist ideals
must be perpetuated, and that this goal is *part of an ideological
system,* not a response to social exigencies. The scope of what can
be changed is thus clearly delimited. Yet, taking the long view of
social change, one has to ask whether this is, in fact, the final and
optimal mode in which socialistic ideals can make an impact on
the future of man, or of Israel. The details of education and child-
rearing are determined by the decisions one makes on these larger
philosophical issues.

Finally, I want to say a word — perhaps even raise a question — about the conscious effort to remove conflict in the relations between parents and children. There is no doubt that our direct contact with the parents and teachers and metaplot was heartwarming; the children did indeed seem to be nested in a loving world. Still, what we have been told about the dissatisfaction of women in the younger generation intrudes on this strong positive impression. Is the parental role, especially the mother's, being abbreviated, from a psychological point of view? Is it not in the *resolution* of conflict rather than in its avoidance that we achieve depth and strength as personalities?

People being people, I am sure there is plenty of opportunity for love-and-hate conflict, ambivalence and resolution in kibbutz life. But it occurs to me that this level of deep relationship exists more *within* the generations — adults to adults, children to children — and not *across* the generations. To the extent that this may be true, is it not possible that the foundation for the transmission of values at unconscious levels, as between parents and children at least, is being weakened?

MRS. WINSOR: The term "visit" seems wrong, in speaking of such an occasion, because long before the day was over we felt like a colleague group. Those who began by offering us their hospitality ended the day becoming truly our conference mates.

Everyone has been in competition here as to who had the most beautiful kibbutz to visit; ours was, of course, the most beautiful, in many ways. In addition to its physical character, the scene presents such a sense of history. This kibbutz is about twenty-two years old, almost a generation; a first generation children born there will be leaving for the Army this year. It is really a dramatic life-span for these children and this kibbutz.

From the oldest buildings (for which there was a great deal of apology; by the way, they did not need so much apology) to the very newest, one senses the social planning that has gone into each — social planning and *concern for people's needs*. Thus, as new rooms — or flats, as they are called — are built, there are differences in design. Some of them have a split-level kind of architecture, delightful, charming and offering a great deal of individual opportunity for decoration, for making the family's living together a true home setting.

There were two important buildings in construction that also gave one a sense of social planning. First, a plastics factory. We were told that this factory is being conceived of as an opportunity for productivity, for those kibbutzniks whose work can no longer be of the heavy variety that they have performed in the fields in the past; as members grew older in the kibbutz, there would still be opportunities for usefulness — a basic human need, as we know well. This is really sound planning, in that a factory so mechanized will take only a score of people to run it, and the tasks will truly not be physically demanding for them. The other new building is avowedly and specifically a school building.

My concerns have been very similar to those of others here. How do these children move into an open society? How will they function even in a kibbutz society that will — because life *is* changing — expect and demand other kinds of roles than were demanded by the agricultural society that the kibbutz was originally?

We seemed to begin our investigations at the end of the years of childhood, and to work backwards in our educational concerns. For example, at the secondary-school level, one had a sense of planning tempered by a flexibility of educational philosophy. They did not consider the educational process as the concern solely of the inner kibbutz group; outside specialists were coming in, and a physics and chemistry laboratory was being built. We saw some of the materials that had been situated in the older facilities and were now being moved into the setting of the modern laboratory. How modest or elaborate this will be, we have no way of knowing; but the thinking of the group is oriented toward *the lives that their children will live,* not fixed on their own ideals or realities.

This was a secondary school for sixty children — which, in itself, posed a vast educational problem. We had a good deal of discussion, later in the day, about whether a *regional* concept of secondary education for the kibbutzim might not be a better answer to their needs. How fully can one hope otherwise to develop the technical understanding, as well as the educational base, that is necessary in this day and age for a child who will be completing his years of formal education in the kibbutz, but will then be going on to tasks that require techniques and knowledge far beyond the level of the educators of the "in-group" of kibbutz life?

In this kibbutz ("our" kibbutz), the answer seemed to be worked out in terms of individualization of instruction — an interesting educational idea. They believe that the children can be so motivated that they will seek and find their own instructional materials. The new building will have a rather elaborate library, to be used by the educational specialists and the adult members of the kibbutz, but mainly by the children in the secondary school. And the man who is responsible for the library said to us that they are well aware that even the textbooks being published today — let alone those that were published twenty years ago — will have very little validity in terms of what children will need to know ten years from now, or even five years from now. Thus they are trying to build a library rich in journals and in source materials, and they hope to develop a curriculum that will demand of these children a great deal of independent study.

Another subject that gave rise to a good deal of discussion was the question of "inter-aging," as we call it at home — that is, the width of the span of age levels. The kindergarten, which *we* conceive of as a very limited age group, is here a group of children from three through seven years of age. As one enters these kindergarten rooms, one has the impression of a highly developed and well thought-out curriculum, in terms of the creative opportunities, especially in art work, or of the more structured activities, such as block-building, construction, and experimentation. The kinds of materials and products that we usually think of as important curriculum evidence all seemed to be there. But more difficult to discern was the structured intellectual stimulation that we have come to regard as requisite for the total growth process of the five- (or even four-) to seven-year-old. Is this wide age range educationally the most suitable for preparing the next steps of learning?

May I tell a story at this point? It is worth repeating because it tells us so much about those questions of parent-child relationships that have been discussed here. The moment we set foot inside the first room, we stopped to admire a beautiful piece of equipment in the form of a boat with a crow's nest high up above it. There were two little fellows climbing up a rope ladder to the crow's nest, and at once, the young woman who was showing us around exclaimed, "Oh, my gosh! That's my kid way up at the top!" Then she yelled to him, "Don't wave! Hold on to the rope." (That was our experience of child-parent relations, almost symbolizing the whole day.)

This same youngster, who was five, then trailed us — and since his mother continued to show us around, he showed up at all sorts of moments — always carrying a pad and a pencil. His mother spoke for him, because he knew no English, and told us that he was writing hieroglyphics. That was what he was studying at the age of five — hieroglyphics! As we looked at his pad, at one point we saw that he had the word "yes," in English characters, written (as in Hebrew) from right to left, among his hieroglyphics!

Well, that's all there is to the story, but if you're an educator, you come back to the thought that here is a five-year-old, offering unmistakable clues of his interest in the symbolic world. Is this the kind of kindergarten experience for him to be going on with until he is seven, the most fruitful period in terms of his next step in educational development? One can assume that this "inter-age" and rather *prolonged* kindergarten style of experience provides a tremendously valuable opportunity for children to enjoy the sibling life that is missing in this kibbutz-family pattern of organization, and in fact, there are many siblings in the group. In thus living together in their rooms with other children from three to seven years of age, apparently very happily, they can be serviceable to each other in all kinds of *affective* as well as intellectual modes. Nevertheless, one wonders whether there does not need to be more specific relationships between adult and child, especially in the intellectual, and, I venture to suggest, the academic realms.

In the high school years, the same thing is true: the age groups have vertical as well as horizontal experiences in curriculum. Here, it seems to me, one faces an administrative problem. You could hardly divide sixty children into the variety of content areas they need in order to follow up their interests, and still have groups of any size left; instead, the educators develop both interest groups and age groups. There seems to be wisdom in providing total group experience in all kinds of festivals, performances and inter-kibbutz activity.

As we talked with our colleagues, another question arose almost incidentally, having to do with the productive work of the adolescents. This was described as requiring from the children eighty-five days a year, including a good deal of work during the vacation days as well as during the holidays. We questioned whether this was being done primarily in behalf of the child's growth, or to serve the economy of the kibbutz. This also brings to the fore the question of the extent of the demands upon the young person, and the consequent loss of — a curious word to use — their "idleness," their time for seemingly doing nothing, a time in which I think all of us, and particularly the adolescent, accomplish a great deal.

Another question that struck me as somewhat of a paradox is the investment that people in our kibbutz put into individualization of the educational process. In fact, the one time when I raised at least a zephyr, if not a storm, was when I asked, "Is there any method of evaluating the learning progress and process?" The answer was definitely: "We know our children so well; why should we subject them to this?" There seemed to be something of an attempt to protect the individual from what was felt to be the aggressive quality of authority displayed in evaluating the child through a somewhat structured process — call it testing, if you must. I was talking of simply giving the child an opportunity, through a method that was not so subjective as the teacher's response to him, to recognize his level on the ladder of learning, his place among his peers.

The paradox lies in the profundity of the *individualization* that is involved in preparation for what is frankly the development of the "kibbutz man" — a *most socialized* individual, with a tremendous responsibility toward and involvement in his social situation. It does seem paradoxical that almost a halo effect of individualization is maintained about the children, with the expectation that out of this there will come an individual ready to accept a profoundly socialized scheme in life.

DR. NEUBAUER: After reading some of the literature about children in kibbutzim, we visitors were rather deeply concerned about the development of the young child. The practice of multiple mothering — of shared responsibility for infant care — is most certain to evoke concern among us as to the regularity, the consistency of affection, and the adequacy of individual matching.

It seems, now, that the immediate focus of our concern has shifted from questions regarding infant development to those about adolescence and the future of the children. I am not referring here to the future of the kibbutz, but to the role of the individual within the kibbutz — questions of his identity, education, individual faculty, and his place within the kibbutz.

We have been much more impressed, I think, with the warmth shown to the children and with the effectiveness of the interrelationship between mother, metapelet, and young child, than we had reason to expect from the literature. It may be that childcare patterns have changed significantly over the last years, producing a modification of earlier findings. (It is true that we have not yet discussed the period from one to three years; I know that Dr. Kris, among others, would wish to explore this separation-individuation phase rather carefully.)

Our comments, therefore, have tended to center more and more on the period of adolescence — that period in which the child's confrontation with society at large comes into sharp focus. Up to that time, the child's relationship with his family, the metapelet, and the group provides his natural environment, Now, it is the integration of the child into kibbutz life that becomes crucial.

In the past, we have had an abundance of material about early childhood, but not an equal amount of information regarding the problems of adolescence. As our exploration proceeds, we will undoubtedly want to inquire into the problems of sex and social identity; the freedom given to role-playing and experimentation; the content of such experiences; the fantasy life of the adolescent; his "free" time; and to what degree a "moratorium" is permitted for this period of fermentation.

Furthermore, some of the educators among us have raised

questions as to the expansion of the curriculum, on which question there may be a conflict between the economic and social needs of the kibbutz, and the full exploration of the talents and capacities of the individual. The kibbutz, with its philosophy of life, its sharing of opportunities among all its members, may find itself with this problem so long as it has not yet reached the position of "to each according to his needs," rather than "to each according to equal distribution." We need to investigate the degree to which such conditions affect child development, particularly during the period of adolescence.

The reports on the visits to the kibbutzim have shown that a high value is attached to the kibbutz ideals of the "return to the land," of man's achievements in tilling the soil, of the moral value of manual labor. Nevertheless, if this aspect is given the greatest emphasis and is regarded as the most highly valued in the hierarchy of human functions, we may find an element emerging which may be described — to put it in the extreme — as "anti-intellectualism."

Let us examine the position of the teacher in the kibbutz. How highly is he regarded? How well is he able to compete with the man on the tractor or in the factory? I wonder what degree of importance, at the weekly meetings of the membership of the kibbutz, is given to questions of educational programs, or concerning the provision of toys for the younger and laboratory equipment for the older children, as compared with discussions of farm or factory equipment and planning.

No one would question the child-oriented character of kibbutz society, the sacrifice for the children, and the deep love and concern for their future. Still, we cannot ignore the theoretical implications of what are dealt with as "administrative questions." I earlier referred to the teacher's position in the kibbutz. But what is the place of the metapelet in the hierarchy of significant work? How is she chosen? How is she trained? How much is she cherished? Questions of this sort are very much in the foreground of our educational dialogue in the United States. Teachers, nurses, "homemakers" do not yet receive the recognition that is warranted by the significance of their contribution to the life of the children, and therefore, to the future of the nation.

An exchange of ideas on such questions should prove valuable to all of us. I would especially ask our Israeli colleagues to consider, in our forthcoming discussions, what limits the kibbutz society places on fulfilling educational aims going beyond those they now hold, and what limits it therefore places on individual aspirations within the framework of the existing social structure.

DISCUSSION ON REPORTS

DR. BERNARD: From the standpoint of questions of child development, our visits were an extraordinarily appropriate experience at this particular time, because they gave us all an invaluable preparation for the rest of the Conference. We really have to get the rudiments of exposure to the total context, the frame of reference, the *atmosphere,* the ideological *gestalt,* within which any kind of meaningful consideration of the children's development can alone take place.

The really great value of these visits came from the opportunity they afforded us to get rid of our previous conceptions of an over-precise and over-neat division between the limit-setting and frustrating functions assigned to the teacher and the metapelet, and the truly gratifying functions of the parents. Some of us didn't feel that real life was lived that way; and, indeed — at least, as far as my observations went — it turned out, to my great reassurance, that it wasn't. Undoubtedly, there are still some issues to be resolved at the theoretical level. However, in terms of the reality of human interactions, we could see, between the parents and children, on the one hand, a great deal of spontaneous and understanding dealing with hostility, along with firmness and saying "no," and, on the other hand, the altogether inescapable security-giving and protection and affection that went out to the children from the teachers and the metapelet.

The diagrammatic way in which we had been thinking had to be replaced by a more realistic understanding of both parents, and the metapelet and teachers. The conflicts we were concerned about lose meaning when one realizes that the teachers, the parents, the metapelet are, in many instances, the same people. Often, the teachers would suddenly turn out to be the parents of the children we observed, who would tag after them and be with them; later, we would find that it was these same people who had decision-making roles. This fusion, this integration, was precisely the corrective — in actual life — for some of the "fractionation" we had been concerned about.

DR. KRIS: I am deeply appreciative of the amount of flexibility that has been shown in our proceedings so far (although I must admit that in certain respects, rigidity is visible too.) The constant raising of questions such as, "What can be changed for the better? How can that be done?" and so on, opens the way for improvement. There is nevertheless one principle that clearly must be adhered to: *"The kibbutz must live on."* Many things are directed towards this specific aim, which must be given first place.

I have been able to observe an example of this attitude, in connection with the prediction that farming will be less important in the not so distant future, while physics and atomic problems will become more important. In line with this, the educational system of the kibbutz would have to be ready to change itself in order to meet these changing needs, and thus safeguard the preservation of the kibbutz.

In the kibbutz that we visited, signs of that sort of development have already emerged. Our host showed us a very impressive schoolroom in process of being built. Already some equipment — electronic apparatus — was standing in its place. The equipment there — plus the plans that were outlined to us for the finished schoolroom — seemed to me to go far beyond the level of most of the high-school physics laboratories I know in America.

My impression is that people here are not too eager to send the children of the kibbutzim out of the area to the universities. On the other hand, I can imagine that in the future, university-like institutes may be established inside the kibbutz area, just as the high schools are now being promoted. Thus, the goal of higher education will be imparted to all members as part of the officially accepted kibbutz goal. In such an atmosphere, interest in this now increasingly necessary intellectual area will be strengthened in the younger generation, too.

MR. ALT: I want to make one comment on the problem of intellectual activity, as related to the emphasis on work with one's hands and production on the land. In our discussions with the leaders of the kibbutz we visited, we encountered the same concern with the intellectual climate of the kibbutz itself — which not only embraced the intellectual activities of the young people and the requirements for their proceeding with further education, but the cultural and intellectual interests of all the members of the kibbutz. In our interviews, this problem was expressed in the form of a number of closely interrelated issues concerning the relationship between the views of youth and of the adult generation; the need for broader educational opportunities for youth; and the need for a general enrichment of the intellectual climate of the kibbutz.

DR. EISENBERG: Is the present generation less intellectual than one would wish them to be? I suspect that some kibbutzniks are not in agreement with the kind of judgment that some of us from the outside have been making.

One immediately comes face to face with the issue: What is it that constitutes "intellectual pursuits?" Is it self-education, of the kind that is permitted and encouraged and apparently widespread within the kibbutz? Or does it require specialized knowledge, in the sense of being a scholar — a full-time scholar — in archaeology or something else? If that is the choice, which is the more important? Which do you want?

Some of us have been concerned that the generation of the founders of the kibbutz — who are closer to us in their origins, and who have earned our admiration for their achievement — may not be replaced by a like generation. Now, either this is true, or it isn't. If it is, is that fact good or bad? There are those of us who tend to think it would be a shame; perhaps some of you do not think so. Perhaps, from some standpoints, if the intellectualized Jew of the past five thousand years were to disappear from the face of the earth, it would be all to the good. That is among the issues we have to face.

But if we were to agree that the character of this previous generation is disappearing, or might disappear, and if we were certain that we *didn't* want it to disappear, what *could* be done to maintain it? What changes would you need to make? And are such changes feasible for you? The kibbutz has just so much in the way of resources; it must survive in some fashion. If you were to spend an extraordinary amount of your budget on education — since it would all have to come from within — that might even bring you to the limits of your resources. This then becomes a practical question.

On the other hand, there is the issue of what some of us feel to be almost a mystique among some of you (it has its explanation, we know, in the historical genesis of the Movement) — namely, this notion that if you raise something with your own hands and it grows from the soil, that is, in some special way, enriching. If that is your belief, then it becomes a matter of asking: Can *this* survive, or can it not? Now, my competence as a social prophet is, I'm afraid, extremely limited; but my own feeling is that you will meet the fate of all the Utopian communes of the past, if you try to maintain something that flies in the face of the technological and material development of society.

SHIMON STERN: On the question of education, we've said many times that our main aim is to educate good members of the kibbutz. But that does not mean that the kibbutz has become an end in itself; it still remains the means for building up Israel. One must keep in mind, therefore, just how many doctors, how many clinics and so on, one needs for a community of five hundred.

We now have scientists who are able to build, let us say, nuclear power stations. But a year or so ago you could find in the newspapers advertisements calling for people who, ten or twenty years before, had been bricklayers or building workers, asking them to return to those occupations. Most of these people, in the interval, had become white-collar workers — politicians, or officials in the labor movement, and so on. (And, by the way, it is now their aim that their children should never become manual workers — in any case, not unskilled manual workers.) So you get this problem: you may build the power station — find the metal workers to build it, and the electricians to man it — but you may not be able to find the people to *build the road* to the place where the power station is to be built.

Another example: we have copper mines in the Negev, and we had to bring in miners from Italy. There were people who said, "it's just a question of experience"; but I was told there was another factor — namely, nobody wanted to work in the mines. Also, there is the growing gap between the salaries and the standards of manual work, and those of the free professions and those engaged in intellectual work. This is a very severe social problem in a country where you have to consider newcomers, especially newcomers who are unqualified. Perhaps, today, the kibbutzim have become the last places in the country where non-Oriental Jews are going on with unskilled manual work.

Against this background, I think you will understand that there is no neglect among us of the need for intellectual education, or of intellectual activities. On the contrary, I feel that we still have not solved the problem of the depreciation of manual work, that we still have to keep in mind the education of those young people who will find their self-realization in the midst of their being manual workers. Of course, I needn't stress that none of this runs counter to the necessity of high technical standards in an occupation, whether it be agriculture or anything else in the kibbutz.

DR. HIMMELWEIT: Some members of the kibbutzim seem to have a sense of anxiety — not shared by those of us from the outside — that if you change one aspect of the system (e.g., increase the diversity of jobs), the structure of the kibbutz itself will be threatened. To my mind, you underestimate the degree of accommodation that can in fact take place. Indeed, some accommodation will be forced upon the kibbutzim through the very age-structure of their population. In some of the smaller kibbutzim, since the bulk of the population will quite soon grow old, the heavy jobs will *have to be* carried out by the young people — not so much because these jobs are suited to their particular talents or interests, but simply because they are the *only ones who will be able to do them.*

In the world outside, the reluctance of people to carry out repetitive, routine or very heavy work has been among the reasons leading to the introduction of machinery, and now, of automation. It may become necessary, and in my view desirable, for the kibbutzim to rethink their ideas about work — for several kibbutzim to share machinery on a scale not so far envisaged, not as a way of denigrating work on the soil, but out of sheer economic necessity.

There is another reason for a far greater concern with machinery, and hence a far greater emphasis on training your members to be not simply repair engineers, but *inventive* engineers and machine *designers*. This has to do with the extent to which important objectives of the kibbutz movement and of its ideology cannot be realized because of lack of manpower. When we talked with the young man from the Youth Movement, I was impressed by the number and scope of the plans he had, not only for the movement, but also for the role of young kibbutzniks in the society at large. Yet there are problems involved in realizing these plans, solely because of the lack of manpower.

Inventiveness and rethinking need to come into play here. I can see no reason why each kibbutz cannot set itself targets in this respect, in much the same way as it sets itself a target in melon-growing or egg production. This target would aim at freeing so many man-hours for other social — often outside — kibbutz work. Once the target is set, ways will be found, even if it is necessary to have closer links with surrounding kibbutzim so as to share costly equipment.

A lot of anxiety seems to be expressed by kibbutz members about the changing society and the changing world in which they find themselves. Such anxiety has real causes, and it must be faced. It will be reduced I think, when each aspect of the problem is considered in isolation, even if artificially so, and its debit-and-credit account is charted — e.g., how can manual work be reduced in the kibbutz? What would be the gains? What would be the negative consequences? Subsequently, the interrelationship of these problems can be studied.

RACHEL MANOR: In my kibbutz, I am always fighting for a higher educational budget; here, I want to say that in my opinion, there is not anywhere in the world a farm — and we *are* farmers — with such a high budget for education.

Nevertheless, if we look at it from the point of view of the Jewish people, who really have been intellectuals throughout the centuries, we have to lay our stress on work done by hand. That is a real value — and as a value, it has not yet become so incorporated in all of us that we can afford to ease up our pressure for it. The set of values that places manual work above intellectual work is something we have to hold to — and I wouldn't want to change it.

I do not think that contradicts anything that has been said about technical development. Almost no kibbutz today is living solely on agriculture. There are factories, and there are specialists, sent by the kibbutz, who are studying to learn how to run the factories. If we find that we can manage the farm — the agricultural sector — with fewer people, then we will have more factories and more industry — which doesn't mean that we will abandon the value we set upon manual work.

DR. MENAHEM GERSON: I've been sitting here with a deep feeling of gratitude — not because of the compliments you have paid us, but because of the really amazing ability you have shown for sizing up our problems and our goals. My conclusion is that I shall be talking to you from here on as *Chaverim* — which means, very openly and without any reservations.

The kibbutz has not grown only out of the necessity of building up the country. That is one reason; the other reason is that we have been impatient to achieve a *Socialist* organization of society. We didn't want to have to wait until, in the wider system, Socialism was reigning in full power; *we wanted to build something*. We have wanted to build a socialist society in our lifetime. Now that you have seen what a kibbutz really means, I think you can understand why this goal is bound up with our whole approach, and is not merely a mental restriction or limitation.

All the great achievements in Israel have been made by the working class. I mean, an "achievement," in *our* sense. Why was this possible? Because we had a very special working class: what we call a pioneering, a *"halutzic,"* working class. People became proletarians, not because they were compelled to do so, but because they wanted to link their own personal fate with the future of society. That's why they joined this class.

Please understand that manual labor and its evaluation have to be seen from two points of view, if you wish to understand us.

One is the Jewish situation: the fact that it was a great experience for us to be able to *plough*, for instance, after centuries of the "intellectual Jew." But the other source of our high evaluation of manual labor is a Socialist one, all of us being convinced that that class, even now, holds the future of society in its hands.

Now, you know — as psychologists, you can probably explain it better than we can — that if you want something very strongly, and if that something is very different from what is currently accepted, you have to *overstress* it, in order to achieve it. Our evaluation of manual labor was born not only out of objective necessity — the objective need to connect our own future with the working class and with Socialism — but also out of our own psychological needs. An intellectual who becomes a worker, i.e., does manual work, still knows that he is *leaving something out:* what he could have achieved intellectually; and he has to convince himself that *this,* after all, is the all-important thing.

In addition to these three reasons for our evaluation of manual work, we have to mention one other objective factor. Israel is very far from being an affluent society. Even though some circles may give you this feeling, or may even themselves live with the feeling that we have already achieved an affluent society — that is a great mistake! The general standard of living in Israel is not what you have seen in the kibbutzim; it is very low.

No, we are not an affluent society; we recognize that our national and social tasks are very far from fulfillment. We need workers; and we still need (this is not just a matter of Zionist propaganda) to "conquer the desert." Taking that into account, we have to admit to ourselves that there is sometimes an astonishing overevaluation of intellectualism outside the Kibbutz Movement. For instance, our former Minister of Education once made this statement: "When the percentage of academic people in Israel becomes less than it is in America, America will cease to esteem Israel." For us, that sort of thing is just the opposite of what we came for; — not only from our subjective point of view, but also as against what is objectively needed.

If you remember these facts, you will understand what is going on in our Kibbutz Movement. You have to see our Movement within the framework of these facts, and then you can see why this overestimation of manual work has arisen. But you must not pay attention only to the psychological aspects; there are social factors involved as well.

What has been said about our youth, about their revolt, is not right, either. I don't know whether the term "the skeptical generation" is familiar to all of you. (I am talking about a wonderful book by Schelsky, called *The Skeptical Generation*.) I'm quite sure that we shall find an opportunity later to talk more fully about our adolescents, and you will see that this drawing further away from politics is not a special feature of kibbutz youth, or of Israeli youth. It is something that apparently holds true all over the world, which is why I don't think it is a form of revolt, as has been asserted here.

Dr. Eisenberg made a very important point when he differentiated between one's career and one's education. I don't know whether you all agree with this distinction between making higher education a career and looking upon it as a part of human development. But it's *all-important for us* — because it's the second one that is linked with the existence of the kibbutz; the first does not go with it. Trying to open up every possible way of making a career for our youth, and then putting stress on their becoming physicists, would not be my idea of the way to preserve the kibbutz. However, if one speaks of the deepening of education as a human value, then I think we are talking of a real necessity that exists now in the kibbutz in every respect.

We need to give our youngsters the opportunity to continue their education after they have finished school; I think this circle of the people of Seminar-Kibbutzim is thinking about it. In my Movement, we have already fixed a time to discuss a plan. Not to send our people to the University; that is not what we need. We would look to the University if we wanted career people; what we need is to give our young people an opportunity to go on with their own education — on an academic level — *right here*. One year of such intensive study for our people — when they are about twenty-five or so — would mean more than three years of being a general student elsewhere. And that's what we intend to do!

Chapter III

EARLY CHILDHOOD AND LATENCY

Problems of Early Childhood

INFANCY IN COLLECTIVE EDUCATION

GIDEON LEWIN

W HEN A CHILD IS BORN in the kibbutz, the whole community is happy. This is an event not only for the immediate family, but also for the whole kibbutz family.

The first contact of the mother and child with the educational system of the kibbutz is in the "baby-house," where they meet the first metapelet. There they establish their fundamental "trust" in kibbutz education. (Erikson speaks of the trust and mistrust that the infant gains during his first year of life. I would like to use this concept in its broadest social sense, with regard to the emotional ties of mother and child to the kibbutz.)

It should be made clear from the outset that the children's houses in the kibbutz are not "institutions." Provence and Lippton have written, in their *Infants in Institutions*:

"The family — father, mother, and children — is the setting in which babies can best be provided with care and influences that support and foster good development. It becomes increasingly hard to provide such care as we get further away from this model. The infant's needs are multiple and complex, and it is difficult and perhaps impossible to meet them adequately under conditions of group care."

This statement, which is probably true when one compares family life outside the kibbutz with institutions, is not true when we compare family education with kibbutz education.

Provence and Lippton mention three elements of deprivation suffered by infants in institutions: (1) The *absence of a specific maternal figure*, which appears to exert a retarding influence on

69

learning in a general sense; (2) The *shortness of time spent* in
the care of infants (a quantitative deficit), and (3) The lack of
personalized care.

As to the first point, which in a sense includes both the second
and third as well, we have to see the baby-house as a successful
combination of maternal and professional care. The metapelet's
experience, training, and point of view, combined with the
mother's tenderness and love, provide the foundations for a complete, unified and wholesome effort at child care. This does seem
to be shown by our infants' development, although unfortunately
we have no exact research data on it.

In speaking of infants, to be sure, we should always keep in
mind individual differences, constitutional factors and specific
personal happenings. With this in mind, we can still say that
our infants have good social contact. They smile, move around,
and play early, and know two or three words by the end of the
first year. The child knows his mother and his metapelet as different persons. His concept of strangers must be different from the
one you are used to: he knows quite a number of "familiar"
strangers — the mothers of other infants, the other infants, the
second metapelet.

Actually, he is almost never alone: for about 90 per cent of
his waking hours, there is the mother or the metapelet at hand,
ready to respond to his needs, and to provide stimuli for his perceptual, motor and emotional activities. Crying of infants out of
discomfort is thus at a minimum. Aldrich speaks about a 117-
minute group average of daily crying in a hospital, which they
reduced to fifty-five minutes by spending more time on care. We
have found an average of only eight to ten minutes of daily crying. This reflects no lack of mothering, surely, in the quantitative
sense of the word, nor is there any evidence of lack of personalized
care.

Collective education has thus proven that the existence of
more than one image in infancy is not only not harmful for personality development, but, on the contrary, may be a very important psychohygienic factor. Identification with the mother alone
is a scientific abstraction; it never existed in reality. The metapelet is not an invention of collective education: there have al-

ways been, besides the mother, other persons who took care of infants, such as aunts, grandparents, baby-sitters, neighbors. Margaret Mead states, too, that "adjustment is most facilitated if the child is cared for by many warm, friendly people."

Identification does not occur *in vacuo*: it is based on such care activities as feeding, cleaning, playing, holding, speaking to. Not every mother anywhere is able to satisfy her child in all these activities; here, the importance of the metapelet becomes quite clear. During the first year of the child's life, the metapelet is not a "mother substitute," but rather a "mother supplement," except in those cases where the mother is hindered from taking care adequately or is too disturbed to do so.

Actually, both "mother substitute" and "mother supplement" are very unfortunate concepts for the metapelet. Nobody is supposed to be, or is able to be, a mother equivalent. There are really *two* emotional centers for the kibbutz infant and child: one is made up of the mother and the family; the other includes the metapelet and the group. Each functions in its own right, producing its own sequence of ambivalence, and presenting in its own way the reality of physical surroundings. As Anna Freud has suggested, attachment in the earliest months is to the experience of satisfaction and relief derived from *being taken care of* by the mother, and is not directed to the mother *as a specific person*. If we see this stage of development as the beginning of personal and social relationships, we may assert that an infant in the children's house anticipates satisfaction from *everybody* around him, and since he actually gets attention and comfort from more persons than his mother, he learns to trust his surroundings *in general*. I think that this is one of the main points one must grasp; otherwise, it is impossible to see the children's houses as their real homes.

Herein lies the answer to Dr. Bowlby's comment after his recent visit here: "The admirable qualities of many of the kibbutz children of age eighteen are products of the excellent facilities the kibbutz provides for children, aged from, say, eleven years onwards. There is no reason to attribute them to the peculiarities of care in the early years." This is an astonishing statement, indeed. If the earliest years and the form of care given to infants

are very important, as Bowlby himself asserts, how can he assume
that education in adolescence is alone powerful enough to endow
our young people so generously, and to compensate so richly for
the supposed "peculiarities" of child care during their early years?

Thus, we believe that there are two emotional centers which
strengthen the infant's ego. Identification with more than one
object mitigates frustrations and conflicts, and compensates for
the suffering from those separations that are due to the necessities
of life. It broadens the images of reality. We encourage every
effort of the infant to put his abilities to use: activities such as
play, feeding, movement and many more are supported. There is
no discrepancy here between maturation of the psychic and so-
matic apparatuses, and their use in adaptation to the environment.

The process of weaning is completed in the last quarter of
the first year. We encourage our mothers to nurse their children
as long as possible — up to eight months; but weaning usually
starts by the fourth month and is gradually brought to completion
by the eighth month. By the end of the first year, the metapelet
is taking over more and more care activities from the mother.
Slavson mentions three stages the child goes through in relation
to its treatment by adults: nurture, discipline, education. Early
infancy is, of course the time of nurture only. With the beginning
of the second year comes the time of habit training, or as Slavson
put it, of "disciplining." This occurs coincidentally with the end
of the weaning process and the infant's first established feeling of
self. That is when the metapelet begins to take over more and
more.

One of the most important aspects of collective education is
that habit training does not have to be carried out by the mother.
This allows for a much more conflict-free relationship between
her and her child, and has a deep influence upon the child's life,
such as would be impossible if the metapelet were to take over at
a later age. This was highlighted recently by a girl about twenty-
three years old, born and raised in a kibbutz, who told me the
following story: "This week we had a meeting in my kibbutz. A
certain woman was supposed to be elected as chairman of a committee. I voted against her. You know why? I always vote against
her. I remember her as my metapelet when I was three or four

years old. She forced me to eat some cheese which I disliked very much. Since that time, I have been against her." This is a sad story for the metapelet; but what would have happened if it had been the *mother* who had forced this girl to eat — as is quite common with mothers?

I would like to make a few remarks on autoerotic activities. Certain body activities of the infant serve as agents of maturation, helping to form the feeling of the body image and the self. They give autoerotic satisfactions and thereby serve as indicators of the quality and quantity of the infant's relations to *other* satisfying persons. Yet one has to be very careful about generalizing in regard to these activities, for they seem to depend, at least in part, on the kind of behavior pattern with which the child is born. Insofar as we value autoerotic activities as significant of relations with others, we find no "deviations," such as are reported by Spitz, Provence and Lippton, and others, for institutionalized children.

Except in a very few cases, we use pacifiers or cradles. Thumb-sucking and genital play are the usual autoerotic activities. Rocking occurs mainly in the developmental stage, when the infant tries to sit or stand up; continued rocking is quite rare. In a few cases, we were able to confirm the fact that Spitz's view is more often true when the mother's emotional ties with her infant are very unstable, and fluctuate between extremes of overprotection and neglect. As far as I know, no fecal play has been observed by the end of the first year.

I would like to conclude with a quotation from the late Smuel Golan, whose searching mind has made contributions to all that collective education stands for: "One must not forget that collective education is not a pedagogical and psychological experiment, which is being carried out in ideal laboratory conditions. It is part of the real life of a social movement that has followed new social and economic principles but has had to face much economic hardship and insecurity during all the years of its existence. We believe that the experience of collective education may add its own modest contribution to the solution of those current orthopsychiatric problems that are common to modern society throughout the world."

ANECDOTES OF CHILDHOOD
Miryam Rot

I have collected, from among our kibbutz anecdotes, some of those which I thought might give you the flavor of the children's life. These little stories may also tell us a great deal about what they think of kibbutz life.

We see, very early, the first signs of the children's give-and-take: for instance, a child throwing a toy into the bed of another child, at first accidentally, but afterwards deliberately. Or a one-and-a-half-year-old child wanting to play with a toy that is in the possession of a girl of the same age; the girl holds the toy very tightly in her hands, whereupon the boy finds a large yellow leaf and gives it to the girl, who then gives him the toy. This is a bargain without words; it is not a very rare incident, you can see things like this quite often.

The children are able to show their sympathy at such an early age, something that is not so often found in other groups of children. For instance, a two-year-old is crying bitterly, and another, of the same age, stands next to him and cries with him, silently; still another girl, two-and-a-half years old, consoles Ram (the boy who is crying) by petting his cheeks. Or, two boys from another group — three-year-olds — throw sand at the head of a two-year-old. He cries. Two girls of his own age-group stand on either side of him; one tries to clean his hair, while the other, Offa, tries to drive away the bigger boy, swinging her hands in his direction. Remember, these are only two- and two-and-a-half-year-olds.

The children receive their directives from the nurse or the metapelet, but they identify with their peers. This is really a regulating factor, an obstacle to the development of guilt feelings. The ties among them are so strong that the children will not do many things except as a group. For instance, they will call to each other: "Come on, let's make something dirty," or "Come on, let's hit somebody"; but they will only do it *together*. They are, of course, able to organize positive group activities, too. You hear this among the three-year-olds: "Come, let's make a nice surprise for our metapelet" or, "Come, let's dress very quickly, so she will find us ready."

All of the parents are away during the day, and all the children are geared to close intimacy with the metapelet. Yet this only seems to bring them closer to each other. We can trace early, friendly relations between children, who look for and get the protection and support of their peers, and reach a very high degree of interdependency. A two-year-old is crying bitterly and a boys tries to console her by patting her cheeks; when a second boy wants to join them, the girls says: "No, no, Mottik; there is no more room on my cheeks."

I think that under conditions of group living, group identification and sharing, as well as group control of individual behavior, can be learned by very young children. Their common experiences make them familiar with reality. The children learn from others' reactions the real character of their surroundings, and share their feelings about it. For instance, Yuva, who is three-and-a-half years old, invites his friend Hagid to meet his father's guests, saying, "Come on, I have uncles and aunts in my parents' room; let's be shy together."

From the time the child is able to walk, he is permitted to go out into the garden. This is an environment that both protects and maximizes autonomy; children have a chance to experience it alone, and completely, yet near the group and near the metapelet. I had the opportunity to follow up a group of two-and-a-half and three-year-olds who had spent a whole year elsewhere. These children — they were kibbutz children, remember — had played mainly on the fourth floor; they hadn't met the daily situations of the village and of the other youngsters. On returning home to the kibbutz, they were unable to cope with simple everyday conditions; group anxiety spread over all their daily routines.

We face this problem about our night arrangements: how can the children bear staying alone the whole night through, without being near their parents? Yet the presence of all the other children in the same room, chatting and singing before going to sleep, calms the atmosphere and helps each individual child not to feel alone at night. Very often, one child will help another, escort him to the bathroom or give him water.

In one of the children's houses, a boy of one year and ten months, was the first in the bedroom. The metapelet still had to put the other five children to bed. Because he was alone, the child cried, and the metapelet sent one of the girls to him, "Go in and comfort Yivtach." This two-year-old girl went in, took a chair and stood on it beside Yivtach's bed, repeating this little jingle several times, "Don't cry. Segal is coming, and Anat is coming, Rahel is coming. . . . All the children are coming to you." The child stopped crying.

We are often asked if the children are really ready for group life. This is not real group life. Yet the children have a feeling of belonging, the earliest signs of sympathy do arise. . . . Still, there are so many dramatic changes in the dynamics of the group. How do they manage, twenty-four hours every day?

An intensive group life of kindergarten children is possible — in the rich surroundings of the kindergarten. There is an abundance of materials there: playthings, crayons, sand, paper, dolls, and blocks. There are play corners and work opportunities: housekeeping, gardening, cleaning, etc. All this helps the children to be continuously active. In their activities, they use the whole of the house space and the garden. The play corners are arranged in different rooms, which makes possible the continuous changing of small group formations. Activities in the house start without any rigid schedule: the children simply begin to play.

I am against separating the children's sleeping and living arrangements from the kindergarten, because that would take away something from the whole picture. The kindergarten in the kibbutz is identical with "home": the children have become used to its rules and arrangements, and the autonomy of each child and of the group provides a feeling of security. The kibbutz kindergarten is not just a place in which the child spends some hours of activity and social life — it is *life itself*.

It is a children's community, with rules that fit the kibbutz society, and the development and needs of the child as well. Let us see how conscious the children are about their "rights." Ruth asks mummy ("ima"), "Ima, tell me, why is this a movie for adults and you won't let me go — but still you always go with me to the children's movies?" Or, the father says to his daughter, a five-year-old, "Please give me your hand," and she answers "You're big enough, you can walk by yourself."

Children are kept informed about farm news: the harvest;

the vintage; the arrival of a new tractor, and so on. The parents work in different branches, and the children are constantly visiting their places of work and seeing their parents at work. Such experiences are part of the basic content of the kindergarten curriculum. A six-year-old boy will say, very seriously, "I am so concerned about its not raining; maybe there will be a drought" — an exact repetition of what he has heard from his father or from other kibbutz members. Even at the kindergarten age, the child feels himself to be a part of his society, with the same concerns and ambitions as those experienced by adults.

What cultural patterns of the kibbutz can be absorbed by the children? How do they feel about them? As you know, Shabbat is the free day, the most pleasant day for children and parents alike. The children know the concept of the Shabbat-day very well. Shmulik, a five-year-old, is walking about in the garden. Hyah comes and bothers him and he says to her, "Leave me in peace! It is Shabbat today and I don't want to hit you!"

Yesterday the group visiting one of the kibbutzim saw the "Commune" — the collective store of clothing. What do the children understand about such things as a commune? A metapelet says to Dalia, "You have beautiful eyes; where are they from?" Dalia answers, after thinking awhile, "Maybe from the commune of eyes." Or, six- and seven-year-olds are discussing prehistoric man, and one of them says, "The ancient people had no clothes." Alicia, six, says, seriously, "I think that's because they didn't have communes then."

Now I would like to tell a story about differences — and equality. Two boys are talking together. The first says, "I can go traveling in my father's car." The second replies, "Good for you: your father has a car, so you can make trips whenever you like." The other boy then says, "Everybody according to his father's branch: I can make trips in my father's car — and you can eat as much corn as you want!"

Although there is a constant struggle for leadership in our kindergarten groups, it is somewhat lessened by the variety of activities, the large amount of space and the possibilities of withdrawing and sitting in a quiet corner. Children accept one leader in one field of activity, another leader in a different one. David is known as a skillful builder; Ruth is the initiator in the doll corner. The children also learn early that in kibbutz society, there are no final roles: everybody can change his role. The teacher often works in the kitchen on weekends, and in the orchards during vacation. The man who used to be the secretary of the kibbutz now works in the garage.

A somewhat different problem is that of the scapegoat. In our society as elsewhere, he is the child who is insecure — in his family, perhaps, or because he has come from outside and is new. But this kind of scapegoat position disappears in a short time.

Dinah wants to go back to the kindergarten, at a time when the children are with their parents. Her mother asks, "What for?" "I have seen there, amongst the tangerines in the basket, one rotten one; I am afraid the other children will leave the rotten one for me." But then there are the children who have overcome such feelings. For instance, when six-year-old Amit listened to the fable of "The Crow and the Fox," and heard that the crow didn't have any cheese at the end, he said, "I have to run after the fox and take back half the cheese. He should only have taken half." This is not the reaction we are used to.

There is a problem of continuities in the kindergarten and in the children's houses, generally. When one child's metapelet was ill, another woman, whom the child didn't know very well, came to substitute for her. At home, the child said to her mother, "Today we had a step-metapelet." Five-year-old Yael said, "I haven't seen my mummy today, and this evening I'll not be seeing my daddy. This is an orphan day." One child is crying, "Ima, ima (mummy, mummy) ," but the mother doesn't appear. A three-and-a-half-year-old then says to him, "Tell us her name, so that everyone will know which mummy you want . . . . You must call not only 'ima,' but her name . . . . Then she will know who is wanted."

The children are very conscious about whether their parents come to get them in the afternoon and play with them. Four-year-old Yonat went to look for her friend Rina in the parents' room. She came back and said, "Rina is not in — her father is playing by himself." Because this is *the time that the father has to play in* . . . but Rina is not there, so he's "playing by himself." A four-year-old boy sees his father through the window. He runs to the metapelet and says, "Hurry, hurry, put my sweater on. My daddy's 'empty' and I have to go to him."

Finally, here are some insights into the children's conception of the metapelet. The name of Zvika's metapelet is Ruth. Zvika looks at the night sky, and seeing the moon and the stars, says, "The moon is the Ruth of the stars." One three-and-a-half-year-old girl is very confused when she sees a hen with its chicks, in the schoolchildren's small farm. She asks, "Is this hen the mother or the metapelet? So many of them are of the same age."

I should like now to summarize the tasks of the metapelet and the kindergarten teacher. They have to practice and to verbalize a number of rules, because they are not only the educational but the main social leaders throughout the day. If we had a rigid atmosphere, that might prove very difficult, but in our warm and close homelike atmosphere, which emphasizes individuality and variety, the children accept it.

The *planning* of the kindergarten is also among the main tasks of the kindergarten teacher. By means of her program, she builds up a direct, strong bond between the children and the adult community, and between them and their rural environment. It is at first a very emotional bond; afterwards, it is also an intellectual bond.

Mention has been made of "two centers." One should not try to compare these two focuses, or ask which one is more important. They are *different*; there are different tasks and different rules. The life of a child in the kibbutz is whole when *both* these centers function well, when *each* fulfills its own role.

The children's community exists side by side with the adult community. They are linked with one another by emotion and interest; at the same time, they are separated by each one's autonomous organization. Thus, there are two circles in which the child moves; that is true. But they are very much interconnected and they have equal importance.

DISCUSSION

Sleeping Arrangements

DR. KARPE: There is a question among us how good or bad the sleeping arrangements are for the children; but there is also the question of how difficult a situation this creates for the mothers. Many mothers may feel that the children's home has a somewhat traumatic significance for them. What opportunities do they have to bring out their gripes, and to get help in resolving what may be this traumatic effect of the children's home?

DR. NEUBAUER: How much opportunity does the mother have to express whatever feelings she may have about the whole setup of having to share her child with the metapelet in the children's home? How much objection *can* she express?

AVIVA MANDEL: In our kibbutz, we have groups of four babies each. Sometimes, when a baby is born, instead of starting a new group of babies, we will allow the mother to keep the baby with her during the six weeks when she is not working. We have found, in many cases, that this has given the mother the feeling that she can cope with the situation slowly, that she doesn't have to take the infant right from the hospital to the babies' home, but can keep it with her.

Surprisingly enough, however, most mothers have not chosen to keep the baby with them. After having tried it for a week or two, the mother would rather have a nurse, who knows that sort of work, feed the baby four times a day. It is true, of course, that most mothers have other children and don't want the rivalry that is bound to occur among them. The important thing is that while we give them the chance to choose, not very many women have taken the privilege. They have found it easier to rest during those six weeks, and have the baby cared for by the metapelet.

DR. KRIS: Is there no possibility of the mother, upon coming home from the hospital, living in the children's house for one week, while the metapelet is there to help her deal with the newborn? Especially with the first child, most mothers are somewhat anxious; they do not quite know how to deal with the new baby, and need a little help. If the mother could stay in the children's house, that would also do away with her separation from the child at that very early time.

There seems to be an awareness in all kibbutzim that the mother needs the child, and the child needs the mother, during the first weeks of the newborn's life. What has not yet become quite clear is *how long* and *how much* the mother is in need of the child and the child in need of the mother. These two questions might be best discussed separately. We would like to know what signs can be taken to demonstrate the child's readiness to leave the mother for some longer period of time, without developing untoward reactions, too much anxiety, etc. Slight signs of uneasiness in the child that disappear readily should be accepted, of course, as normal variants, rather than as constant or stronger signs of disturbance.

AVIVA MANDEL: We have a room next to the babies' quarters for the mothers. And in every baby's room there is a bell connected to the mother's room; the minute the baby shows signs of waking up and needing his meal, we ring for the mother, day or night.

NECHAMA LEVI: There are people who think that if only they can take the children home to sleep, the children will be happy and the parents will be happy. Another group wonders: if the children sleep in the children's home, then who is to put them to bed at night — the parents or the metapelet? I try to think of *what is better for the child* and *what is better for the parents.* How will the parents be more relaxed; how will the child be more relaxed?

RACHEL MANOR: We have had an experiment with children sleeping at home with their parents; the parents were happier than those parents whose children continued to sleep in the children's house. *In one generation,* there can be that kind of change. When the parents themselves accept our sleeping arrangements, they don't raise conflicts in the mind of the child. Remember, to the child, this not only a question of a place to sleep; the place where he sleeps is also a corner of life — that corner of the room, that shadow on the wall, that flower. . . . Although we may change, the child cannot, and you will not solve this problem just by having children sleeping in the same house with their parents.

EMI HURWITZ: My point has to do with the importance of inner security — confidence — which is the product of tradition, regardless of methods and techniques. A member of a certain kibbutz has told me that the *veteran members* of her kibbutz are quite confident when they put their children to bed. They consider it a good thing that the children sleep in the children's house: everyone is satisfied — the parents have no doubts, and the children no night fears. However, when the *younger members* come with their children — the educational or psychological guidebook in one hand, and the child in the other — then it doesn't work so well. They are a little doubtful and a little insecure; this has an impact on the child. It is more difficult for the child to separate from the parents, and the result can be — although not always — night fears.

Both these situations go on in the same house, in the same environment, and actually all the people involved are doing the same thing. The only difference that does exist is the difference in confidence and inner security. That is why I regard tradition as an important factor.

SHMUEL NAGLER: Our most important problems do not have to do with "arrangements," but primarily with the *relations* between parents (especially mothers) and the educational staff. We recognize that it is essential to provide mothers with the opportunity to express their feelings on the subject of the educational system and the educators themselves. This does not mean that they can have the final word on any principled educational matter, such as whether the child should stay overnight in the parents' home or in the children's house. There are, it is true, instances in which kibbutzim delegate that sort of decision to the parents. However democratic that may sound, in my experience, it turns out to be nothing but a rationalization of confusion and an evasion — a poor one! — of possible conflicts.

If the practice of children sleeping away from the parents and in the children's house were no longer to be an integral part of a pattern, and to become instead a matter of individual decision by the parents, then the whole situation would acquire a totally different meaning. There have been instances where the transfer of a child from the metapelet in the infants' house to that in the toddlers' group, at the age of six to eight months, causes night-crying. I myself have dealt in such cases with what were considered to be matters of "arrangements," yet the effects on the child of rearrangement proved to be short-term rather than long-term. In almost all the cases where we found pathogenic effects of such situations on the later development of the child, we also discovered deeper disturbances that had their origin in the mother-child relation.

Sex, Aggression, Fantasy

Dr. Kris: I should like to ask a question regarding attitude of permissiveness towards children's genital play. What is your attitude toward it? What is really meant by "permissiveness" here? Do you ever openly say, "Don't do it!" If you do say it, at what age do you start? That is, at what age do you start to be prohibitive?

Gideon Lewin: If genital play were acted out in front of adults, there would surely be less permissiveness than when children were doing it amongst themselves. But since you are asking about adults and their attitudes, once again that is a question of individuals. I remember one metapelet who said, "In my kindergarten, there is no masturbation." (She even put her hand before her mouth, so as not to mention it.) Generally speaking, however, I don't think that the metaplot interfere with play unless it is going too far.

Miryam Rot: It is going too far if there is the possibility of any physical damage. We provide ways for sublimation, such as doctor toys; the children can sublimate in this way, and we don't interfere directly. For instance. I have seen play about childbirth: they put a big ball beneath their dresses, and afterwards they have childbirth. We don't interfere.

Dr. Kris: Is there a routine way in which such situations could be handled? One way, of course, could consist of not interfering at all. Another might be for the metapelet to suggest an alternative form of play, without directly mentioning the unwelcome activity itself, if the intimate play between the children is becoming too exciting. In this way, the child would be prevented from going on with the undesirable action; it would also be conveyed to him — even though indirectly — that this play should go no further.

I am trying to determine what regulations and routines exactly, what happens at the conscious and actual level of dealing with this problem. We ought also to know the inner taboos of the adults, and what these indirectly convey to the children. They may have the effect at times of allowing even less freedom than you might prefer to have established. If an eight-year-old openly masturbates, or has sex play with other children, would you feel that this is appropriate or satisfactory behavior, or would you judge that such activity should be halted?

NOOMI BEN ISRAEL: I don't think we regard it as either good or bad. That is one very fundamental attitude of ours. It is necessary, we think, for a child to explore his own body and the bodies of others; on the other hand, I don't think that we are indulgent enough to allow our children to explore and play this way for a long time.

Now, what is a long time? I think that every educator knows how long a time a child can profitably spend drawing or playing in a sand-pit, it's a feeling that he has. I could say ten minutes, or five minutes, or a quarter of an hour. I think that this is very important to the children — which is why they go back to it all the time.

Very often during the day, however, we will definitely interfere, by suggesting different kinds of play. We think that the children have many other things to do, which are creative, whereas *this is not truly a creative kind of play*. Its significance lies solely in the fact that it plays a part in their personality development. It is important for them to know how the body is built, and even for them to touch, in order that they should know the body is not bad; but it is not creative play. This is why we suggest to them, "Come, let's do this or that." "Look, I've brought you a box of clothing." "Come, let's have a dramatic play." That is how we would try to handle it, I think.

SHMUEL NAGLER: In our therapeutic family plays, children express chiefly sexual and aggressive drives, as well as their anxieties. For example: two dolls are put together on the bed; then follows the "killing" of the dolls, "attacks" on the dolls by wild animals, and finally the "killing" of all the adult "human beings," leaving behind only one lonely, sad child.

With regard to guilt and shame, as dealt with in Spiro's book, let me first say that the children referred to us tend to have strong guilt feelings, which may lead to self-punishment — mostly of an unconscious type. On the other hand, there are, of course, feelings of shame, primed by the highly developed pressure to conformity.

GIDEON LEWIN: It seems to me (I am aware, of course, that generalizations are always dangerous) that the oedipus complex lasts longer with our children. We can see this conflict at its highest point at six and six-and-one-half years old — even as late as seven. I don't think that this is a symptom, but the outcome of a more tolerant education. Group life tolerates the freer expression of all kinds of genital play and genital curiosity and genital acting-out at this age.

Susan Isaacs once wrote about how experiences with siblings are brought into group life; we may have this, too, but we also have it the other way around: experiences with peers are brought into sibling relations. All the experiences of boys and girls in group life seem to intensify the relations between siblings, because group life is, in a sense, a trial to find out what is really involved in these relations.

DR. NEUBAUER: There are two issues I would like to speak on. (1) The prolonged oedipal period, and (2) family play of children in treatment:

1. Dr. Lewin has mentioned that he was under the impression that the oedipal period seemed rather prolonged, as compared with the normal developmental duration. This, it would seem, deserves to be carefully checked. If it were found to be true, one could then consider the following questions:

(a) Do developmental phases become shorter or longer as the result of cultural situations? Is this part of an adaptive process? What are its advantages, and what are the hazards? If the oedipal period is prolonged, does that mean that solutions cannot be found for the process of sex and social identification and integration?

(b) What can we see of superego formation? Is there a delayed superego development — and with it, a delayed repression, which then also delays the emergence of the latency period? Is there a connecting link to the children living in the children's home, rather than in the family? What is the relationship of this to the primal scene experience?

(c) If there is a delayed solution of the oedipal conflict, does that fact signify that neurotic symptom formation will probably occur at a later time among kibbutz children — at least, those crystallized symptoms that are based on the neurotic conflict?

The shortened latency period may have a special effect on the child's learning capacity. Does the prolonged oedipal conflict stimulate curiosity and exploration? Or does the shortening of the latency period result in preventing the emergence of a long conflict-free learning period? This question is obviously connected with the degree of instinctualization of life — in other words, with the degree of ego control of the drive elements.

2. Dr. Nagler has given us material on play association with children in treatment, in which he has discussed the child's attempt to reconstruct the family in fantasy play. The fact that the family emerges is in itself, as he has said, quite significant. Dr. Nagler may also be able to tell us about the contents of such fantasy family life. What goes on in such a family? Who is seduced, and who is punished? Where are the fears; where are the death wishes? In what form is the oedipal conflict stated, and is there a common pattern in the family scene? Has he also found that the primal scene is part of the reconstruction?

Sex differentiation can easily be observed among our children in the nursery. Here, in the five-year-old group, there is a clear separation of boys and girls. While until this time, they have played together, the boys now go into aggressive play — "Cowboys and Indians," or "Superman" — from which the girls seem to become excluded. The girls play in the special family corner — they cook, take care of babies, become very interested in how they dress, love to put on mother's clothes, etc. Have you observed a similar differentiation among the kibbutz children?

EMI HURWITZ: The social differentiation of the sexes can be observed very early in our children's houses. At one-and-a-half year, it is already an established fact that the boys play with motor cars and tractors, and the girls with dolls, and at keeping house. In spite of the fact that at this early age, all the children are cared for entirely by women, the behavior of the boys already differs significantly from that of the girls.

Secondly, in many groups, it appears to be not enough *to be as good* in performance as other children. There is also a tendency *not to attempt to exceed* the performance of the other children. I remember my daughter asking me, when I criticized her, "Do you really want me to do *better* than the other children?" She was genuinely surprised to hear that I thought that she could do so. This attitude exists in school work as well: the lack of desire to surpass. It has its drawbacks.

SHMUEL NAGLER: Small children tend to reveal their strivings and feelings more by means of fantasies than through actions. During therapeutic play, anxieties, aggressiveness, and sexual drives are expressed directly, as well as in symbolic ways. There appear monster crocodiles, elephants and snakes, in a way very similar to that which you have experienced in your own practice. In our culture, the Arabs serve as a means of expression for the child's anxieties and aggressive tendencies. In their make-believe play, father and mother dolls are used frequently, and the primal scene finds direct or symbolic representation, as may be gathered from our recorded play-sessions. This is in spite of the very different bedroom accommodations we have, as compared with those of the traditional family setting.

(*Question from the audience*: In the children's fantasy play is there any reversion to the original family structure, as opposed to the kibbutz family structure?)

DR. KRIS: The child has probably had no experience other than the kibbutz family. He has had no opportunity to witness the primal scene, as it is often observed by children in a family home.

SHMUEL NAGLER: I am not so sure about that. It is quite possible that the primal-scene play sometimes reflects actual eyewitness experience, and is not a mere product of fantasy. It happens, from time to time, that guests have to be accommodated overnight at the children's house, or that there are some cases of illness; or there may be instances in which the parents are too weak to withstand the children's expressed desire to stay with them, and hence these children may stay a night or two in their parent's room. To sum up, we may say that kibbutz children do reflect the traditional family structure in their therapeutic play. That, of course, does not mean that the figure of the metapelet or the night-watch is out of the play scene. They are there, all right — particularly the "bad" metapelet (the one who shouts, scolds and even strikes) ; she takes on the image of a witch.

DR. KRIS: The problem of nightmares has been mentioned. This is a symptom which frequently makes its appearance during the hegemony of the oedipus complex; it should not be understood merely as a reaction to some daytime occurrence with the mother. We may have, in our discussions, paid too little attention so far to the inner dynamic processes of the child. The fantasies that occupy the child around its various inner conflicts have very much to do with these nightmares; they sometimes use the incident of the day in terms of their own needs.

DR. EISENBERG: The state of our theoretical knowledge — even that of our factual data — is taken to be sufficient to make determinations of issues. Yet what developmental tests we do have are mainly related to the child's cognitive development. We have little about the inner psychic life — which is, in fact, impossible to measure in a young child. Satisfactory methods of determining the nature of the child's psychic life at one year are practically non-existent; we measure only certain functions of the infant — how he manipulates his environment, etc.; about the rest we cannot say very much. Many youngsters seem to function perfectly well at school, although sometimes emotional trouble pulls down intellectual achievement. When we are told that developmental tests have shown the kibbutz children to be the same as other children, this gives us one important respect in which they did not fail. Still, we have to recognize the present limitations of our examination.

DR. NEUBAUER: To what degree can one generalize about neurotic children from the material that is available? A diagnosis of neurosis can be properly applied, of course, only to that group of children who are able to achieve an oedipal phase of development. What about those who are not — who are either fixed at the pre-oedipal stage of development, or can avoid fixation on the oedipal conflict? We in America are quite concerned about the "nuclear" family: how very small the family has become, and how each individual therefore has little space for maneuvering, so that it becomes quite imperative to work things out among the very few, which thus brings about an intensification of the conflict. Does the availability of others minimize for some the drama of this conflict? Or is it the group that can alone avoid this solution, because it offers so many "escape hatches?"

Sibling Relationships

DR. BERNARD: Could we talk a little about the infant's siblings? It would be helpful, for those of us who are not acquainted with this problem, to learn more about the ways in which kibbutz conditions either foster or impede interrelations between older and younger children, and especially those from the same family. We would like to learn about the actual relationships.

EMI HURWITZ: The sibling problem is generally quite serious, particularly where there is only a small difference in the ages of the children. I do not find this to be any simpler among us than it seems to be outside the kibbutz. But there are certain constellations that may complicate the sibling relationship even further — such as, siblings being in the same group, nursery school or school in a small kibbutz, where there is no other alternative. Then there is *competition not only inside the family but also within the group,* and this causes constant tension.

That sort of thing can happen even when the relationship as such is a good one. Whatever the home relationship, siblings will always feel responsible for one another, will defend the brother or sister when he or she is attacked in the group. Some suffer from the failures of their siblings in the classroom or in social life; they look upon the sibling as a burden. In some instances, this situation is perpetuated all the way through childhood.

AVIVA MANDEL: In our kibbutzim, the kindergartens are for mixed ages, from three to seven. We felt that sisters and brothers of a family group were being needlessly separated, and that we could find a way in which brothers and sisters, and children of the same age group, could all be put together — to begin with, during the first three years, and then again from three to seven — from the oedipal age until school age (We don't have a direct learning process in the kindergarten. Our children go to school at the age of seven, entering the second grade; what we call the "pre-learning" period is handled in the kindergarten, in a very individual way.)

Our feeling was that the special rivalry between brothers and sisters in the parents' room (this is for a very short period only, since they meet only from five until seven) had become even sharper. We tried to lessen it by bringing brothers and sisters together where the *object of their rivalry* would not be present — for example, in the kindergarten, where the mother and father do not play any role as educators. Instead, there is the metapelet, who is responsible for all eighteen children, and therefore has a different relationship with them; through her, the actual brothers and sisters would be able to establish a positive relationship toward each other.

DR. KRIS: If the relationship of the kindergarten child to the teacher is intensified, the rivalry among the children will also increase. That is why some educators think that such a change as Mrs. Mandel has indicated would make the handling of the child in the group that much more difficult. In my opinion, this situation might be used beneficially to help the child deal with these feelings, to teach him how to face and control them, since they are less intense than the feeling in the family situation, where the parent is present.

It would be interesting to experiment with a variety of situations, in order to determine whether the working through in the kindergarten of the sibling rivalry situation might help to control the ambivalent feelings altogether, and thus render service to the total developmental process.

MOSHE AYALON: We do have kibbutzim that do not keep siblings in the same kindergarten, when the relations between the siblings seem to call for their separation. If one of them is very possessive and bossy, for example, they are not put together.

DR. KRIS: If the bossiness of a sibling is very intense, this might be the opportunity to have that child work out his problems, without his siblings participating in the kindergarten group with him. This quality has a better opportunity of being successfully mitigated and worked out, in a situation marked by the less intense feelings directed towards the substitute sibling.

ELI ILAN: I was much impressed by Mrs. Melzer's observations derived from the longitudinal study that she did with her own children. I must say, however, that the behavior of the siblings in this instance is not typical of that of ordinary siblings in a private family. This very good relationship between the siblings in the younger age group is *not* the characteristic relationship among the siblings of one family, where there is generally open strife. In this instance, no open strife was to be seen. Here, in fact, is the difference that we should keep in mind.

These children had a better opportunity to *displace negative feelings against the children in their groups* than the ordinary child has in the family in which he lives with his siblings. *The possibility of this displacement is a mode of defense that has been opened to the children in the kibbutz.* This sort of thing is very often sought for in private families, but I think that here it presents itself more easily to the children, and thus has something to do with the problem of avoiding conflict. "You can avoid conflict by displacement." That is what came into my mind when I heard this.

Group Relationships and Group Pressure

DR. KRIS: There are two different kinds of education or nurturing. One kind might be called "conditioning" — namely, putting the child again and again in a specific situation designed to achieve a reaction, but before any real ego capacity and object relationship has been established. In that case, the only result can be an *automatic* response. In England, they used to start bladder training from almost the first day of life. They achieved a relatively early bladder control; yet this training did not hold on as well as the bladder control achieved via object relation — i.e., for the sake of the relationship with the adult-caretaker, which at the same time fostered ego involvement. With this second kind of training, the goal set by the adult is *internalized* by the child, and the achievement is thus able to withstand stress.

There seems to me to be a parallel problem in the matter of group adjustment. Is group pressure, with its demands, brought to bear on the child *too early* — as in the previously mentioned "conditioning" — taking place before relationship capacity has fully developed in the child? The child in the kibbutz has un-

doubtedly as strong an attachment to his mother as a child anywhere else, i.e., the opportunity and basis for the development of
relationship capacity is given. Is this capacity — which we consider
essential for many of the ego functions — permitted under these
conditions to function to its fullest extent?

MIRYAM ROT: I would not use the word "group" here in the
sense of "unit," because this is a very small grouping, and these
children do not yet have the ability really to lead a group life.
This is, instead, an *identification on the part of individual children*: one child identifies with another; one child has an influence
over another — sometimes in the direction of the fulfillment of
the regulations, sometimes in the direction of the second child's
progress. Everybody, however, feels that each child has a very
wide range within which to act according to *his* urges, according to
his *own* drives.

We now have smaller groups than we formerly had: four
children living together. We have seen that four children makes
a better group than six, and that, if the metapelet is very close
to the children and can keep in contact with them, the children
generally function better. (Even when schoolchildren go into the
yard to sit there in the sandbox, or to be near the younger children, the whole atmosphere changes: the children become quieter.)
The metapelet can perform her duties merely by being near the
children: they just have to be able to see her; she can speak to
them, or just go around and smile.

NOOMI BEN ISRAEL: The term "group pressure" has been used
here. Can it be that *peer group pressure* is in fact less disturbing
for the child than adult pressure? A child who grows up in an
adult society is under very strong pressure from the adults. One
of the reasons we wanted children to live amongst children was
precisely *in order to relieve them of this adult pressure*. Aggres-
sions that children would not hesitate to show toward their peers
they dare not show to adults. That is why we thought this arrangement might have a good result in the acting-out of aggressive wishes, directed in fact toward adults, but diverted toward
their peers, after which they become friends again.

On the other hand, I think that the peer group not only imposes pressure, it also provides a lot of help. I don't think this is

given enough emphasis. Children think, "Everybody does it; I'll do it too." That helps them a lot.

SHMUEL NAGLER: I do not question the existence of close relationships between one child and another, even as early as one year. But I rather doubt that there can be a close relationship between the child and its group as a whole, and I do not think that the group is therefore able to give the child of that age needed support as well as an adult can.

When motor development is at its peak (during the second half of the second year, and the third year), children are running about, always in a rush and pushing about things, as well as other children. Generally, there is a very noisy and active atmosphere. We assume that since the needs of children of the same age are almost identical, there will be a mutual identification in the satisfaction of these needs. However, in our clinical work, we meet children who turn out in fact to be the prey of this need for satisfaction on the part of their fellow children; they become "bullied," frightened and driven to withdrawal from motor and general activity. These children, by contrast with the rest of the group, do not get any gratification of their motor needs out of their being in the group; on the contrary, this very fact is the cause of their frustration.

DR. KRIS: Everyone seems to recognize here that a proportion of six, eight or ten infants to one metapelet is not the ideal situation, and that it cannot now be changed, for practical reasons. What was disturbing in the articles sent to us was the omission of any reference to the child's need for "emotional refueling" during the day — especially the small child. This cannot be done for the one- or two-year-old by another child of the same age. At that age, this very important ingredient — emotional warmth — has to be made an integral part of the daily routine. That, at least, is our impression; it is partly but not as yet fully scientifically proven knowledge.

I do not doubt that very good experiences can be created by one two-year-old for another. But there are some things which they have not as yet acquired the ability to supply to each other. They are not yet able to *give love* in anything like a mature object-relation. They are still at what we call the narcissistic level —

which means that although they are in need of *love being given* to them, they cannot yet *give* it. Furthermore, they are not yet able to master on their own how to limit their drives. In this, as in many other respects, they need guidance by the adult.

After visiting one kibbutz and listening to our discussions, I am now convinced that it is *no deprivation for the child* to be in a small group with the metapelet during the whole day, so long as she is a warm person, who gives — both in quality and in quantity — the appropriate emotional supply.

DR. NEUBAUER: There are studies that have revealed the ability of children to turn to each other for satisfaction when adults are insufficiently available: the group seems to become stronger, the more limited the one-to-one relationship. The kibbutz children are placed in a group with a limited age range. I have always been interested in knowing whether you have discovered phenomena here similar to those found among twins: mirror reactions — in this case, imitation and identification among peers. The shift of the pattern from activity to passivity seems to be characteristic of the "twinning reaction." What is the "pecking order" in the group? How often does it change? What factors decide this? Is it generated by the adult or by the children's group interaction?

DR. KRIS: It is very interesting to deal with situations which exist in one culture but not in the other. We might ask why they are not present in the other culture, and whether there would be any value in their appearing in the other culture as well. Or is there some negative factor involved that might make this less desirable? These questions should be applied to group experiences.

Group situations with children are familiar to me from various day-care centers in New York, where a considerable number of children live together from eight in the morning until about five or six in the afternoon. They, too, are grouped according to age. There is one factor that seems to stimulate these children adversely — the continuous noise, which is interrupted only by relative silence during the nap-time after lunch. I do not know what sort of neurophysiological and psychological studies have been made in regard to this stimulus of sound jointly produced. I wonder whether such studies have been planned in the kibbutz.

DR. NEUBAUER: Would our Israeli colleagues tell us something about the problem of separation from the group — not the earlier "separation" from mother or metapelet, but the process of individualization in relation to the group? If one has lived in the group from infancy on, how does one regard the fear of the loss of the object (fear of losing the group), followed later by the fear of the loss of the love of the object (fear of losing the love of the group), and then, finally, the fear of punishment by the object (fear of being punished by the group)?

GIDEON LEWIN: We should discuss group life, I think, in developmental terms. As we speak of group life here, we seem to have in mind certain types of relations — between ourselves for the most part, or between youngsters during the periods of latency and adolescence — times when relations are somewhat more socially regulated. But before group life comes to be *socially* regulated, there may be a phase in which it is *emotionally* directed: "I love you; I hate you; I would like to be with you; I don't want to be with you," and so on. There may even be an earlier phase.

In the age group we are speaking about now — two-, three-, and four-year-olds, and possibly an even earlier stage, at the end of the first year and the beginning of the second year — there may be a kind of relationship which I would call "perceptual group relations." There are not too many emotional ties yet; still, the child knows that this or that baby "belongs to my group": if a child of twelve or fourteen months meets another child of his group in his parents' room or somewhere, he smiles at him. Since he knows and recognizes his group-mate, there must be some sort of perception of a group.

If we speak about group relations, then, we are speaking of something in which there are definitely different stages. We should make it quite clear which of these stages we are dealing with, because in every stage the pressure is different. If one speaks, for instance, as one mother has spoken, about the "struggle for life" in a group of two-year-olds, one is using, I think, a bad term: "struggle for life" in a group of adults or grown-up persons or adolescents is altogether different. The younger children are in one way more emotionally involved: they scream more, they hit more; but, in another way, they are *less* involved, because they don't "carry a grudge," and that, surely, is something that works against group pressure.

ERIKA KNOLLER: It has been said that we need to find ways of getting information about the influence of the group on younger children, but that we are not able to get such material from analysis because we don't carry on analytic treatment. But even if we did have the opportunity to perform this kind of analysis in individual treatment, would that be the best way to get information about the two-year-olds? I ask, not only because it is such an early age, but because the analytical situation with its specific transfer doesn't afford us the opportunity to bring to light the kinds of group feeling that may be present. Group analysis with older children would probably give us better information about the specific influence of peers at this early age.

It would be interesting, I think, to compare the group treatment of kibbutz-reared children with the treatment of children reared outside the kibbutz. If this specific question of group dynamics can be reached through analytical treatment, then the differences between the life of the kibbutz-reared child and that of children outside the kibbutz will find their expression.

MOISHE AYALON: It is very important to take note of age differences in regard to social pressure. I am not sure that we should always speak of "social pressure"; perhaps it might be better to speak of "social influence," since "pressure" has such a negative meaning. There is one age group — from ten to fourteen — in which I do feel the social *pressure* of the group on the individual: these children do not *dare* to be different, to do something different from the group. As a parent and as a teacher, I sometimes worry about this.

There are not only groups of children, there are also groups of parents. In the children's houses, the parents form a group, too, not only in relation to the children but also in their relations amongst themselves. That makes it a sort of "peer group" of parents, with great influence.

We sometimes feel the competition between parents who compare their children. This occurs mostly in the evening, when parents go from the private atmosphere of the parents' room to the public atmosphere of the children's house. This is a very difficult transition, and it therefore creates a difficult situation. Take the question of how the parent succeeds in getting his child to sleep. There is a great deal of competition, of looking at the other parents to see why and how it is that they succeed in quieting their child.

We have not spoken enough here of the role of the fathers. In European culture, the father is not as important for the baby as he is in the kibbutz. Here, a father can be very important for the whole group — one father, a special father. He does not stop with being the father of his own child, but becomes something like a collective father of the group.

Another thought about competition between parents: we have instances where the parents sit at the bedside of the child in the evening, because the child cannot sleep. We say to the parents, "Please stay at your child's bedside." But it appears that they have problems about staying with their child; they are concerned what the other children will say. The children, we find, understand it better than the parents do: *they* understand that there are some children who cannot sleep, and that the mother therefore sits with them. It is the *parents* who are jealous: the *mother* feels that it is not right to sit with her child when the other mothers do not.

SHMUEL NAGLER: Striving to conform is generally present among preadolescent children, in all the Western cultures outside of the kibbutz. But our material suggests that *in the kibbutz, the need to conform — or rather the fear of not conforming — is much more prevalent than it is in outside societies.* This should not surprise us, since it is only the natural outcome of the very structure of the children's house.

In urban societies, a child who has failed to be accepted in one group — for instance, in his classroom — may attain his social prestige in another group, such as the youth movement. In the kibbutz, on the other hand, *no such chance for "escape" is available to the child,* since he happens to belong to only one group. Therefore, it is quite natural that the possibility of being excluded from the group should revive very strong separation anxieties, which in their turn may have long-lasting effects on personality formation. It is thus not surprising that the kibbutz child is actually *afraid* to find himself different from "the rest of the flock."

Pathogenic Factors

ERIKA KNOLLER: Do we find in the clinical material evidence of a pathogenic factor in early group life, which affects some types of children by reinforcing their character; or, do we find the effects of this pathogenic factor (if it is that) among *all* those children who have participated in the group? In the pathological material, we come upon disturbed children for whom early group conditioning has clearly been a disturbing influence, but we cannot determine whether this early group conditioning had a similar pathogenic influence on other types of children.

SHMUEL NAGLER: The problem in regard to these conclusions is the well-known difficulty which one experiences in all the behavioral sciences — *how to isolate factors.* In most of the cases referred to, we discovered the existence of very disturbed mother-child relations. It cannot be expected that we should have found how to isolate specific influential factors solely on the basis of clinical material. This problem must be approached by direct observation of children in the one to two-year age group.

DR. NEUBAUER: I am not too sure that it is the observation of children during the first two years of life that will give us the answers to these questions. While it is true that any additional data will help, the problem of observation remains that of not being able to decide, from among the events in a child's life, just what is "experienced," and what, therefore, is most significant for either health or pathology.

I am in full sympathy, however, with the desire to isolate factors; this is an important scientific requirement. It reminds me of the situation which exists today with regard to the problem of smoking: the causative factors are still unknown, and therefore constitutional factors may also be important, for many people have smoked all their adult lives without any severe results. Can we be said to know for sure what produces a certain outcome? Yet, there would be little hesitation — on scientific grounds — in calling for a general limitation on or avoidance of smoking, on the part of the whole population. From the viewpoint of public health, the indications are clear, in spite of our less than full knowledge of the causative factors.

Psychoanalytic investigation has made a broad and meaningful contribution to development, in that it has forced the analyst to reconstruct the genetic scene — that is, the developing conditions out of which the pathology emerged. With this, the genesis of pathology can be described, as well as the processes of normal development.

Dr. Nagler earlier indicated his concern about the fact that there is a shift in the metapelet and a simultaneous withdrawal of the mother through weaning. His recommendations were quite clear, in spite of the fact that we cannot say for certain that all children suffer from such a situation. The scientist, of course, works for a careful corroboration of his hunches before he will commit himself; on the other hand, the practitioner has to translate knowledge into actions, and if he waits for strict scientific proof, he may wait too long and the proof may come too late to be of any use in most situations.

SHMUEL NAGLER: In our clinical practice, we meet youngsters who are noncooperative. As you may well imagine, such symptoms cause us the greatest concern, since they occur in a society which has cooperation as one of its cornerstones. Let me quote a few mothers and metaplot interviewed at our clinic: "He had to struggle for his life from the very beginning"; "He is an 'individualist' "; "He does not fit into kibbutz education; maybe not everybody is able to accustom himself to collective education"; "He is not a kibbutznik by nature."

In some of these cases of noncooperative children, aggressiveness could already be detected as early as during their second year of life; with regard to others, we discovered that the children had previously been extremely apathetic. These are, for the most part, the ones referred to by mothers and educators as "individualists." The statements I quoted above were accumulated primarily by the use of the retrospective approach in taking case histories, or during actual treatment. As for myself, I must admit that, so far,

I have not made sufficient use of direct observation of the toddlers in their group.

In our interviews with the parents of these children, we were sometimes met with a description of a situation that went like this: "While I was working one day, I heard my Micky crying; mind you, where I work is rather far away from the children's house. So I rushed to the scene, only to find Roni hitting poor Micky rather brutally with his fists. That Roni is a spoiled one! As a matter of fact, nobody came to the assistance of Micky, and I really wonder where all those metaplot were at that time. They were probably out having a stroll."

This Micky had unquestionably one of the characteristic features of the passive "individualist": he was slow in his motor development. On the other hand, it was also unquestionable that he did not get the needed support from an adult. Even if support may be expected to come from among the child's own age group, such group support cannot be counted on to replace adult support.

I am convinced that a metapelet — who, in addition to being charged with the care of six toddlers, has to see to it that the children's house is kept clean and tidy — cannot be expected to devote enough time to the satisfaction of any one individual's need for close contact with an adult, a contact on which that individual's security may be largely dependent. Insufficient contact with an adult, especially in this age group, may be regarded as a potential pathogenic factor. Everything must be done to prevent that potential from growing in due time into a reality.

ELI ILAN: There is a certain danger in putting the question as it has been put here: What is pathogenic? What is not pathogenic? Changes of the metapelet do not have any pathogenic influence; this is an everyday influence. We should not ask "What is pathogenic?" but rather, "What is the need of the child and what is the need of the mother?"

I think the kibbutz has gone a long way toward giving the mother and child increased opportunities to be together, and I do not think that it was done because we have seen our children become sick. They did not become sick; I don't think that there were any more sick children at the time when there was a sharp

separation between mother and child. And I don't think that
there was a larger proportion of sick children in the kibbutz,
from a psychological point of view, at the begining than there is
now.

DR. NEUBAUER: What you are saying would seem to be that
you are now addressing yourselves to the child's needs, but that
it has not made any difference from when you were *not* addressing yourselves to those needs. Is that it?

ELI ILAN: I would say that it does not make a great difference
in terms of pathology, although it may make a great difference in
terms of personality development. I think we should keep this
differentiation in mind, because although there are children who
do develop pathology, the question of influence, in terms of personality development, is of much wider scope. That is why it is
so very important.

EMI HURWITZ: It is necessary to stress one point which is important for the record. It is the background for many instances
of pathology in the kibbutz movement, perhaps throughout the
Jewish world. We have found no greater proportion of such cases
than there is elsewhere in the Western world, and it may be that
we have an even smaller proportion. Yet, *we could have had even
fewer, had the history of our entire generation been different.*

The holocaust appears in almost every anamnesis of children
and parents. Parents of some of our patients mention their own
parents, who perished in the concentration camps; others, their
brothers and sisters, about whose fate they still know nothing.
Some parents lost their entire first family — all their children;
they come with their second set of children, born after the war,
after the first children had perished. We hear these same histories
repeated in a thousand variations. People who settled in Israel
many years before the Second World War show strong guilt feelings; they ask, "Why did *I* survive?" To this day, many accuse
themselves of not having done enough to save their families.

All this cannot help having a very great impact on the relationship between parents and children; the strong emotions involved are transferred to the children in many strange ways.
When we speak of the psychological problems of Jewish children,
we must not forget this painful background. *We now know what*

Hitler did to the dead; we do not yet know and we cannot even imagine what he did to the living, and to future generations.

SHMUEL NAGLER: In what way can collective education be said to manifest an influence on child personality development, in view of the fact that the existence of such influence has not been directly revealed in the clinical material? In my opinion, this influence makes itself felt correctively, rather than pathogenically; in fact, I would estimate it to be the most significant among the corrective factors.

Under what circumstances might the children's house have to be regarded as pathogenic? When the metepelet's character traits clashed with the children's needs, for example, in the very same fashion as their mother's character traits did; in that case, the metapelet would serve as a reinforcing factor. This can be easily observed, for instance, in cases in which the child of a compulsive mother is under the care of a metapelet who is also distinctly compulsive.

During the earlier stages of collective education, there was a tendency to overvalue the countervailing effect of a constellation in which the child of a compulsive mother was brought under the care of a very permissive metapelet who, let us say, permitted the child to dirty itself with sand and mud. As we went along, however, we were confronted with negative results from such a constellation. In these cases, in which the attitudes of the mother and the metapelet were in sharp contrast, we found that conflict and confusion on the part of the child was accelerated, with resultant bad effects on its personality development.

DR. KRIS: Where we come from, we see something parallel in the case of children who come early to a nursery school, from very restricting mothers. Such a mother may be rigid in matters of control because of her own needs, or sometimes because of the father's intolerance of disorder of any kind in his home. In these situations, we hope that the nursery teacher, if she is not of a compulsive nature, can exert a mitigating influence. The way the nursery teacher can do this best is not to place herself outspokenly as a hostile counterforce to the parent, as someone "on the other side of the fence," but to tell the child — and the mother as well — that, although those restrictions *do have to be maintained at home,* in the nursery school they are *not necessary.* If this is acceptable to the mother, then the child can — without conflict, without guilt feelings or anxiety — go ahead with the now permitted activities.

Such agreements are important. It is evident that there is frequently a kind of hostility between mother and metapelet; that the metapelet is critical of the mother and vice versa, on the question of the extent of control or of leniency. The pathogenic factor may then be not so much the attitude of either adult, but the conflict they convey to the child by way of their contradictory attitudes — a conflict which, at that age, is too great a burden to carry without bad consequences.

This is similar to situations we often see arising in the home itself — between mother and father, or mother and grandmother — that is, between two people one of whom is more restrictive than the other can tolerate, thereby provoking in the latter a tendency to bend over backwards and to go to the other extreme. These divergent attitudes of two adult people concerned with the nurturing of a single child are more than likely fostered in reality by their mutual hostilities towards each other, rather than by their desire to help the child.

DR. NEUBAUER: We have to translate the conditions of co-ordinated child-care in a collective into developmental terms — in other words, to try to ascertain in what way these conditions affect each developmental stage.

We have raised these questions: Where does the child-rearing actually take place? Under what conditions? Of even greater importance, we want to find out to what degree one can assess the *quality* of the relationship, going beyond the questions of "who is in it?" and "where is it taking place?" When the process of child development is being studied, the *quality of human interaction* is one aspect to which we must attach significance, and which we must find the means of evaluating under existing cultural conditions.

In this respect, it seems strange to hear that the frequency of symptomatology, and the content of the clinical picture, of kibbutz children does not differ too much from that of children who have been reared outside the kibbutz. If this is true, the implication then emerges that even such a drastic change in social structure as that undertaken by the kibbutz along with its innovations in collaborative child-rearing is of little significance with regard to the health or pathology of children.

Such a finding is difficult to accept. The whole intent of kibbutz life is the creation of a society that will benefit the individual. A new social structure and ideology are primarily justified in that they hold more promise for the life of the individual, even if immediate gratifications may have to be postponed in the name of future generations. I have not heard anything which spells out the limitations under which child-rearing *may actually be taking place* in the kibbutz, although there seems to be agreement on the benefits that *should accrue* to the child as the result of the circumstances created for him in this society.

Mother and Metapelet:
The Problem of Multiple Mothering

DR. KRIS: Dr. Margaret Mahler has been studying for some time what she calls the child's "separation-individuation" phase — roughly, the time between one and three years. This is a study of the child's development from his unity with and dependency on the mother to the first steps he takes toward independence. The child begins to be able to leave the mother — even if cautiously, to explore the world around him, and thus to become slowly capable of taking surer and surer steps towards independence. More and more he differentiates himself from the mother — there are a "you" and a "me" establishing themselves. But *it takes a considerable length of time for this state of mind and emotion to become fully stabilized and integrated. The mother's continuing availability seems to be essential for the child's healthy development toward real independence.*

The questions that come forward, on the basis of this picture, can be formulated as follows: (1) Is it wise to separate mother and child — or, in this case, metapelet and child — at a time when inner independence is still in the process of establishing itself? (2) Is it better, for the building of a solid foundation for the personality, to maintain constancy of relationship to one and the same adult, at least until the process of inner independence has reached a certain degree of solidity?

In general, our tendency has been to adapt nurture to what we believe to be "natural" development. But we do not have enough scientifically structured observations, with follow-up studies, to prove that this is sound and correct, even though it may appear so to us. Again, there seems to be a fertile ground here to make use of the differences of living arrangements among the children in the various kibbutzim for scientifically conducted observations.

DR. NEUBAUER: As Dr. Kris has stated, continuity of relationship is necessary in order to achieve separation and individuation. What is so interesting about the separation-individuation phase is that *the child needs stability of the object precisely in order to be able to achieve separation from it.* In the process of separation, the child returns to the mother, again and again, *so as to be able to leave her again.* This phase, therefore, cannot be seen as one in which the child "takes a giant step" away from the mother; it is rather a stage in which the child proceeds with small steps, constantly enlarging the circle away from the mother, *so long as she remains the central figure in the circle.* A central-figure concept is therefore necessary not only for need satisfying, but also for the encouragement and furtherance of the process of separation. Such a person must be *available over a period of time* in order for this process to take place.

ELI ILAN: The assertion has been made here that the dynamic relationship is much more important than the geographical. With a small child or an infant, however, there has to be some *relation between the quantitative and the qualitative.* One can hardly expect a satisfactory dynamic relationship to develop without adequate time and contact with the infant. These two aspects — adequate time and physical contact with the infant, and the development of adequate dynamic relations — are in some fundamental way connected.

I am influenced in my thinking, among other things, by a clinical experience with a mother who was herself a child of the kibbutz, and is now the mother of two kibbutz children. Of course, this was a clinical case — and a very serious one. For this woman, the break had come when she was weaned, so that weaning had become a fixation point for her; a psychotic breakdown was the outcome of her weaning her first child. With the second child, there was also stress occasioned by the separation during the weaning period; but this time, I was able to help her overcome it.

Now, I have the feeling that this weaning situation is a difficult period for both the child and the mother, and that its difficulties are reinforced in the kibbutz by the fact that a mother who has been able to devote quite a lot of time to her child suddenly has to give up, not only breast-feeding, but even being in contact with the child. To a very great extent, I think that was the stress in this clinical case. But I am certain that it has repercussions on every child during this same period. It seems to me quite unfortunate that at that time, the mother goes back to work and leaves the child with another mother figure, the metapelet, so that the separation becomes quite complete and difficult.

Noomi Ben Israel: That is not the situation in the kibbutz now, although it was many years ago.

Dr. Kris: Does the mother in the kibbutz have the right to nurse the child as long as she would like to — that is, as long as her milk supply lasts — or is there some regulation that she must discontinue after a certain number of months? Has each kibbutz its own rules in regard to this and similar situations?

Eli Ilan: She can nurse the child as long as she wants to.

Noomi Ben Israel: We have arranged a schedule of weaning that is not connected with breast-feeding at all. The mother who has milk and the mother who has no milk both have the same status. If a mother breast-feeds the baby until six months, and then has to stop because she has no more milk, she will go on bottle-feeding or spoon-feeding. Today, it is no longer true that a mother who has no more milk has to go back to work.

For six weeks, the mother does not work at all; at that time, she feeds the baby — five, six or seven times daily, if necessary. Up to the age of five months, she goes on feeding the baby five times a day. When the baby gets one meal (fruit), she works one hour longer: from the fifth or sixth until the ninth month, she gradually weans the baby — which means that she omits one meal and goes to work for one more hour. Only when the infant has reached the age of nine months does she work a whole working-day, coming to the baby mornings and afternoons until it is one year of age. After that, she comes to the baby as all the other mothers do; but up to one year, she weans the baby very, very gradually, taking away one feeding hour at a time, and putting in one working hour instead.

ELI ILAN: Still, this weaning — which outside of the kibbutz means going on to *other food* or *other means* of getting it — here means getting food from *another person*. I wonder how the mothers take this — if it is easy for them. I can well imagine that it is not easy for the child. From all the experiences we have had, and from our theoretical considerations about the development of the mother-child relationship, we know of the difficulty the child has with the individuation process and separation from the mother; here it is tied in with *another person* coming in, so that, after one year, the mother has *nothing at all* to do with feeding the child.

AVIVA MANDEL: I think we must keep in mind that this "other person," this metapelet, is *present in the house from the child's very first days,* although she does not feed the child then; the child feels her presence and takes in her image *during all the beginning months of its life.* She bathes the child, she cleans it, changes its diapers; she is not simply *another person* who has come to feed the child.

DR. KRIS: Separation from the child can certainly mean the loss of something for the mother. It may go beyond the partial loss of this specific relationship; it may be a reminder of problems that occurred during her own toilet training, when something precious — her autonomy in regard to the bowel movement — had to be given up, and was, so to speak, lost to her. Recall of other problems of early development might also be stimulated at such time of "loss" — namely, the link with the castration complex, the feeling about the female self. In some cases, women continually feel castrated; it is the experience of child-bearing and of nursing the child that somewhat replace the woman's sense of loss. When these experiences are taken away, the early castration trauma may be revived.

DR. NEUBAUER: As child phychiatrists, we are very much interested in the question of separation. We are always raising the
question, *When* is the child ready to leave the mother and the
home, and go to the nursery and the group? We say that the
child is ready to move when he has "incorporated" the mother
sufficiently.

Now, under your circumstances — so very different in this
respect — at what point do you encounter difficulties of separation? When the child is at home, and then has to go back to the
group, or when he is attached to the "metapelet" and the group,
and has to leave them? Or is it when different occasions arise that
somehow involve having to move away from the person with
whom he has made contact? When do you see signs of separation
anxiety?

My next question has to do with possesion. To what degree do
these children have *possession* of the objects that they carry
around with them? In spite of the group distribution, do they
make any attempts to hold on to what we call transtitional objects, or objects as a substitute for the mother? To what degree is
this so?

MIRYAM ROT: Every child has a play corner in his parents'
room in which he keeps some of his toys and some other very be-
loved objects. On occasion, he brings these objects with him to
the children's house. You can see small children holding on to
them very tightly; they will sometimes hold on to them the whole
day long. One little boy who got a toy car from his father couldn't
leave it for one moment. While eating, while sleeping, he held on
to that toy; it was his symbol of the father.

But we also see the opposite: the children want to take something from the children's house to the parents' room and they
can do it. There was a time when we told the children that everything belongs to all of them, "you have to share," and so on. *Now*
we no longer do that; we have learned something. We have observed that every child, during early childhood, has one or two
toys in the children's house which he loves much more than any
of the others — and the other children accept that. "This is Anat's
doll," they'll say. It is not really Anat's doll, it belongs to all the
children; but the children themselves go along with this.

Now, as to whether the children have any difficulties in having to go back to the children's house after being with their mothers. There are children who do find this very difficult, but that does not depend on them alone. For instance, there are some mothers who, at that moment, are not satisfied; *they* cannot separate, and they keep saying, "Shalom, good night," but they still hold the children very tight, so that they cannot leave. Sometimes the mothers even come back with them.

It also depends on whether the child finds the right metapelet at the right moment. The metapelet must be waiting for the children when they come back to the children's house, and welcome them warmly. If she does, it is easier for the children to part from the mothers. Sometimes, putting the child to bed, calming him down, soothing him before he goes to sleep is less difficult for the metapelet than it would be for the mother.

GIDEON LEWIN: I wonder whether the concept of separation doesn't actually mean something different in kibbutz life. This is not a clear-cut separation, it's something in-between. Complete separation takes place when a mother turns over a child to an institution; the complete opposite of that would be putting a child to bed and saying, "Well, you stay in your room — I'm going back to my room — and now good night!" Then the child is somehow alone and not alone: the mother is *in the next room*. Now, in kibbutz life, when the child separates from his mother, he immediately joins *somebody else who is close to him* — either the metapelet or the other children.

When we speak about peer groups — about groups in general — we always have in mind a structured group. That probably doesn't start to exist before the age of four or five, I think; but I have observed, among children ten to fourteen months old, some feeling of "togetherness." After the mothers leave the babies' house at six or seven o'clock in the evening, those babies who can't sleep — well, they just try to speak, to let their presence be felt by the others, and there is a give-and-take, of some sort, until they all fall asleep. This is a group, too — not a structured group, to be sure, but a feeling of *belonging to somebody, somewhere*. The problem of separation, in such a case, is not so clear-cut.

DR. NEUBAUER: I am impressed with the degree of intensity

of the relationship between parent and child here, and the variety of forms in which it expresses itself. It seems that over the years, a good many changes have occurred in this respect in the kibbutz. The parents seem to have extended their influence into the children's home, and as a result, there appears to be a less stringent separation between, on the one hand, the child in its relationship to the metapelet and to its peers, and on the other hand the child in the parental home. Under the circumstances of life in the kibbutz, the question is really not *where* early child-rearing takes place, but *how,* and *what qualities* go into it.

Dr. Lewin has spoken about the differences in the separation experience outside the kibbutz and within it. Among us, when a child leaves home to go to a nursery, he faces an unknown environment and an unknown person. The degree of separation anxiety, therefore, is dependent on the child's capacity to form a new relationship with a stranger. In a kibbutz, separation does not assume the character of moving from a known person to a stranger, but rather of going from one person to whom the child has made an attachment, to *a new, often equally well-known person,* to whom a new attachment must now be made. The mother and the metapelet are *both known.* The entire kibbutz, from the viewpoint of the child, is one large family. Strangeness is not associated in the child's mind with kibbutz life or any of its elements, but with that which exists *outside the kibbutz.* This must have some effect on the child's change from one object to another.

Dr. Kris: I am happy to hear that most metapelets are known, to a certain extent, to each child, through the close contact that the members of the community have with each other. I agree, therefore, that the separation problem in general in the kibbutz is *likely to be quite different* from the situation *we* are so frequently confronted with. Nevertheless, I would imagine that the very small child is handled by one and the same metapelet during its first months; when, after some time, there is a change, it could have an impact similar to that made on the infant among us, when the nurse in a family situation leaves her job.

The infant cannot be "prepared" for the change; it is bound to react to the loss with regression; whatever functioning it had achieved may be given up for some time, through anxiety or uneasiness. One might have the metapelet of the next stage handle the child a few times before he moves to the next house, so that the suddenness of the change may be lessened. Or one might take care not to change the child to another metapelet and another house at such an early stage.

Dr. Neubauer: I am impressed with the care with which you proceed; the depth of your understanding, and the degree to which you are really attempting, within your given circumstances, to carry out your ideas of child-rearing.

As we have already found, one can easily place a greater emphasis than is warranted on the differences between the life situation within the kibbutz and that of other societies; one can consequently speak in exaggerated terms about the effects of these differences on the children. But, as has been stated, it is not only the question of *what* happens or *when;* what seems to be of major importance is *how* it happens.

One can lose oneself in a detailed discussion of a training period: *When* does it occur? *Where* does it occur? *Who* takes part in it? Yet, as Dr. Kris has indicated, the specific effect on the child of weaning or training depends on *the underlying personality of the child-care person.* The final outcome is influenced most by those individuals who have the greatest impact on the full range of events during each developmental phase. Therefore, *how mother and metapelet interact,* whether there is *supplementation* instead of substitution, *complementation* instead of conflict, will be more significant than any of the detailed arrangements that are part of the practice.

Eli Ilan: I think that the relationship between metapelet and mother is quite definitely a pathogenic factor; we have seen it too often for there to be any longer any doubt of it. There still remains this question, however — what is this shadowy quality of the metapelet, which we come across time and again in the analysis of these children, or of adults who have grown up in the kibbutz?

In a few cases that I have seen, the metapelet did *not* seem to be a very important figure for the child. Now, there may have been several reasons for this. Perhaps it is because we have been trained to see the mother-child relationship only. Or, it may be that these two figures, during the first and second year of life, in a way are fused for the child. There is also this splitting of good and bad mother figures, even when they form one figure.

I have the feeling that a bad experience with the metapelet becomes merged with a bad experience with the mother; as a result, the good experience with the metapelet and those with the mother are able to be united in the single picture of the good mother. Perhaps that is why, at first, we get material from one figure: the "mother figure." Our material is from two figures when children reach the age of four and five; this material shows displacement. While the mother is idealized, the metapelet "was very bad, because she did not let me eat the cheese" or "she forced me to eat the cheese." But this, I repeat, is material from the four- or five-year-old, not from an early experience.

GIDEON LEWIN: The importance of the metapelet's influence is so strongly stressed by the child that we cannot deny it. I am reminded of an observation: A little girl of three and a half years always woke up before the metapelet came in. If the bed was dry and she was clean, she would greet the metapelet with "Boeker tov, Miriam tova," which means "Good morning, good Miriam"; if she had wet her bed, however, she would say, "Good morning, my good-bad Miriam."

EMI HURWITZ: Let me give you another example of the socializing influence of the metapelet — and of the complementary influence of the mother.

A boy of two had already been toilet-trained and didn't even wet his bed when his nurse left the kibbutz for several months. When the second nurse fell ill, a third came to take the group. The training held good during the period when the second nurse was working with the group, but there was a regression when the third one came. One day the little boy told his mother, "Ulla (the first nurse) will be angry with me." When the mother asked, "Why should Ulla be angry with you?" he told her that he had soiled his pants. His mother reassured him by telling him that Ulla would certainly not be angry with him, as such a thing could happen any time. *This was when Ulla had already been gone for three months.* When she finally returned to work with the group, everything was all right again. The boy is now two and a half years old.

Two interesting points emerge. The first is the socializing influence of the nurse, which directs the child. Even when she is not present for a time, she still remains the representative of socializing demands. The second is that it is the mother who reassures the child in a moment of failure, who assures him that he is all right.

DR. KRIS: Have you made any full-scale observations in support of your idea that it is better for the child and his development that he be trained by a person less involved emotionally with him than the mother? One measure of validation might be evidence of the child's capacity to retain the control achieved, even under situations of stress. One could also ask whether it would not be best to have the person with the *strongest relationship to the child* help with the training; and then again, whether in relation to the metapelet, *her* emotional involvement with the child should be fostered?

Clearly underlying some of the thinking here is a "conviction," or rather a hypothesis, which runs as follows: "It is important for the benefit of the child's development that the relationship with the parents be at all times 'conflict-free.'" One consequence would be that it is the metapelet, and not the parent, who then becomes the representative of the larger community's demands upon the young child to assume control over its own drives. This process of assuming control takes time; during it, anger is likely to appear among the child's emotions, mixed with positive feelings toward the parent or his substitute. Since the emotions directed toward the parent are stronger than those directed toward any other adult, the conflict inherent in the ambivalent feelings just mentioned will also be stronger.

The goal is the efficient and thorough solution by the child of the task set for him. In this, the adult can help the child by the means he uses in pursuit of these demands, which result in strengthening the child's ego capacity. The idea of deliberately leaving this to the metapelet may be based on the intention of helping the child to attain a specific and practical achievement in the easiest way. Yet this may, at the same time, have the effect of negating the opportunity to help the child develop inner strength.

One example might be bowel-training. The child resists the demands of the adult, preferring to pursue the freedom of instinctual gratification. This creates a conflictual situation between adult and child — a situation that is eventually resolved by the child's acceptance of the adult's goal. That acceptance represents a strengthening of the child's ego. If the situation is handled properly, the result is not a disruption or disturbance in the child-parent relationship, but often the contrary: a deepening and maturation of that relationship.

I wonder whether there may not result a delay in the achievement of such a control as bowel training, if the child is moved from one house to another, where another metapelet takes over. Separation from a person to whom the young child is attached is usually followed by regression. Are already established controls relinquished at such times of shifting metapelets?

It might be worthwhile to study the development of the personality, especially with regard to ego strength and depth of relationship, through a comparison of children who have been mainly trained by their parents with children mainly trained by the metapelet. It might also be worthwhile to review the question of the length of time that a child should stay in one and the same house — i.e., with one and the same metapelet. I should think that during the early years, a longer stay in the same place, or with the same person, would be preferable to the yearly or two-yearly change.

MENAHEM GERSON: There are two reasons, I believe, why we have been trying to liberate parents from the burdens of habit-training: one is our concept of the importance of unconditional love, which a child has to get somewhere; the second is that parents are much more emotionally involved in these things. We have some mothers who are very nervous as mothers, yet make very calm and good nurses. That is why we make this sort of division.

This does bring up certain problems — which are not always for the best. There are tendencies in communal education to spoil the child: one seldom finds a rejecting metapelet. Are our assumptions in this respect really right? Or is conflict with parents in the field of habit training to be regarded as essential, something that we should not try to eliminate? (In any case, we have not succeeded in eliminating it.)

Noomi Ben Israel: The person responsible for toilet-training cannot, of course, be a stranger. Therefore, a nurse will never start toilet-training if, for instance, she is about to leave the group, even for holidays; instead, she'll put it off until after the holidays. If she is about to leave one house for another, she won't start toilet-training, for she knows that it should be carried on *in the same place, with the same person, and under the same conditions.*

It is important that the nurse does it and not the mother, because the mother is too much involved with the problem. She wants the child to eat the cake she has baked, because she made it with her own hands; if the child doesn't eat it, she is offended. In that way, the question of "yes cake-eating" or "no cake-eating" may involve an *"offense" against the mother.* With the pot, it's the same: if the mother asks for it, and the child doesn't give it, she may be offended.

Finally, it's much more difficult for someone to do the training who has to wash the diapers afterwards and clean up. The mother is often quite exhausted; she has too cook, clean, do everything around the house. Training is the nurse's work, however, and she therefore does it in a much more detached way — not so detached, of course, as not to be in contact with the child.

Miryam Rot: I would like to discuss the question of what motivates a child to accept habit training from the metapelet. What can *she* do for him?

Not only does the metapelet demand, request, ask the child to perform such and such duties, to follow this or that pattern of social behavior; she also *loves,* she also *gives* much. The child feels that, for all that he may be dirty, may smear dirt and clay all over himself all day — in this small area, he *has to be all right.* We keep forgetting that there is this transfer of the child's feelings from his mother to his metapelet and to the children's house. The whole day, sometimes, the child will call the metapelet "Ima," and his mother by the name of the metapelet. I have experienced this, both as a mother and as a metapelet.

All of the family problems come back to the children's house. Sometimes the mother will bring the child in the evening, and tell the metapelet, "You will have trouble with him today, because it was a very hard day with him." If he did not sleep enough, or something, it will be very hard; the child will bring his troubles with him. There is a theraapeutic value in the fact that the metapelet receives these troubles and can handle them.

We can see, then, that the two persons are separated. We have been asked, "By how much?" But how can I tell you by how much? I can only tell you for certain how much a child is stimulated, how much he is excited or disturbed, by noise.

I would be very eager indeed to hear the "scientific principles" involved in — and the scientific "proofs" for — the notion of giving back to the mother her old role. We would want to base that practice — in order to be able to do it well — on such *scientific truths.*

DR. MARANS: Most of the concern expressed so far has been about habit-training as it affects the parent-child relationship; but I am sure there is also much reason for concern about habit-training as it affects future personality traits. A recent study was presented by Hetherington (University of Wisconsin) and Brackbill (University of Colorado) at the April 1963 meeting of the Society for Research in Child Development. This study seems to indicate that it is not the method, timing, or severity of the toilet training that produces the later personality characteristics usually attributed to those aspects of the training, but the personality patterns of the parent with whom the same-sexed child identifies.

DR. NEUBAUER: May I return to a question that is so basic and has so often been asked: "How is a metapelet able to care for six or eight children during their first year of life, when we so often hear from mothers that one baby is a full-time job?" Can the metapelet distribute her time equally to all? If not, then how does she proceed to keep up with the individual needs of each child? Whom does she feed earliest? To whose crying does she react first? Do those who have the capacity for delay of gratification have to wait the longest? Or is there a general position that all ought to be treated alike, in order to foster the principle of equal rights, thus overriding the assumption of unequal needs?

MIRYAM ROT: How can a child endure waiting for the meta-pelet, while she takes care of the other children? I have the impression — based on visits to many children's houses — that our metaplot know their children very well and are sensitive to their individual levels of tolerance. She knows, for example, that she must put on her apron as fast as she can because if Dani cries, he has to eat immediately. It may be that in this one group, two or even three of the children are like Dani. Then it is very difficult. Usually we can deal with these problems precisely because children are *not* the same. But you must have an individual approach to children; you must know who Dani is, who Ruti is, who Ilana is. "Dani cannot wait for his food; Ilana cannot go on an outing without first taking my hand . . . "

DR. KRIS: It has been mentioned that those who have been trained as nurses for the infants' group want to keep on caring for the infants and are not inclined to take charge of children of more than a few months to a year old. Such an attitude could interfere with what we consider to be so important: *constancy of presence during the transition* from one metapelet to the other should be guaranteed.

We can see parallels among mothers who deal with their own children better at a certain age level than they do at another. Some mothers, in the beginning, are not well related to their very young children — and then suddenly, at a later time, the mother will seem to blossom out in her parental functions, where-upon the child follows suit and blossoms out, too. Other mothers, while they are excellent with their newborn or young infants, are not able to go along with their children in further development, especially towards independence.

The psychological consequences of the parent's not respond-ing to a child in need, and the child's reaction to this, will differ according to the age of the child. The child may not be so ready to blame the individual parent, because he will have become aware of the fact, relatively early, that there is a super-organization to which the parents are subordinate. He may use as concrete evi-dence for this the worksheet that tells parents where to go and when, in order for them to do their share of work. The existence of such a superior entity, "in charge of" his parents, may or may not make a difference in the structure of the child's superego; under these conditions, this "super-parent" replaces in the child's mind the otherwise religiously conceived supernatural.

MORDECHAI SEGAL: They know one major force: "I have got to go to work." That is that; there is your *force majeure*.

DR. NEUBAUER: How do the mother's sensitivity pattern, perceptual mode and affective tone fit those of the child? Or, viewed in a reciprocal way: how do the child's activity pattern, sensitivity level and perceptual range match those of the mother? In the kibbutz, we would have to extend this concept of "matching" to include the relationship between metapelet and child. If there is a greater complementation between mother and child, how does it affect the child's interaction with the metapelet? How does it affect the maintenance of harmony between mother and metapelet, if the mother feels that the metapelet is "preferred" by the child? How do you address yourselves to this, which is, presumably, a frequent occurrence?

EMI HURWITZ: Everything rests on the very delicate balance between the factors in our education: the children's house and nurse on the one side, and the mother (parents) and home on the other. Here, the question of permissiveness comes in. Sometimes the mother can fill in what the nurse leaves out, and sometimes it is the other way round.

A certain elasticity does exist, which is quite good if it doesn't mean *very big swings* between the two centers — children's house and parents' room. When parents think that a nurse is too rigid, it may be that the mother is too permissive at home, and vice versa. This is one of the problems we deal with in our child guidance clinics: we try to explain to both educators and parents that they make it difficult for the child when the gap between the two approaches is too large. Those are the more extreme cases, of course; in a great many instances, the polarities work out and an equilibrium is created.

ERIKA KNOLLER: It has been suggested that the children transfer their relations with the mother to the metapelet, and that the metapelet is then able to deal with habit-training. But, what sort of transfer is it when four children in one group can each transfer his special relationship from his mother — and perhaps also his father — to this one figure of the metapelet? What we have is now four different relations with one figure, aside from the fact that the children identify with each other. (In such a young group, can we truly speak of "identification?" Perhaps it is imitation, or something of that order.)

What sort of group dynamics do we get under such circumstances? There isn't only the fusion of the figure of the metapelet with the mother; there is also — through the identification of the children — the fusion of the *four different* metaplot into one metapelet, and then the fusion of *that figure* with the mother of *each* child. It is not that I think this is too complicated to be real. The reality of psychic life is still, assuredly, considerably more complicated than we are able to express.

DR. KRIS: I do not think that it is so important whether it is mother or metapelet who administers the child. What is important is the "mothering," and the quality of the feelings, that either the metapelet or the mother brings to the child. The articles we received as preparation for this meeting seem to have misled us to some extent about the kibbutzim. They gave the impression of a great discrepancy between the emotional atmospheres created by metapelet and mother.

The metapelet comes through in these articles as not emotional, not really tender, although functioning very well and knowledgeable. The mother, in contrast, appears to be extremely emotional — in effect, someone who should not have too much to do with the nurturing of her child, precisely because of her terrible emotions (although, occasionally, some good emotions are attributed to her, too). But we know that mother and metapelet are human beings and have essentially the some emotional capabilities and deficiencies. (That the metapelet also has some specific knowledge of the techniques of child care is certainly an asset.)

MORDECHAI SEGAL: For us, it is not really a question of "mothering." *Not only the mother is able to do what we are speaking of.* As far as the kibbutz is concerned, we do not need the term "mothering" (for which, by the way, we have no Hebrew word), because we do not want a misleading connotation — namely, that *only* a mother can do this, and the others are a sort of *substitute,* or *less than a mother.* The point for us is the variety of sources of social and physiological stimulation for the child at the very earliest ages. This can be achieved, first of all, by the constancy of the metapelet: it is very important that the infant should come to know another figure as well as the one with whom he is most familiar.

This would further mean linking the work in two children's rooms, so that two metaplot would, in a certain way, become a collective figure. It has been suggested that the metapelet is a shadowy figure for the child. Well, perhaps it is shadowy — in one sense. After all, we do not want it to penetrate too deeply into the child's personality, since it is a changing figure; but we do want a *general sense of the metapelet* as a representative of our culture. If we succeed in combining all these sources of rich and varied social stimulation for the very young infant, we will then succeed in producing, we hope, a better sort of development than we have seen so far, perhaps even better than one finds outside the kibbutz.

Dr. Kris: In our society, there are usually one or two persons who are the loved ones; they make demands on the child at the same time. This, we think, can be easily managed; as has been mentioned, it should strengthen the child's personality. Under such circumstances, even if some tense moments do arise — perhaps because of some irritation on the part of the mother — I doubt that, except for extreme cases, they would have a detrimental effect. I think they would give the child the opportunity to develop the means — both adaptive and defensive — to deal with the situations of tension that it will meet later on in everyday life.

During the war, a situation that occurred in England — probably it is known to many of you — has been described in the book *Children Without Families,* by Anna Freud and Dorothy Burlingham. I shall summarize it briefly.

A residential nursery had been established for children whose parents were not available to them because of the war situation. Many of the children were very young, so toilet training had not even been attempted by the time they entered the nursery. At first, the policy had been to have the nurses shift every eight hours for the entire group, the understanding being that all the nurses would handle all the children at various times. Under those conditions, toilet-training took much longer than usual. A new policy was then established: each unit was called a "family," and four to six children were assigned to one special nurse, with rotating substitutes. Following this change, the control of bowel movements — or toilet-training — was achieved in a time close to the expected average. (It may also be of interest to mention that in these nursery "families," sibling rivalry suddenly turned up, just as in ordinary families.)

There seems to be no doubt that children develop strong and lasting attachments, and many of these "family nurses," on the basis of the loving attachment of the children, were able to help them more quickly to complete bowel training, etc. In some cases, where the mother is especially troubled and disturbed, it would be better for both mother and child if there were another adult substituting for the mother in helping to toilet-train the child. These seem to be the exceptions, however, not the rule.

PROFESSOR WINNIK: You cannot compare our children with the children described by Anna Freud. Ours are with their parents in an intensive way every day, and it is unquestionable that the development is completely different. During intensive treatment over the years with a lot of people from the kibbutz, I have found that the metapelet is, on the whole, a very shadowy figure. The two main figures are, in reality, the parents. The children have the same difficulties as children brought up in other environments; they are the same from the point of view of the main conflicts.

MORDECHAI KAFFMAN: I feel that something is missing here: the important role of the father. Very often, babies look to their fathers even more than to their mothers (I am talking about infants in the second half of the first year). This is not surprising: the fathers spend a lot of time with the infants, they take care of them, etc.; at times, they even replace the mothers.

One thing is certain: the most constant figures for the infant are the father and the mother. There was a delegation of English psychiatrists here, who were amazed at this: how was it possible that even though the infants spent more time with the metapelet than with the mother, they were more attached to the mother? At two months, they were responding more to the mothers than to the metaplot; they even smiled differently. If we analyze the relationship quantitatively, we can see that the infants, from the beginning, have had more contact with the parent figures than with the metapelet, if only because the latter has had to take care of four, six, eight or more children at once.

MR. ALT: If I thought that the metapelet was the principal mother figure, I should be much more concerned about young children in the kibbutz than I am. This second mother figure, who may be described as an "auxiliary" mother, is not permanent. She may continue with the child for one year, after which she is replaced by another metapelet; a few years later, the same process is repeated. She is not as important to the child as his own parents.

ELI ILAN: Which age are we discussing — first year, second year, third year? Throughout, the mother is the main figure, the metapelet only a supplementary figure. The kibbutz has gone a fairly long way in letting the mother play an important role during the first year of the infant's life: some fifteen years ago, things looked very different, but now the mother has ample opportunities to frustrate the child.

I think we should concern ourselves more with the *second* year in the child's life, where relatively few changes have so far taken place in the kibbutz' attitude. When the child is weaned, he gets another metapelet; sometimes that makes for a very problematic phase. Problems must come up, according to all that we know about child-rearing, during the second year of life — problems that should be of great importance: the fact, for instance, that these different figures are each playing a part; that the mother is retreating while another mother figure comes to the fore; that ambivalent feelings are being experienced by the child.

NECHAMA LEVI: There are not two circles in the lives of our children. I think there is one circle, with two very clear roles: that of the metapelet, and that of the parents. When a child lives in one circle, and knows clearly what everyone's role is, then he has confidence. Knowing what the mother's role is and what the metapelet's role is, he doesn't have to compare them and he doesn't have to become confused about them. He understands what demands the mother can make, and what can be demanded by the metapelet. Even more important, he knows what are his emotional reactions to the metapelet's demands, and what they are to the mother's.

Sometimes the metapelet will say, "Oh! you know, when you take your child, he immediately starts to cry. When he is with me all day, he doesn't cry." Now that is not very surprising. A child cries when the mother comes because he feels, emotionally, that *with his mother he can cry;* he doesn't feel as free to cry, even among his peers or with his metapelet.

We ourselves have to know clearly what is the role of the metapelet and of the parents, if we wish the child to be confident and clear in his reactions and relationships.

Noomi Ben Israel: I don't think the question for us has been whether the mother or the metapelet is more important. Perhaps we can see the real question better, by looking at it somewhat indirectly, at first.

What happens to the child when he fails? It has been said that if a child can't learn, but is a good athlete, for instance, then he can make up for his weakness in studies by his excellence in sports. But very often, the child *can't* make up for it, because his mother wants him to be an academic child, and she doesn't think sports are so wonderful. A child can play ball all day long, but his mother would like him to sit looking at pictures. Or we find a mother who says, "Yes, I do have a very sweet child, but he just can't concentrate." "How old is your child?" "Three." What should *he* concentrate on?

That is where the metapelet comes in. She doesn't make such demands on this child. She loves him and values him — whether he concentrates or doesn't concentrate, whether he plays ball or doesn't play ball. She likes him *just as he is,* precisely because her emotional ties to this child are not so involved. At this very moment, for example, the metapelet can give the child a wonderful uplift, because *she* sees in ball-playing something wonderful. And she can say, "Well, of course, Moishele doesn't draw so well, but he plays ball wonderfully and he laid the table yesterday in such a wonderful way."

The metapelet is also often a corrective force in a child's life, at a time when the mother cannot give enough love to her child, because she herself is disturbed or is just not able to give her love (which can also happen in a kibbutz). The warmth of the meta-pelet means a great deal then.

Wherever the mother and the metapelet complement each other in their demands on the child, or in the love situation, we achieve an ideal basis for the child's development. If both are very demanding people, we are in danger of putting too many demands on the child. On the other hand, when we combine a very demanding mother with a lenient metapelet, we may "even out."

The point that has been made about the security a child feels in its surroundings is very important. A kibbutz child knows his room first, then his yard, then the space outside his yard; very soon he comes to know the whole kibbutz. *There is nothing strange in his life.* I think that this is a very important part of our children's lives from the very beginning — that they do come to know their surroundings, and that it is no strange world that lies around them.

Another important point is the nearness of the *chaverim* all about the place. On its visit, my group found that the children were all very friendly; they weren't afraid of the grownups, even though we were all strangers to them. To them, every grownup is a friend; they have had no bad experiences whatsover with grownups. This is not only because we are kind to the children, but because, in our community structure, we have no "persons in authority." Even the Secretary, the man in the highest position, is someone whose beard you can pull, or whose lap you can sit upon. A mother will never be able to say, "Now be quiet, or I'll call the Secretary (or the policeman)." No teacher can give a child a note that says, "You bring your mother tomorrow and we'll tell her what happened."

DR. KRIS: What does it do to the mother emotionally, and to her present and future relationship with the child, when it is the metapelet who handles the child most of the day: bathes it, dia-pers it, and has most of the close physical contacts with it. The other question is: how does the *child* react when the mother reduces her contacts — especially the feeding contact?

This seems to be to be an extraordinary opportunity to study the reactions of mother and child in close detail, and thus to learn about the consequences of such events. It might be necessary for the metapelet to acquire some knowledge of methods of observation, etc.; for instance: Is there any sign observable in the child's behavior, upon its first contact with the mother after her prolonged absence?

Dr. Himmelweit yesterday commented to me that there would be a great advantage to all of us if the metapelet were able to carry through such observations. My impression is, however, that the metapelet's busy schedule hardly leaves time for additional work. Another solution might be for some other female members of the community (who are apparently not so occupied with work in the field as they were originally) to function as regular (professional) observers for various studies of this kind. Young high-school girls could also become steady assistants, after being taught how to perform this kind of observation; in that way they could do important work for the kibbutz, as well as for the whole scientific community.

Dr. Neubauer: I was puzzled earlier, as I think I stated, by the clinical material indicating equal frequency of pathology in kibbutz and in city children. Furthermore, the oedipal conflict was reported to be equally centered around the parental figures (to the exclusion of the metapelet). Our discussion here has enabled me to formulate a hypothesis to explain this. It is the assumption that the term "father" or "mother" refers to a *variety* of earlier primary images, which have since become more crystallized and more focused, and are now presented as *single figures*. What I have learned here is not so much how important the parents are to the child, but how important it is for the child to be able to *create a single parental figure under these circumstances of multiple care.*

I think that we have here an extraordinary opportunity to make an essential contribution to the field of child development. Multiple mothering provides the child with two need-satisfying objects, and later, with the possibility for identification, at different levels of development, with two different persons. Dr. Lewin has suggested that this offers to the child the opportunity to separate "good" and "bad," associating one with the metapelet and the other with the mother.

We have referred to the necessity of *fusing* various influences in such a way as to facilitate ego integration. Processes of diffusion are generally regarded as pathological. How, then, does the child's ego integrate metapelet and mother? How does he make of them *one model*, around which imitation, identification, gratification and frustration can be so integrated as to maintain the unity of psychic function?

Perhaps we can formulate this hypothesis: No matter how many mothering persons may be available to him, *the child's developmental tasks demand that they become integrated and unified.* The child is not able to cope with a number of parallel primary figures; he will merge these, instead, into *a single figure, which functions in a unitary sense,* as if only one person of significance was influencing his upbringing.

What is involved in the merging of this unified image of a parent? In which stages of development does it take place? How close to reality is the image that emerges? The young patient may refer to "mother"; nevertheless, he may in fact be speaking about the various influential personalities in his everyday life, who have become merged and are represented in this one word "mother."

ELI ILAN: We have spoken here about the possibility of different mother-figures merging into one figure; but one of the tasks of individuation is to combine, to fuse such splitting as is found even in the normal family situation, where there is only one mother: the splitting into the representations of a bad figure and a good figure. It is a problem to bring the child during the individuation process to some sort of unity of the mother figure, and from there to a solution of this difficult task of seeing the mother as a *separate whole.* I have the feeling that both these tasks — seeing the mother figure as a whole, and separating from this figure so as to attain individuation by that separation — are being made more difficult. On the other hand, it may be that the defense mechanisms are being reinforced here — namely, those of splitting and of displacing aggression outside onto some bad figure — so that the child can keep an idealized figure and thereby avoid depression and depressive feelings.

SHMUEL NAGLER: Dr. Neubauer's hypothesis that the ego in early childhood is capable of fusing multiple mother figures into a single one seems to me most helpful, from a theoretical point of view. Nevertheless, we should not overlook what Dr. Kris has reminded us of — namely, that it is not so much the question of whether a child is *capable* of accomplishing a certain task at a given stage of his development; the real question is whether the accomplishment of this proposed task will be *beneficial* to its further development. In other words, we must first ask ourselves whether this necessity of fusing different mother figures is a *proper* "developmental task," and then find the appropriate conditions for *strengthening the integrating capacities* in these early developmental stages. I believe that a genuine and permanent mother figure should be the nucleus around which the child's ego can exercise its "mingling-functions," and that such a mother is essential for healthy personality development.

THE DYNAMICS OF CHILD DEVELOPMENT IN THE KIBBUTZ
(Summary of Discussion)
DR. E. J. ANTHONY

Our group sessions dealing with the dynamics of child development in the kibbutz developed productively under the chairmanship of Dr. Marianne Kris. The visitors were able to obtain firsthand information, of both clinical and nonclinical character, about child behavior and care within a communal setting. It was helpful for us to have this opportunity for a close interchange between participants and perspicacious observers, just as it had been salutary for us earlier to visit the kibbutzim and see their life for ourselves. As a consequence, our comments lost their previously abstract, theoretical quality; they now seemed more pointed and pertinent. Having started as "experts," we soon found that we had a good deal to learn about local ways and means. For this we had to divest ourselves of some of our Western "expertise"; whatever we came prepared to teach, we had first to do some learning of our own.

By the end of our final session, we were still not integrated as a group; it would have been too much to expect that we should be. It continued to remain "we" and "they" — the visitors and the kibbutz people; but we had begun to explore the problems together, jointly, helpfully and hopefully, and with less defensiveness on either side — certainly with less criticism on the part of the visitors. It was altogether more of a two-way process: neither the questions nor the answers stemmed exclusively from one or the other side. This could be attributed in part to our moderator, and in part to an intermediate group of analytic clinicians, who skillfully brought us together once again on the numerous occasions when contact between the groups threatened to become lost because of misunderstanding. Whenever the two main groups were inclined to exaggerate their positions, carried away either by idealization or by an over-critical appraisal, the intermediate group would re-examine and re-interpret the issue, and so bring us back to a more balanced point of view. (We learned later, without any great surprise, that both of these clinicians, in addition to being analysts, were also experienced group therapists.)

It was to be expected that the group would carry over from the plenary session the challenging observation that psychologically and psychopathologically, there appeared to be very little difference between the kibbutz and the non-kibbutz child, even though they had been brought up in radically different ways and in radically different surroundings. Here were two quite distinct philosophies of child-rearing; yet the end result was apparently the same, at least as far as gross clinical assessment was concerned. The so-called "conflict-free" development that took place in the kibbutz appeared to make no difference as to either the quantity or the quality of the conflicts that subsequently reached the clinician, nor did the developmental traumata involved in group upbringing turn out to be quite as pathogenic as some of us may have expected that they would.

We examined the sleeping arrangements, for example, from two points of view: the one dealing with the "geography" of the arrangements — that is, where the children slept, who also slept there, the distance between the sleepers; the other, with the emotional dynamics involved. It became abundantly clear that the structural and functional aspects were closely bound together. The arrangements were far from fortuitous; they reflected the developmental philosophy practiced in any particular kibbutz.

The crucial element seemed to be the age at which the children were housed separately from their parents' room. This was related, in turn, to the controversy going on around the so-called "anti-familistic" trend in the kibbutz.

We were now beginning to recognize that in order to evaluate any kibbutz procedure, you first had to consider its background — its history and its relationship to other kibbutz procedures. You could not deal with it piecemeal; it had to be viewed in its proper perspective. Any attempt that we made as a group to examine some developmental detail in the kibbutz, in the light of our Western experience alone, caused great uneasiness among the kibbutz members. It had become out of context and unrecognizable — no longer part of any meaningful whole. This meant that to try taking up a nuclear question, such as the amount of time to be spent by a child with its parents, and handling it through a re-arrangement of the sleeping conditions, without reference to the totality of the child's experience, was to condemn the attempt in advance to producing nonsense.

The clarification of this sleeping problem led us to scrutinize two closely related and important developmental processes: the "separation" process, involving the distancing of the child from the mother and the mother from the child, and the "surrogation" process, entailing the substitution for the mother by the nurse, the metapelet and the peer group. With regard to both these basic processes, the chief interest lay in the timing: how early and how rapidly were they to be effected?

In this matter, the "we" and "they" differences within the group came to the forefront. The "we" members (the visitors) felt that some degree of stability needed to be established in early object relationships, before the child could be subjected to either separation or surrogation. "We" spoke of the importance of the mother's closeness, her range of contact with her baby, and her availability at all times; "they" discussed closeness and contact in terms of the enormous expectations of love and gratification to which the child would be conditioned, and the greater likelihood of subsequent disappointment and frustration. There seemed to be a minor clash of principles here: on the one hand, some sort of belief that the less one expected the less one was disappointed, and that too much of a good thing could become a bad thing; on the other hand, the belief that too little of a good thing could also be a bad thing.

During this interchange, it became clear that both sides were sophisticated enough to appreciate the fact that positions were being deliberately exaggerated in the service of greater clarification. None of us was really talking of all-or-none phenomena — that is, either "no one but the mother" or "the mother not at all." We were concerned with *degrees* of contact, with a *spectrum* of mother-child transactions.

It was the outsiders' inclination to examine the problem *sub specie aeternitatis* (in the light of the basic psychoanalytic principles), whereas our hosts preferred to regard the issues within the context of the parochial, the particular, the pragmatic. The more direct data forthcoming from the teachers about everyday kibbutz life, the more we were able to appreciate their point of view. Without this "grinding together" of experience in the discussion group, each "camp" might easily have been left with an uncorrected personal and habitual sort of perspective.

One could readily understand why the kibbutz movement has been roused to indignation in the past by visitors who have come, seen, recorded, and pontificated — without submitting their opinion to the fire of interchange. The pity of it, on this occasion, was that the group, having successfully delineated its central concerns, was left without enough time for the essential movement towards a group consensus. Although it might well have turned out that after six months of group transactions, our final standpoints would be no different from those we did arrive at after three sessions, nevertheless, they would still be no longer quite the same standpoints, having been saturated in opposition for a while.

The mother's giving up of the care of her child is not a

peculiarity of the kibbutz; well-to-do families in every century and in every continent have adopted the same procedure, without any special philosophy of child development to guide them. As one sociologist has pointed out, wealthy mothers have never, in the past, brought up their own children, for reasons of status; in this century, working-class mothers are ceasing to bring up their children for reasons of need, and professional mothers for reasons of their intellectual and cultural interests and responsibilities. This leaves the hard core of middle-class women who, despite all temptations, stubbornly insist on doing their own mothering.

In the kibbutz, the mothers turn over the raising of their children to the metapelet on both ideological and practical grounds; they see the justification and the need for men and women to share equally in the running of the settlement. We could not gauge how many mothers have had to struggle with this problem of early separation, nor to what extent it has been a manifest problem, requiring intervention on the part of the kibbutz. We were given some illustrations of covert difficulties in which a mother, on parting with her toddler at the end of the evening visit, would offer him a series of "double-bind" communications, directing him to return to the children's house and yet holding him tightly by the hand; imploring him not to cry when he left her, and yet weeping a little herself. Such scenes, we felt, might well create a great deal of floating anxiety and conflict among the group of young mothers. The desire to put her child to bed and to be carried into his sleep as his final conscious image must be deeply imbedded in human mothers; it is surely not given up without a good deal of internal struggle.

The visitors were concerned as to how much opportunity these young women had for abreacting their feelings about parting from their children, and for expressing any opposition that they may have felt toward the idea. Was it possible, we asked, to institute some therapeutic or quasitherapeutic arrangement, whereby the mothers — singly or in groups — could come to terms with this difficult demand? The kibbutz members replied that it was axiomatic in community life that people were accessible to one another for comfort and counsel. Mothers had opportunities to talk with other mothers in the mothers' group, and with the teachers and the metaplot at the regularly held meetings of teachers and mothers.

In the early days of the kibbutz movement, it was true, women had frequently insisted that their natural instincts were being thwarted by these sleeping arrangements; today, however, when they looked upon themselves as an integral part of the whole movement, they understood the need for separation from their children and willingly accepted it. There would always be a few with greater difficulties than others in this respect; but this was a recognized problem, dealt with *ad hoc* by the community. If a mother raised a really great outcry, some professional person was designated to deal with her complaint.

At this point, the kibbutz members of the group suggested that the outsiders might be idealizing the "maternal instinct," and viewing it as too large and too pervasive a question. They informed us that even in the early days, when mothers had been offered the opportunity of rooming in with their infants, most of them had been quite content to leave the matter to the professional "know-how" of the nurse (later, to the metapelet), and instead to return to their work groups and their "honeymoon" lives with their husbands, undisturbed by wailing and demanding children.

The group next turned its attention to the child's side of the problem of separating from the mother, and his readiness to do so during early infancy. Dr. Margaret Mahler's views about the separation-individuation process were referred to by the American visitors, with emphasis on the dangers of accelerating the separation process beyond the infant's capacity to tolerate it. According to Mahler, separation should take place gradually, in stages, the child himself determining the tempo of separation, the distance he can travel from his mother, and the amount of time he can remain at this furthest point away from her, without returning for "emotional refueling"; furthermore, the child should be heeded as to the length of time he can bear to have his mother out of sight — a tolerance level that correlated closely with his stage of development.

The whole course of infant development is seen as taking place within the framework of this dyadic arrangement, with the mother as the continental center of the crawling and toddling child, who is tied to her by an invisible cord which allows him to explore the limits of his primary world for short periods of time. He has a "love affair" with the world, flirting with every section of it promiscuously; but he is always ready to return to the center for sustenance and reactivation. Accelerated separation gives rise to anxiety, in extreme cases panic, however good the surrogation may be. The problem with regard to the nurse in the baby house or the metapelet in the toddlers' house, is that in the nature of group upbringing, neither can be completely and indisputably at the service of any one infant or toddler, so that the latter cannot practice the first steps of separation within a fully secure setting.

In place of the model constructed by Mahler, which is attuned to the mutual needs of each mother and child in an "average expectable environment," the separation process in the kibbutz is scheduled according to a preconceived plan, the time aspects of which have been carefully considered from both theoretical and practical points of view, before being put into practice. The programming of early separation differs from kibbutz to kibbutz. One schedule went as follows: For the first six weeks of the baby's life, the mother stays in her house and away from work, visiting her baby five to seven times a day in order to feed him; at the end of this initial period, she returns to work. By the time the child is five months old, she has dropped one feeding and taken on an additional hour at work; at seven months, she drops another feeding and takes on still more work. This continues until, at nine months, she is doing a whole day's work and seeing her baby in the morning, at midday, and in the evening. By the end of the year, she has taken her part in the routine schedule of parent visiting common to all children in the kibbutz.

In the modern kibbutz, the mother is prepared for this postnatal routine. As a member of the kibbutz, she has already been made aware of its history on the questions of child-care, and she is given the further opportunity of talking over these matters with knowledgeable people. During the last five months of the prenatal period, she is given relaxation exercises by a physiotherapist, and encouraged to undergo "natural childbirth." There seemed to be something almost paradoxical to us about this emphasis on the "natural" mode prior to birth while, after the birth, there was what amounted to a prohibition of "natural" responses, with regard to the mother-infant interaction. Once again, we had to be reminded that it was the needs of communal life, and not "nature," that determined the way of life for the community members.

The group then shifted its focus from the separation to the surrogation process, in which the nurse, the metapelet and the peer group undertake in turn the supportive role with respect to the developing child. There was not much to say about the nurse, who is an expert in baby care and has full charge of the infant in the baby house. In general, the mothers recognize her skill and authority, and are guided by her in their feeding and handling of the infant. It was obvious that they regard the nurse not as a substitute-mother, but as a professional.

The feeling about the metapelet was of a different order. In this case, there is more obviously an emotional replacement, with someone substituting for the mother in most of her maternal functions, and taking over the care and training of the child altogether. It is true that the mother has visiting rights at all times, and is able to discuss her child freely with the metapelet; still, it is the metapelet who is in charge. The mother herself may be a metapelet, but in that case, she will be carrying out her child-caring functions with the children of other mothers.

The triadic relationship of mother, metapelet and child was referred to by the kibbutz members in our group as a state of "very delicate balance"; like many such states of equilibrium, it is subjected, from time to time, to phases of imbalance. It provides an additional source of conflict for any developing child. In ordinary family life, he would have experienced conflicts of the dyadic phase in relation to care, contact and control provided by his mother; these would have been followed by conflicts of the triadic phase, which involved both parents simultaneously. Under kibbutz conditions, a triangular situation of a different character, yet still fraught with conflict, is superimposed on the very first stage, and has its repercussions through all the succeeding stages of development.

The interrelationship between mother and metapelet can take several different forms, depending on the personalities involved and the degree of dependency established. At its best, the relationship may work out as a complementary one, in which the functions lying outside the mother's competence or her time-schedule are fulfilled by the metapelet.

The second kind of relationship is of a more conflictual nature: in it, mother and metapelet compete for "ownership" of the child, struggling against each other for its love and attention, sometimes in the fiercest and most overt rivalry. The child is caught in a conflict of loyalties, just as he often is in Western family life, when the mother is working, and a grandmother has first assumed training responsibility for the child, and then gradually taken over in all areas. In the case of the metapelet, the mother may openly show her resentment of the other woman as a woman, and her mistrust of her as a surrogate: "She has always been against me in the General Assembly." "When I applied to go to Oranim for training, she voted against it." "How can she bring up my child when she has no control over her own behavior?"

In the third type of relationship, the conflict is even more extreme because it is based on a clash of personalities. For example, a compulsive mother may feel that a permissive-minded metapelet has been teaching her child "loose habits," and she may therefore direct a lot of criticism and anger against the hated surrogate. The metapelet may also contribute her share to the conflict by reacting openly to the obsessive concerns of the mother. Once again, the child is "caught in the middle" — this time between two basic attitudes toward child-rearing — and becomes a victim of both.

A fourth type of relationship is one in which the metapelet compensates for deficiencies on the part of the mother, and yet this compensation never takes the form of a confrontation, with consequent exposure of the mother's incompetence or neglect. This is different from the first relationship described earlier, which is more in the nature of a "team approach" to the child. Here, for example, a covert rejection on the part of the mother can be mitigated by overcompensatory acceptance by the metapelet. Differences in character between the metapelet and the mother are not by themselves conducive to pathological developments, unless they are exploited by one or the other, and thus foster in the child a negative image of the "rival."

One problem generated by this triadic relationship is the transference of negative feelings stemming from the separation response. That this is well-nigh universal was suggested by one of the kibbutz clinicians in the group, who had found that in play therapy, the figure representing the metapelet was almost always treated with the greatest hostility, while the parent figures were idealized. In any toddlers' home, the metapelet may find herself the target of five or six such "transferences"; while they may not necessarily come together at any particular time, they may add up in the metapelet's mind at the end of a hard day's work, leaving her with a feeling of having been emotionally "beaten."

The visitors now expressed their interest in the exacting demands on the metapelet, and inquired into the methods of selection and training for that task. They were also disturbed by the succession of figures that made their appearance and exit in the child's life during its early development, thereby creating a marked discontinuity of relationship. It was recognized that the kibbutz child in no sense lived an "institutional" life — being in fact reared in an atmosphere of intense "belongingness" and "togetherness," with its parents remaining real parents, deeply involved in the development of their child. However, there remained the possibility that the lack of continuity in surrogation might create emotional problems similar to those met with among us in cases of multiple fostering.

The kibbutz members in the group freely admitted that they were not satisfied with the present system, being as cognizant as their American colleagues of the need for constancy in the substitute figure. It was regarded as impractical to make a metapelet out of the nurse after the children's first year, since her highly specialized abilities would serve no purpose for the children as they grew older. Having a metapelet as assistant to the nurse during the first year, however, was a fairly usual practice; it was quite possible for this woman to carry on, into the toddler and kindergarten homes. We were also told of a recent experimental innovation, in which two metaplot worked together with two groups in the same house, performing overlapping functions. This has made the groups equally responsive to their own and each other's metapelet, so that on off days and sick days, the children still had a familiar person taking care of them.

The problem lies in not having enough metaplot of good quality: not everyone is suitable for the job, and not everyone who is suitable wants the job. The visiting group felt that since group upbringing is regarded as a cardinal feature of kibbutz life, an extra-special effort should be made to recruit more directly and vigorously into this sphere, which could be indicated as a high-prestige job.

With regard to selection and qualification, the difficulty was once again shown to lie in the fact that demand is greater than supply. Although appointments are made through committees and have to be ratified by the General Assembly, only the very simplest criteria are actually used in selection. It is enough for a girl to show an interest in such work, and to have the backing of one of the metaplot. No vocational training is offered, except on the job. While the more dedicated metapelet remains on the job, others tend to graduate into teacher roles, so that there has been a certain amount of personnel loss.

The new metapelet frequently has her first experience in an overlapping role with a more experienced metapelet. In some of the kibbutzim, she can take her problems to a working group, presided over by one of the professional teachers or psychologists. We were told of one case in which a metapelet who was looking after the child of an extremely depressed mother, was trying hard to cope with the effects of this situation on the child. For several weeks, she brought this problem to her metapelet group, where she was given a great deal of support and advice by her more experienced colleagues.

It was this illustration, along with other information about the occupational hazards of being a metapelet, which made the visitors feel that the whole problem was still not being adequately handled, and that what might be regarded as the cornerstone of the whole kibbutz educational structure — the selection and training of the metapelet for her role as a continuous figure throughout the young life of the child — needed to be given immediate operational attention by the directors of the kibbutz movement. What the visitors were saying was, in effect, that for a mother-substitute to be good enough, she has to be at least as constant as the average mother, as well as better trained, and also better at the job of "mothering" since she has a more difficult mothering task to perform than the mother herself.

Our next theme was the surrogation provided by the peer group in the life of the kibbutz child. The group system certainly enters into his development earlier than it does anywhere else in the world, and the visitors were surprised to learn just how early, in this type of setting, the infant is capable of group responses and group recognitions. Although he cannot, in reality, be looked upon as a "member of a group," he seems to be aware of the others growing up along with him, and especially of their feelings, as these are expressed in laughter or crying. By the time the child has reached the kindergarten stage, the group has already begun to influence and support him much more directly, and to pressure him towards group or community conformity.

This group pressure begins to reach its peak around late latency and prepuberty. Even in the earliest groups, however, collective influence is apparent in such matters as showing emotion, making noise, creating a mess and so on. Many of the tiny kibbutz child's activities are strongly reinforced by his being able to see what he is doing reflected six or more times in the group. Everything is done together and in much the same way: they imitate each other and follow each other, and the totality of feeling engendered by all this conduces to an inner conviction that group-oriented activity has a special kind of rightfulness all its own.

In discussing this aspect of kibbutz life, the visitors realized that whereas *they* had been thinking in negative terms — of children being deprived of their mothers, lacking continuous figures in their development, having to compete as a group for one harassed metapelet — their *kibbutz counterparts* saw it in quite a different light. As people of more than average sense and sensibility, they were able to appreciate some of the deficiencies in their system; but their own enduring picture of the kibbutz child is of a much-loved, even pampered darling who lives a care-free, permissive existence, always in the close company of his peers, always in an intensely familiar environment, seldom hearing a harsh word, and never treated punitively. He experiences complete acceptance and tolerance, and many of the children's symptoms — such as bed-wetting and thumb-sucking — are regarded as evidences of tolerance, and not of deprivation. To a great extent, the peer group has taken over the role of the family in the life of the child; once again, the absence of the parents removes the stimulus for jealousy in its more pathological forms.

In some kibbutzim, an effort is made to keep siblings together in the children's houses; in others, it is felt that this creates problems and veers toward a "familistic trend," a reconstitution of part of the family. One of the kibbutz teachers gave us a beautiful illustration of "sibling surrogation": a little boy got up at night in the children's home and set off for the toddlers' home to visit his little sister, with the firm conviction that he had heard her crying. She was, in fact, crying, and he then wondered whether this was because their baby brother was crying. He was about to continue on his mission of consolation when the night-watch-woman caught up with him and was able to reassure him. It would seem that in the absence of functioning parents, a rudimentary sense of parental responsibility can be awakened in the child, sensitized by his own needfulness.

In keeping with their country's tradition of "individualism," the visitors expressed great concern for the child who, for various reasons — genetic, constitutional or environmental — would not or could not conform to group norms. Our colleagues were aware of this problem. They described to us two types of children who were really not suitable for kibbutz life: the one they described as individualistic, aggressive, hyperactive and oppositional; the other as introverted, isolated and "shut-in." These two types (in

Israel, as in America) finally found their way to the guidance clinics; here, they eventually took their leave of the kibbutz altogether.

It would seem, therefore, that communal life is best suited for a "middling" sort of child, neither too extroverted nor too introverted. There is no place in it for the child who is excessively curious about the world beyond the boundaries of the settlement, and all too eager to explore it. Nor is it a place for the quiet, inward-turning child, in search of a private nook in which to indulge his fantasies, read a book, or write a poem. One has to remind himself that this is still a pioneering community, with a pioneering job to do in cultivating the desert, and that a special sort of "no-nonsense" pioneer stock is therefore at a premium. However, you can never "breed true" in human genetics, nor can you insure that a predisposing environment will do the job properly. There are bound to be "odd ones" produced from time to time, who will remain unable to adjust to the stringent requirements of the kibbutz, even after prolonged indoctrination.

During the final phase of our group discussion, we turned once again to look at development as a whole under this system. It was clear that although a "conflict-free" kibbutz development was theoretically intended as the result of "splitting" the mothering figure into a loving one and a nurturing one, in practice this process has produced as many conflicts as it has resolved. From many points of view, it might well be harder in the long run to adjust to two mothers than to one.

Psychoanalysis has taught us that one of the crucial developmental tasks that must be undertaken by the child is the resolution of conflicts of ambivalence towards its objects, without resorting to such psychological maneuvers as idealization, denial, splitting, reversal of affect, etc. The concept of "conflict-free development" for the human child is, in that sense, unrealistic. Moreover, it cannot be guaranteed that the child will continue to love the mother who has given up her training role, since he may view her instead as an *abandoning* figure. He may *displace* his hate onto the metapelet; nevertheless, as the analysis of adult kibbutz subjects has shown, he is unconsciously aware of *whom he is really hating*.

One of the kibbutz clinicians presented clinical data which suggested that in their inner lives, the children react *as if* they were being reared under normal family conditions. They manifest, for example, an oedipal development that is normal, although somewhat delayed in its onset and resolution. To what extent this retardation impedes the formation of the superego and delays the functioning of repressing mechanisms (with the emergence of guilt in the handling of conflicts) remains uncertain. Where group pressures are so predominant in controlling behavior, it may be that shame rather than guilt is the determining measure involved. The ego ideal, with its scheme of mechanisms stemming from group ideals, has probably replaced the superego and its guilt mechanisms in many of the conflict situations.

Nevertheless, there is still a great deal of guilt attaching to the nuclear conflicts. In this respect, the gross symptomatology and psychopathology are similar to those of children brought up under quite different conditions. The kibbutz child makes attempts, during play therapy, to reconstitute the family along traditional lines, and to involve this classical family model, rather than the kibbutz family arrangement, in his various life themes. The child also brings in fantasy "primal scene" material, *as if* he has actually been occupying a bed in his parents' house.

The general atmosphere of the kibbutz is so benign towards the child that occasions for anger and hostility directed against significant grownups are probably much less frequent than is the case in familial environments. In the play situation, we were told, the kibbutz child sometimes shows as much rage as any other child, but he projects a large part of it outside the kibbutz altogether — against the Arabs, the Egyptians, the Jordanians, etc., who are very much the "official" enemies in the kibbutz. Part of his rage he reserves for his metapelet, who is often a witch figure in his play.

At this stage, the metapelet is a highly significant and prominent object for the child; as he moves into adult life, she gradually fades into a shadowy figure which eventually fuses with the image of the mother and loses its identity. Thus she will play no part in the analysis of an adult patient, although some years earlier she may have made tempestuous appearances in his play therapy. The metapelet is therefore "lost" in the course of development, while the mother, who has been idealized in the early play, emerges in the adult treatment situation as the villain of the piece, much hated and much reviled.

The question of why the psychic apparatus needs to fuse the two early separate images into the later single one made for an interesting discussion. The child brought up under ordinary conditions may "split" the maternal image into good and bad mother images under conditions of intense ambivalence, and so preserve its good mother — at least for a time. In this respect, one can say that it does its own psychic work. As development goes on, it fuses and de-fuses the maternal images until, in the adult, a more or less coherent image is achieved.

In the case of the kibbutz child, the maternal image is artificially bifurcated, in the service of "conflict-free" development, into a good, loving, indulging mother and a bad, frustrating, training metapelet. There may be a primary need to fuse these two images, as a normal development, or at least to restore the abrogated maternal function to the mother. The result is that the metapelet and all her conflict-laden activities are eventually incorporated into the maternal image, with the hostility re-placed onto the original mother figure. (In this context, one American analyst informed this reporter that in all his analytic experience, he had never encountered such mother hostility as appeared in a woman patient who had been brought up completely in the kibbutz.)

Our kibbutz members reminded us of the normal psychological process whereby events are shortened, sharpened and distorted by time, so that multiple events of long duration are often telescoped to create a single foreshortened screen memory. The fusion of metapelet and maternal images may be brought about by the same sort of process. This takes place over time, however, so that one will find the elements still separate in early life. In the child's play therapy, the two images remain discrete.

Thus the kibbutz members of the group felt that we were still tying the mothering function too closely to a single mother figure, and therefore making too much of a fusion process that is normally operative. While recognizing that there is a developmental lag during the second year of the kibbutz child's life, they attribute this not to the fact that the toddler does poorly in the absence of his mother, since he has not yet learned to make full use of his group, but to the amount of stimulation given to the toddler during his second year — which is, in terms of current kibbutz practice, inadequate. What the toddler therefore needs is, in their opinion, *more stimulation,* not more mothering; *this* they were eager to obtain for him. There appeared to be something of an impasse here, which three sessions of group discussion were not sufficient to overcome.

One final contribution to the group meeting, although it was not made within the same context as the other contributions, should not be overlooked. From a kibbutz member came the suggestion that since the child of the kibbutz is to all intents and purposes a "group personality," having developed under group conditions, it might be logical to conclude that analytic group therapy would be more helpful than individual therapy. At this point, it emerged that many of the kibbutz clinicians, being group therapists, were in a position to provide us with some instructive clinical data from group therapy settings. We of the visiting team, all of whom were also clinicians, could have made use of much more clinical data from both group analytic and child analytic sessions. The blending of clinical with nonclinical information would surely have thrown light on many of the problems raised. As analysts, we would especially have liked to hear what they could tell us about the nature of the transference response in kibbutz children.

Finally, it is my opinion that the helpfulness of these group discussions would have been enhanced by:

1. An extension of the time alloted to the mixed discussion group, so as to allow for some "working through" of problems.

2. Verbatim observational data from non-clinical members.

3. Verbatim clinical data from individual and group therapy sessions (child analytic sessions, if possible).

4. Direct access by the visiting clinicians to children, parents and metaplot. (The language barrier could be met by means of an interpreter.)

5. An extended living-in experience in the kibbutz itself.

Problems of Latency

SOCIALIZATION OF
SEVEN TO TWELVE-YEAR-OLD CHILDREN

Rachel Manor

Socialization is the process whereby children acquire sensitivity to social stimuli, to the pressures and obligations of group life, the process whereby they learn to behave like the others in their group or culture. It is the process, in short, of becoming a social being. Socialization is achieved by the inculcation in individuals of the skills, traits and values prerequisite for the performance of present or anticipated roles; in our case, it is the preparation of children for kibbutz life.

Different socializing agents are at work during the process of the kibbutz child's education: parents, siblings, other family members, educators, the peer group, the children's community, and the wider community of the kibbutz. In each developmental phase, one or more socializing agents exercise the main influence. For the seven- to twelve-year-old child, the peer group becomes the important socializing agent, side by side with the parents and educators. The child has a strong feeling of group solidarity: he feels secure in his group, and wants to fulfill their demands, in order to be loved and accepted by them.

The group thus becomes an emotional center, giving the child the feeling of belonging — a second family. (Some of the kibbutz children take, as their family name, the name of their group.) There is an unbroken unity here of learning of content and education (as a person): the classroom is one of the rooms in the children's house; the peer group *lives and learns together.* The group helps the children to give up their infantile dependency on adults; they learn to take care of themselves — to wait, to share, to take their turn.

At that age, learning ability advances hand in hand with the repression of infantile sexuality and the development of the ability to sublimate. Life in a kibbutz group provides a wide field of opportunities for sublimation. The children generally enjoy learning, and there are rather high accomplishments in study, without punishment and without examinations, marks, report cards, etc.

At the same time, my experiences reveal that "taking time away from" formal learning, in the traditional academic areas, for group discussion of the means of developing good group living — and that *does* take time — does not hinder normal growth in the academic areas. The children themselves take part in deciding which rules to learn; together with the teacher, they prepare an outline for their studies. The individual, or the group, learns to weigh values, measure alternatives, make selections. Not all our teachers are able to work in this way, but it is the basic philosophy of kibbutz teachers, and ultimately, the key to successful education.

Erikson sees an overall danger in the imbalance, characteristic of our times, between passive stimulation and active outlet. In the children's group, there is no such imbalance. Group life, work experience, developing and laying stress, in turn, on all kinds of creative arts and crafts help to create the necessary balance between stimulation and outlet. The children learn both to be led and to lead. From the last third of the school year — that is, from the second grade on — the children live in a democratically organized children's community, comprising three to four different groups, from the second to sixth grades. Since all of the children's houses are in the same area, there is much spontaneous playing together, and the development of friendships among children of different age groups. On this vital level of conscious interrelationship, there are all sorts of activities in the children's community, organized by their own committees: sports, work, parties, library, newspaper, etc.

Each committee is in charge for three months. This practice of changing the members three times during the school year ensures that many children are able to serve as active members of these committees. Every committee has an adult — teacher or metapelet — in charge throughout the year. Every group in the children's community sends its representatives to every committee. The basis for selection is the child's own wish, along with the group's recognition, influenced by the educators, of everyone's need to develop along the lines of his own specific experiences. Every child is eager to be active on a committee; he thereby develops initiative and responsibility. Beginning as the youngest member in a committee that includes different age groups, the child grows slowly in self-reliance and security.

The children master — better than many adults do — the art of living together, of keeping a balance between society's demands and individual needs and weaknesses. At the end of the fifth (sometimes even the fourth) grade, they are expected to serve as responsible committee leaders; as a matter of fact, they often prove to be creative initiators, as well as thoughtful friends to the younger committee members.

I want to speak on the idea that one has to pay a price for this intensive group life — not being able to be alone, and so on. In this age group, the children do have the time to read and they do read; but I have the feeling that this is an age at which children *want to be busy and to stay together.* I think the other question is for adolescents, rather than for this age group. At this age, they don't really want to be alone very much; we sometimes have to urge them to go on individually.

At the end of every term, there are community meetings. Here the committees give their reports, which the children evaluate, thus marking the path for improvement in both their individual abilities and the community's activities. Living in the children's community makes it possible to transfer values, to demand controls, and to cast aside renunciation and frustration. However, these achievements are not imposed by powerful adults upon helpless children; they are accepted and incorporated as values by the children's community, through discussion and through identification by the younger children with the older ones.

The children work on their own farm, a small area loved by every child. It includes animals, poultry, and a flower and vegetable garden. They clean and arrange their own rooms, lay the table and wash the dishes. At work, the principle of age-groups is abandoned; every child meets children from different age-groups.

The existence of the children's community strengthens group development. Intergroup relationships make it possible for the group to look at itself in relation to the larger society. With that intent, the educators organize meetings and mutual visits with the same age-groups in neighboring kibbutzim, in moshavim, in the cities, in Arab villages, etc.

In the sixth grade, the group enters the Youth Movement; it thus comes into contact with a large youth organization, which is spread all over the country. At this age, they get *madrichim* — generally a boy and/or a girl, only a few years older than the children in their group. Here is another socializing agent of strong influence.

There are obvious differences between children of the same age group, with regard to the cultural and human values they absorb from the family. School children spend about two hours every day with their parents — more on Saturdays — and, during their vacations and on school holidays, they visit their parents at work. On many occasions, they work with them. They thus identify with their parents in their social, as well as their sexual roles.

We find many cases of extended kinship families in the kibbutzim. In my kibbutz, for example, there are some families that comprise four generations; families of three generations are rather common. The grandparents play a specific role in the children's life, a different one in each family. Sibling rivalry exists, but there is also much give-and-take among the siblings in any one family. The parents of the children in a children's group often form a group themselves and follow, as a group, their children's development, giving the children a kind of "our parents" feeling, which is gradually transformed into an "our kibbutz" feeling.

In modern Western society, children and youth are to a great extent isolated from society. In contrast with the past, when children were regarded as an integral part of community living, they are today relegated to an isolated realm of their own. Small families, apartment-house living, the increased specialization of the adults, and similar factors — all contribute to this isolation.

In the kibbutz, on the contrary, the child becomes an organic part of his society early in life; he grows into it, gradually "conquering" every part and corner. The children take an active part in kibbutz holidays and festivals, without being dominated or swallowed up by the adult world. Moreover, since the kibbutz is not an isolated island, but a part of the world family, influenced by such means of mass communication as radio, newspapers, magazines, etc. — television will become an addition in the near future — there is a trend within kibbutz society towards *light, passive amusement,* marked by a preference for the role of *spectator.* This trend is counterbalanced by those kibbutz members who initiate and organize choirs, dramatic groups, chamber music ensembles, orchestras, etc., reinforcing *active participation* in recreation, festivals, etc. The outcome of the struggle between these two cultural roles — passive and active — will be rather significant for the cultural development of the children.

The special form of the second- to sixth-grade children's group life puts before the teachers and metaplot unique problems, and calls for particular qualifications and knowledge. The educators of a group are a teacher and a metapelet. They work together in close cooperation, their fields of work not being strictly differentiated. Both are responsible for the group climate: the metapelet is aware of everything that happens in the classroom, while the teacher, on the other hand, has two meals every day with the children, and also puts them to bed at night.

Teachers do not specialize in particular subjects: they shift, according to situations and needs, from subjects that demand intellectual attention and concentration to the arts and crafts, which bring relaxation and stimulate creativeness. In this sort of school system, there are no half-year promotions: one teacher may remain with his group for a period of from three to five years. (This continuity of teachers and metaplot can cause some difficulty, however, in the socialization process.) Strong emotional bonds are woven between the teacher and the children; this is the source of his strength as an educator — the fact that the children love him and identify with him.

"There was an old world clock" (speaking of the big clock that directed life, year after year) . "Suddenly this clock was damaged; then it started to go backwards. Everything that had happened in life returned to happen all over again." Here the teacher stopped telling the story and asked the children, "Which event in your life would you like to happen again, and which one would you not like to have happen again?"

One after the other their tongues loosened; the children told of amazing things that had happened in their lives — things they had never before told to anybody, and which they now dared to tell, in the accepting atmosphere of the group classroom. "A" — an eight-year-old girl, who stuttered, and generally did not participate actively in group discussions — told the group of an event that had taken place, involving herself and her father, when she was three years old. Her father had frightened her terribly then; she told about the event in such a lively manner and was so stirred up by it, that it almost seemed as though he had done it only the day before. From that day on, the teacher established steady contact with the little girl's father, and, after a short time, "A" stopped stuttering.

Performance and success in education are dependent in the long run upon the educator's personality, as well as his talents, skills, and knowledge. The educator's study, supervision and in-service training therefore deserve our chief consideration and concern. In older and more experienced kibbutzim, we find staff groups — all the teachers, and the metaplot who work with children of the second to sixth grades — holding regular meetings. They exchange experiences, offer mutual help, plan common activities for the children's community, and discuss educational and psychological problems. Every kibbutz has an Education Committee that supports the educators in their work. Among other things, it picks up the criticisms made by parents and tries to straighten out conflicts between parents and educators.

I want now to discuss some special problems. Intensive group life has its stresses and strains for seven- to twelve-year-old children. Groups, as well as individuals, have their needs; if these are not met, there is frustration and maladjustment. In order to meet the needs of a group, you must both love them and limit them — in both ways you are helping them to achieve. The teacher has to give a great deal of thought to the dimensions of the responsibilities that he assigns to the children. There must be clear limits to the relevant areas, so as to avoid confusion; but these limits should be designed to widen the children's growing maturity and skills. In a group that lives so closely together, there is also the danger of constant roles — specialists, stars, leaders, scapegoats, etc. The teacher needs special awareness and skill in order to avoid this.

Good group-living requires respect for deviation as well as for conformity. Kibbutz children are in danger of too much conformity, of having no legitimate ways in which to express their aggression or deviance, precisely because the environmental influence is so unified. Educators, parents, the whole community — all move in the same direction, without any of those negative influences to which children outside the kibbutz are exposed. However, a small number of outlets are deliberately left unsocialized. For instance, during the winter, on fine, sunny days, one gives the children some hours when they are without any adults and can do whatever they want to do. Not all acts of aggression are prohibited, some are even sanctioned.

There is a social pressure within the group that pushes each of the members toward growth, development and achievement. Everybody is generally pleased by the contribution and improvement of the group as a whole, and of every member individually. Such pressure may nevertheless have the effct of discouraging and unwarrantedly limiting; educators have to be aware of this when it shows signs of occurring, and to reduce the pressure.

Because they are always together — and in this age group, I repeat, they *want* it that way — they have to be *helped to be alone,* to be able to spend their leisure time individually. The teacher has to help the group to discover individual abililties and to assist and employ them. Individual hobbies, spontaneity, and the initiative of individuals and subgroups are encouraged, where necessary, to go outside the range of the officially organized programs.

As its members grow older, the group acquires more and more autonomy — which provides the children with a new opportunity: to live their lives as children and adolescents, and not as little adults, expected to behave "like ladies and gentlemen." They are active, but as the youngsters they are, without any exaggerated pressure to "behave."

Along with competition, there is a great deal of cooperation, starting in the first grade and continuing on into adult life. In kibbutz society, competition mainly takes the form of "socialist competition" — that is, of competition between two groups. The capacity for cooperation is one of the most estimable attributes of the child's personality. It is the process of socialization that brings the children toward the realization of this set of values. Erikson describes the emotionally healthy child during the latency period as "developing industry," saying that he can at that time become an eager and absorbed *unit of a productive situation.*

But there is also a danger at this stage; it is rooted in the underlying sense of inadequacy and inferiority. The group climate in the kibbutz, by emphasizing cooperation as against competition, helps the children at the same time that it provides them with productive situations. The security the children find in their groups reduces their dependency on adults and with it, perhaps, also the need to revolt, to revenge, to protest, as well as the accumulation of guilt feelings.

We have to consider whether or not the price a kibbutz child pays for all these advantages is a decrease in its capacity for emotional ties, a certain coldness and flatness of affect, as is sometimes suggested. Judging from my personal experience, which has consisted of living with both parents and children, I would not say so. It may be that the need for love and affection, as it appears in the Western family today, is in fact exaggerated, because the children are conditioned to feel it. I agree with Green, when he says that ". . . not the need for parental love, but the constant threat of its withdrawal after the child has become conditioned to the need, lies at the root of the most characteristic modern neurosis." The child's personality has been, in effect, enmeshed; he can now be thrown into a panic by a disapproving glance. Such a child feels caught and helpless; he has anxiety and guilt feelings and a sense of inferiority. He is "alone and afraid, in a world [he] never made."

That is not the feeling of the kibbutz child. It is wrong to think that collectivity and conformity are the same thing; we strive for individualization and differentiation. During latency, kibbutz children identify with the social role that has won the highest status; at this age, they aspire to become tractor-drivers, or any kind of responsible workers. Since they are used to work, they enjoy the mastery of materials, cooperative situations, the feeling of being both creative and productive. For a kibbutz child, it is not only possible but desirable to live up to the norms and values of his society. There is no discrepancy between social requirements and the child's own hopes, and every child has access to the means both for meeting those requirements and for fulfilling his hopes.

I want to speak a little here about the superego formation of the kibbutz child. Some see convergencies between the nature of social systems and the nature of the individual superego. We have already mentioned that, in the kibbutz, we have no delinquency. It is true that this term means different things to different individuals and different groups at different times. Fritz Redl, for example, considers it bad to use the term "delinquency" as one uses "bellyache" — without differentiating between appendicitis, and a simple case of "too much ice cream" — and then to think that a theory can be built around such a loosely defined concept. Anyway, in the kibbutz, there are no gangs performing anti-social actions. There may be single deviant acts — breaking into a refrigerator in the communal kitchen, going on a trip without permission, using a jeep or a tractor without a license — all of which are pranks, rather than instances of delinquency.

The mastery of materials is the backbone of identity formation. Ego identity provides the specific ego strength that helps youth to manage both increased drives and conflicting standards. Ego diffusion, on the other hand, leaves you wide open for explosive drives and shattering conflicts.

According to some sociologists, delinquency is not evidence of individual failure during the process of socialization, but rather a measure of the breakdown of society itself. The absence of a meaningful and structured social life produces a society in which the individual, supposedly "free" of all genuine social bonds, finds himself in fact abandoned, isolated, demoralized. Society becomes a scattering dust of individuals. All of this is effectively counteracted in kibbutz life.

There is no clear-cut differentiation between parents and educators, in regard to discipline. Kibbutz children form their superego by identifying with their parents, who have reinforcing as well as disciplinary functions. However, there are also cases, in the extended kibbutz family, in which there is retention of the dependent role of infancy, the individuals in question looking for care and reassurance even after they have become adults and have their own families.

I want to touch on the problem of emotional disturbance among latency children. In the kibbutz society, just as in differently structured societies, there are emotionally disturbed adults. It seems to me that kibbutz life can actually reinforce emotional disturbances. Every emotional disturbance results in regression, and we have been able to observe some manifestations of regression and immaturity, such as could cause emotional disturbances in the children of these disturbed parents. Such adults tend to look on the kibbutz the way children look on parents, as both protecting and frustrating; they react with the same infantile ambivalence as the child does toward his parents. These are the kibbutz members who want only to receive, and are not able to give. Embittered, they project their own failures and shortcomings onto the "mother" (that is, the kibbutz). One may fairly assume that kibbutz life can have the effect of reinforcing such regressive tendencies.

The rationalizations of these members are for the most part presented as ideological arguments against the principles of the kibbutz. Their relationships with fellow members may be disturbed by the very fact of their perceiving them as siblings. Regression in such a case takes the form of longing for the family life that they experienced when they were children: having negated kibbutz family life, they strive in an idealized and distorted way for the restoration of their childhood family. The fact that the kibbutz is a small island in the wide ocean of a different way of life makes it easier for them, whenever there is a crisis, to peer outside, instead of trying to change whatever needs improvement inside.

These infantile and immature persons would very likely have emotionally disturbed children wherever they lived, since they are not able to give their children the love of mature parents or see to their emotional needs. Yet it seems to me that their confusions and ambivalence *about kibbutz life* cannot help aggravating their child's disturbance. If kibbutz parents impose frustrations on their children about the things that they themselves resent, their children too are likely to be disturbed. When these children feel the antagonism directed by their family against their children's house, they become confused and deeply insecure.

The concept of "anticipatory socialization" is important in an everchanging society. Children have to be prepared to play the role that their parents have not succeeded in playing themselves. In this context, the existence of a peer group, the children's community, which establishes identification with older children and younger adults, in addition to the child's identification with the parents, is of crucial importance.

David Riesman sees in the peer group one example of the "other-directed" type of society. For him, the fate of many "inner-directed" children is loneliness, in the home and outside it, yet the "other-directed" peer group makes efforts to "cut everyone down to size," as soon as he stands up or stands out in any direction. The child is thus at the mercy of the judgment of his peer group (except that these are matters of taste, and not of morality). "The function of the group is to have fun": existing in and surviving in that kind of peer group requires a highly sensitive response to — things of fashion. This is training in "consumer taste," calling for the ability to adopt new sets of fashions rapidly, and creating a real fear of nonconformity. The relatively stable and idealistic pursuits of the "inner-directed" person are thus, according to Reisman, replaced by the fluctuating taste that the "other-directed" person accepts from his peer group.

The climate of the kibbutz peer group, however, is not "other-directed." It might be interesting to consider which of Riesman's categories of society he would assign kibbutz society to — the traditional type of "closed society," or the "inner-" or "other-directed" type of society. It seems to me that kibbutz society is, in fact, *an altogether new sociological type, and does not fit any of Riesman's categories at all.*

DISCUSSION

GUSTI MELZER: Young children are very closely bound to each other: in the afternoon, for instance, the older child will go to the children's house and bring the younger child home to the parent's house. You can see the bigger child holding on to his smaller brother or sister by the hand. There is a lot of that sort of sense of responsibility between brothers and sisters, younger and older.

My three children, for example, live in three different houses, far away from each other. One night the night-watch found my boy, who was then eight years old, coming from his sister's house (she was two years old), and when the watch asked him what he was doing there outside in the garden at that time of night, he replied that, in his sleep, he had heard his sister crying, and "I went to see why she was crying." When he got to her bed, she told him that the reason she was crying was that their baby sister was crying. He said to the watch that he was now on his way to the baby sister to soothe her; but she told him to go on home, that she would see to the baby.

A very interesting development takes place during the later years, when the role of the group becomes more important to the child. After the children have identified themselves with the group, personal competition between brother and sister becomes hidden behind group competition. At the ages of ten and twelve, they don't say: "You aren't doing that well," or "You're doing that badly," or "I don't like you." Instead, they become aggressive in the name of their groups, and say: *"Your group* didn't work well!" *"Your group* went out yesterday to pick apples, but everyone said that they worked badly"; "We're going for a trip, but you aren't allowed to go."

It is very interesting to watch the children hiding their personal rivalries behind group rivalry, and to observe how the children express this. They do it in many different ways. When my two daughters quarrel, for example, they don't quarrel personally — they identify their personal quarrel with their groups.

DR. KRIS: Incidents such as the one just described with one sibling going out in the night to help his younger sister do not involve only the sibling; they can also be viewed in the light of the very important process of identification with the parents that makes its appearance more sharply at this stage.

Often, we also see the older child in the family taking care of the younger one spontaneously — but under one condition, namely, when the mother is absent. At such times, the older child identifies with the caring person, and takes over her function. I am sure that in the kibbutz there must frequently be situations that provide an opportunity for the expression of this attitude. It may even be a source of special incitement to the older child, to know that there is no parent or parent substitute present with the younger sibling at night in the children's house; it makes him adopt a basically protective, watchful attitude, such as comes into action, for example, when he hears the younger child's cry in the other house. In some ways, there may even be present a *double identification*: he understands readily and identifies readily with the younger sibling's needs, and he satisfies these needs via identification with the absent parental figure — that is, by acting as he knows the parent would in such situations.

DR. REDL: I would like to know what these kids are actually doing most of the time. What kind of possessions do they cherish? Which of them do they consider exchangeable, which expendable? How do they feel in relation to "territory?" What does a kid do when he wants to start a fight? What does the adult do to keep it on a reasonably friendly basis? What are the most widely used forms of face-saving? Is there any similarity between the children's methods of saving face and the ones the parents use?

JEHUDA MESSINGER: I would like to answer Dr. Redl's question about what children "do." Parent and child in the kibbutz are both so different in character from their counterparts outside, I feel, that the emotional problems are of a quite specific nature.

We have heard here of "over-indulgence." The atmosphere in the parents' room reflects the fact that the parents are not so much determined and demanding as they are satisfied. In those two hours together, the children and their parents are not "in conflict." I don't say that there are *no* conflicts. There are, in fact, frequent differences between parents and children, and there are conflicts as well. It may be that the parent presents a good image and the metapelet a bad one; it may be vice versa. In some cases, hostility is transferred from the children's room to the parents' house; in some cases, the other way round.

MIRYAM ROT: We have spoken here about one child being pitted against another. The children themselves have strong feelings about this, and also their own ways of dealing with it. They see the danger to each other. There are children who obey and children who disobey. There are children who want to know; they also know what will happen when they do revolt, and whether or not it is dangerous to revolt.

SHMUEL NAGLER: By contrast with the general readiness to cooperate that prevails among children during the latency period, we have met with some extreme cases of noncooperativeness among lower-grade children in the kibbutz. Such disorders have caused a great deal of disappointment to kibbutz educators, who had believed that early conditioning would serve to strengthen the cooperative attitude. It may be that this extremely aggressive *counter-attitude,* directed against the kibbutz philosophy of co-operation, is the result of *too early* attempts to condition to co-operative life, carried on at a developmental stage at which the child is *not yet ready* to fulfill the task of a cooperative give-and-take.

DR. NEUBAUER: Is this difficult to overcome by treatment? How stubborn is such a child?

SHMUEL NAGLER: The methods of treatment differ according to the case. There are, however, some cases of antisocial acting-out that are so deeply rooted they can hardly be overcome.

ELI ILAN: If this supposition is correct, then not only should the fact of being placed under group pressure too early result in severe pathology, but there must be some sort of continuum in which a decrease in this kind of pressure would produce a correspondingly lesser degree of pathology or personality disorders. Has Dr. Nagler considered this kind of continuum?

SHMUEL NAGLER: The general belief is that during military service, kibbutz-born recruits, who have completed the kibbutz secondary school, are group-minded and very cooperative. Unfortunately, this is, so far, only an opinion; it has yet to be put to the test. The idea that premature group pressure may be one of the antecedents of antisocial behavior is based chiefly on the investigation of symptom formation, and not of personality formation, which lies outside pathology.

DR. KRIS: I wonder whether the less disturbed ones come to you at all. If they did, you might really have a wide range of material.

SHMUEL NAGLER: I agree. In this setting, educators are more prepared to deal with open aggression by themselves, and without feeling the need for our clinical services. Hence, at our clinic, we have, for the most part, only the most severely disturbed children — those who show definitely antisocial symptoms.

Chapter IV

ADOLESCENCE

SOME ISSUES OF ADOLESCENCE

MONI ALON

IN A KIBBUTZ, the children's house is generally a "quiet corner"; problems are kept out. Most of our "problems" with children occur during adolescence.

I would like to begin by stressing two specific points about the adolescents in kibbutz life. The first is that the older generation of parents have had great expectations for their children. These are not the different personal expectations that every parent has for his son or daughter; the older generation as a whole have looked to their sons and daughters for the answer as to whether the kibbutz would continue.

The second point is that we, the generation of parents, are really not altogether certain what sort of relationships we want with our children. While we want these relationships to be very friendly and close, we nevertheless have to recognize the fact of adolescent rebellion. We ourselves had it, and we see that our adolescents have it. We want our children to be healthy, with undisturbed roots in the country; yet we ask, "Where is the intellectual disquiet that we brought with us?" because we want them to have that, too!

I do not think that this is a rebellious generation. The youth in general seem to accept the values of the kibbutz movement, and of the kibbutz in which they live. I am speaking here of work — manual labor — both as a value and as a job. I am speaking of democratic cooperation as a way of life — and I am speaking of equality, too. Our youth accept these things, cling to them; they love them and conform to them. In that respect, this is a traditional society; at the same time, it is an open, dynamic society. In the Army, our children meet youngsters who were brought up differently; yet their identification with group values and the kibbutz way of life remains powerful.

What conflicts exist between youngsters and their parents? There are conflicts in our daily life — but these are not ideological conflicts. When our children come back from the Army, they go to work alongside their parents. I think they now see them in a more realistic way (that does not necessarily mean that they see them clearly.)

Parents don't interfere in the daily lives of the children — they don't ask them whether they have done their schoolwork, or when they came home the night before; there are no discussions about the keys to the car, or about money. While there is thus no conflict around such questions, in adolescence there is a certain withdrawal: the children speak less to the adults about their intimate problems; they ask fewer questions of their parents. (On the other hand, they are very much attached to the special atmosphere of the family room. There they speak about cultural things — books and music.) We often see how, at the tender age, children unconsciously accept their parents' traits; at this age, however, they argue with their parents, they become critical of their outlook, their interests, and so on.

What I want to stress is that the children not only have their own lives, but their activities are very *structured*. Besides learning and work, there is a lot of cultural activity. On Friday evenings, we have discussions of various kinds. There is a newspaper, in which they can criticize the school — or write their first songs. The children themselves set up the activities, although they are helped by adults. We see in this the possibility of mixing children, of bringing some of the educational activity of the older child within the orbit of the younger child.

We don't have any problem of boredom — of young people not knowing what to do with themselves, and therefore looking for some activity that is gratifying only in an emotional sense. Our problem is really that the children have less time for themselves than they should have — especially the older ones. We have yet to decide whether they are working too hard, and if there are ways in which we can reduce the work.

We are not interested in having the children take examinations, because we built the schools for all the children. We think that every child in the kibbutz is entitled to an education up to the age of eighteen. When you give examinations, the school starts becoming selective. Further, our curriculum is different from the curriculum of urban secondary schools in Israel, because we are preparing the children for life in the kibbutzim. They learn less physics and mathematics, more agriculture and chemistry. They also learn less by heart; we teach the Bible, but not by heart.

Similarly, we are against giving marks; we are, in that sense, against formal education. We try instead to motivate the child by raising problems, by integrating different things. We are opposed to any form of competition in the classroom, and we try to bring about a friendly relationship between teacher and pupil. We don't have some irrational aversion to examinations, we just teach for a different purpose and in a different atmosphere.

If a child is gifted, and if the kibbutz is interested in having him go on to higher education, such a child generally does not have trouble passing the matriculation examinations. But we are really not interested in facilitating this for a large number of children, or in changing our basic outlook on education.

We are not only teaching, we are linking our whole educational system with kibbutz life. This creates conflicts, especially among children who aspire to a profession. You might compare the problem with that of the Orthodox Jew who knows that if he were to go into a certain profession, it would conflict with his religion. He may give up his religion because he truly wants to accept another religion, or he may give it up in the name of some specific opportunity. On the other hand, he may give up his dream of a profession, and remain instead with the society that he most wants to live in.

DISCUSSION
The Problem of Goals
"Articles of Faith"

SHIMON STERN: There is, in my opinion, one main problem about our educational process, especially at this age. On the one hand, we would like our children — we are, in fact, very keen on this — to stay in the kibbutz; on the other hand, we wouldn't like them to do that just because *we* would like it. They do have a special problem, after all, such as we never knew: we *decided ourselves* whether to go the kibbutz or not, while you will hear very often from our youth that they were *"born into"* the kibbutz, so that it doesn't really seem like a problem to them. (Perhaps, for the more philosophical-minded, the more serious among them, it is a problem, sometimes a very complicated one.)

It has been said here that in kibbutzim where the set of values — of kibbutz values — is held to, fewer daughters and sons leave the kibbutz. That is why it is very important at that age to make these values very clear to our children; in other words, to teach them about the kibbutz. My experience, however, is that many teachers who work with this age group are missing the point: they feel that they do their job better, the more they verbalize about the kibbutz. However, the point is whether or not there is a serious gap between what our children *hear* in their school about the kibbutz, and what they *see going on* in their own kibbutz. The problem, then, is not *to teach about* the kibbutz, but to give our children the opportunity *to live* in the kibbutz manner.

It has been said that the youth have the opportunity to identify themselves with the kibbutz; yet, in every kibbutz, they find different objects for identification. There are members who identify themselves with the kibbutz; but there are also members who go on living there just because they are too old to go outside. Even the parents will sometimes say: "If I were your age, I wouldn't go into a kibbutz; but now it's too late." From them, our youth can't learn how to live in a kibbutz.

DR. BARBARA BIBER: Through many of the problems that we have been discussing, there seems to be a cross-pull between uniformity and diversity, adaptation and autonomy. The dangers that conformity holds for personality development — for example, in the form of strong group pressures — are thoroughly recognized by kibbutz members. But the extent to which a child or an adolescent can safely run counter to his group lies, in fact, within very narrow limits. Some of the guide-lines have been clearly expressed to us as among the basic articles of faith of the society.

Trends that might lead to *"careerism"* are considered undesirable; critical thinking — that is, negative criticism — must be channeled toward the *society outside the kibbutz,* for purposes of maintaining internal social stability. Blocks in communication between parents and children seem to involve the affairs of kibbutz life — from which we may assume, rightly or wrongly, that these represent an area of conflict for the adolescents.

If all this is so, then the question arises of where — with what alternate figures — adolescents can communicate, not just at the level of familiarity or friendliness, but at a dynamic level, where the resolution of conflicts becomes part of the complex process of forming ego-ideals. In this connection, we hear mention of people outside the family — metaplot, teachers, youth returned from the army. Yet here again the range of variation is limited — these people have all *accepted the kibbutz way of life* as the realization of their socialist ideals. Conformism, in personality terms, on the one hand, is antithetical to the ideal of the kibbutz man; on the other hand, exposure to diversity, to variation, has its institutional limits.

This dilemma would not be so troubling, if we (perhaps I should talk more personally here, and say I) were not so deeply impressed with your great concern and advanced techniques for developing each child into a fully developed individual, not only secure but autonomous, and capable of independent thinking and decision-making. I keep remembering the goal one of you expressed: that the child shall come to accept the kibbutz system *through his own independent processes,* not through being indoctrinated.

Is it really possible for you to educate children toward the autonomous resolution of problems, and the internalization of a value system, when there is so much feeling of the possible danger to the society that may arise from exposing children to *too much variation and diversity,* either of ideas or of alternate identification figures?

DR. REDL: There must be many issues about which we are still not quite sure as to where they belong: Are they articles of faith, or do they belong in the realm of *modifiable procedures* —

only *steps to a goal,* not the goal itself? This sort of thing happens in most societies: what has started as an undifferentiated article of faith, has to be moved later into the area of procedures that one can experiment with, while other questions remain, or move into, the "basic value" category.

Even where we were able to detach certain issues from the "basic value" category, things do not become altogether simple or black-and-white. Every advantage that we gain through adopting certain techniques or arrangements may be counterbalanced in some other direction; conversely, some of the prices you seem to be paying at times can be shown to be bringing a gain somewhere else. All we can try to do here is to determine which arrangement will carry which price in its wake. As to the price you are willing to pay, only you and the basic philosophy you hold can decide that.

I would like to add a few more illustrations of the type of issue that may not be as wholly faith-attached as it seems — issues which the daily practitioner in his work with adolescents is confronted with, and on which some experimentation could well be done, without any harm to basic principles. You obviously have a good many group management problems, since your adolescent group is part of a larger group-oriented society. The adolescents themselves, as you have indicated, do handle some of their own problems. You are going to have to set a limit somewhere, of course, as to the decisions they can make on their own; yet, within that framework, there would remain a certain leeway within which they could still make their own decisions. Right there, within that range, there are many more or less technical issues that have to be considered as technical issues.

There are ways of helping adolescent groups to "make their peace" with the boundaries within which they are expected to live; there are other methods that would simply rub their age-typical sensitivities the wrong way and make them angry or antagonistic, or else induce them to become apathetic and withdraw. As another illustration, your adolescent group may need help in deciding how to react constructively to such issues as privileges and penalties, or in determining what should be the meaning of those terms. Finally, most groups need help on the issue of "deviation tolerance," or else, in their very enthusiasm for their group goal, they may begin to act destructively rather than supportively towards those members who do have trouble fitting in.

Adolescent groups have to struggle with all these issues, and many more. They will not always be able to cope with them on their own; there will be times when they will need counsel and help from you, or when their group leaders, or the adults themselves, will be eager for advice from you. Now, all this is not a matter of basic values and belief. For instance, whether you do or do not want to have a democratic decision-making process established in your youth groups is a basic value decision, of course. But once you have decided on it, there are many technical problems of group leadership that can be handled only on the basis of experience, research, technical know-how and skill.

You yourselves have raised the problem of communication. Now, in any group society there are always a number of channels of communication that are wide open, between people in their various roles. There are others which, for some reason or other, seem to be closed. Do your kids always know to whom they can talk or go for help, and on what issues? Are some of the potentially available channels temporarily closed or shut down entirely, or are they just boarded over, so to speak, during a given developmental phase?

In some of our adolescent groups, for instance, you run into this problem: The adults of a given institution are more than eager to offer full access, for guidance and counseling on all matters, for their kids. But in some of the youth groups, their subculture puts a heavy taboo on such communication: one would be considered a sissy, a coward, or even something of a traitor, if one used adult confidences instead of "taking it bravely and bearing proudly what has to be suffered after all." This pattern, by the way, may change from year to year, even within one and the same group. But in this way, otherwise usable channels of communication get to be jammed up; then it becomes the task of the educator to help the kids open them again.

The Question of Continuity

SHIMON STERN: Now for a question — and I would ask our friends to be as direct or hard-hitting as they need to be, in order to answer it. As outsiders, have you developed the impression that many of the problems (perhaps most of them) that we have spoken about in connection with adolescence in the kibbutz, are not really the problems of adolescents at all, but *our* problems? For example, all this fuss about individualism, as if we were not the *most individualistic* people in the world, and all our behavior did not point to our respect for individualism. Or take the queston of "loyalty"; isn't that a projection of our own anxieties?

Sometimes we do what a man does when he is approaching a very narrow and dangerous bridge: if he hadn't been told that it was going to be very narrow or very high or very dangerous, he would have crossed over it without any trouble; but, since he was warned, he starts to tremble. I have the feeling that we do the same thing with our youth when it comes to the question of whether or not they will go on in the kibbutz, whether or not the kibbutz has yet convinced them (and ourselves) that they will go on.

DR. SCHOUTEN: One must guard against the danger of getting oneself into a position comparable to that of the fathers in our society, who, having established a beautiful firm (or even having continued their fathers'), succeed (merely by their wishing so anxiously for the sons to continue in their footsteps) in *pushing their children out, instead of keeping them in.*

MR. ALT: I would not be willing to discount or to prize too lightly the extraordinary element that has pervaded this discussion, as well as life in the kibbutz, as we have observed it — the remarkable sensitivity to children, their needs and their problems. Even granted that one can also err on the side of over-sensitivity, over-articulation, over-intellectualization, I still would not minimize the tremendous importance of this sensitivity.

DR. EISENBERG: I don't think that what we have been dealing with is merely a preoccupation that the adults have transferred from themselves. It seems to me that you face a unique situation

— to begin with, the fact that those of you who founded the kibbutz movement were a highly selective, conscious, articulate group, who made their choice and underwent considerable sacrifices in order to make the movement succeed. I'm sure you weren't all heroes: there have been people who failed, those who proved inadequate, some who had to be "carried"; but, by and large, I cannot believe that you could have been anything less than a most extraordinary group of people to have succeeded under conditions of such difficulty.

Now, this movement is not, in a sense, "guaranteed"; it continues to operate as a sort of island, with the rest of the world still all around it, and it has to demand certain things that we would perhaps look upon, from our individualistic point of view, as sacrifices. Your problem, as I see it, is simply this: heroes may band together to form a society, but they don't always produce heroes — they often produce ordinary children. The question then is: What *capacities* are there in your new human material? We waste a lot of ours. I'm sure that our children in the States, taken as a whole, could do much more than they are doing; many of them are neglected, and many of them get a poor education. But could we, even under optimal circumstances, turn every new human being into an extraordinary one?

I see your concern about your adolescents as stemming, in part, from that most difficult question, which has never been answered: does *everybody* have the capacity to be a hero? to be extraordinary? to withstand difficult circumstances? And because these are, in effect, the actual demands on your young people, I think you are properly concerned about the characteristics of your education and your society.

It *has* to produce extraordinary people; it cannot succeed with just a *small percentage* of extraordinary people. I don't know what percentage you do need, but I suspect that it's higher than it is for much of the rest of humanity. Thus, it becomes a very important concern of yours that every possible avenue be opened for the fullest development of your children, because they face stresses greater than the ordinary ones — at least until the world as a whole becomes a very different place!

MENAHEM GERSON: I would like to comment on the so-called

"second-generation" problem. Dr. Eisenberg has suggested that we can't reasonably expect all our children to be as extraordinary as their parents were, or something of that sort; but the fact is that not all the people now living in the kibbutz are — or have been — extraordinary. There are many, many things about them which did not show up quite as clearly in their youth as they have since. You can find rooms in a kibbutz — in the same kibbutz, in the same house of a kibbutz — which are centered around, let's say a library; and you can find in the very same house rooms that are centered around the dining-table area, if you know what I mean. Differences exist in the first generation as well.

Still, the problem does exist: what will happen to the sons and daughters of this extraordinary generation? I fully share this concern. A new sort of motivation has become much stronger with the second generation than it was with us: a sort of feeling "at home" — not really an ideological connection, but simply a feeling of being "at home" in the setting in which they have grown up, where their parents live, and so on. Now, if it were possible to rely on *that* alone for the continuation of the kibbutz, we would be quite content. But if this sort of feeling turns out to be the prevailing — the *only* — motivation in the second generation, then the kibbutz itself will change. It will become no better than an ordinary village.

We know quite well that for this second generation — which has been called "the skeptical generation," a generation not really keen on ideology, and so on — it must be very, very difficult indeed to find another than the ideological basis for continuation. Yet it is clear that what we have achieved — our kibbutz movement — will not continue, cannot continue, if it is based only on that second-generation "at home" feeling. Why? Because experience has already shown us that a utopian village that is, so to speak, cut off from the outside, without an active influence, even an active interest in it, will surely come to decay.

Now, *that* is a difficult problem, and with all my high estimation of our colleagues here as experts, I do not want to burden you with that problem. I just want you to understand this: that we cannot be satisfied with being told, "Things are like that everywhere; it's only natural: in the first generation, you always have this sort of pioneering approach; and in the second generation, it is always different." Maybe that is "natural"; but if you are concerned with the future of the kibbutz movement — and surely you understand now why *we* are so concerned— then you can see why this answer will not satisfy us. We somehow have to find a way to imbue our children with the *spirit* of the first generation, let's say, even if we know for certain that it will now take a different *form* of functioning.

Relationship with Parents

The Problem of Communication

MENAHEM GERSON: Let me put a question for your consideration. You know, by now, what the situation of the kibbutz child is during his adolescence. What then are the desirable relations for him? What are the desirable connections? Is it really desirable, as we thought for a time, that the adolescent become close to his parents, that he be able to talk with them about his intimate problems? If that is so, then I believe that it can be achieved easily in the kibbutz because quite a few of the "normal" barriers do not exist here: you don't need to pester your child about whether he has done his school work, is clothed properly, and so on. Under those circumstances, it is easier, perhaps, to create the sort of relationship we would like.

But I wonder whether you think that this is really the desirable thing to do? Or do you have any misgivings about it, from the standpoint of the independence that the adolescent must achieve?

KIBBUTZ MEMBER: Adolescents in the kibbutz today are on more intimate terms with their parents than we were with ours. That, I think, is the general impression of the parents of my generation. These parents, of course, may vary widely, according to their background, their country, the class they came from.

Secondly, I have the impression that there are adolescents who do have intimate discussions of sex problems — but more often as private or group discussions with their educators than with their parents. Parents generally turn to the educators when the children are thirteen or fourteen, especially on matters concerning a daughter. They ask the educators to start conversations about contraception, and so on, saying, "You know, I cannot get through to him or her on this point."

There is another kind of intimate material, and on this the parent has some intimate material, too. It is what we might call "kibbutz gossip." Our children live together on the same farm, or near the same factory; and while outside the kibbutz, in a large town, father and mother may more easily discuss in a very frank way problems of the father's business, the boss, and son on, they are reluctant to do so in the kibbutz, because it always touches on people known to the children. Especially when the parents are very education-conscious, they try to avoid that sort of thing.

Then there arises a situation in which the children get the feeling that the most important things going on in the kibbutz are not discussed in their parents' room while they are there. They say, "Our parents don't discuss important things with us; why should we discuss with them the things that are important to us?"

JUDIT GILAN: The teachers of children of the adolescent age-group are, for the most part, not educators; they are *teachers* in their attitude and aim, rather than educators. There are not many among them who become the objects of conversation of adolescents and adults, as the metapelet is. To the latter, adolescents speak a great deal. They meet with her often, both privately and in unorganized groups, to speak about themselves and their problems. They also speak amongst themselves; even though the group is not organized, group like gives them the opportunity and the feeling for speaking together. Many also find an opportunity to speak while working together with adults; still others communicate with the youngsters who come back from the army, who are now grown up, no longer adolescents, no longer children. There are also children who have very strong attachments to youngsters only two, three, or four years older than themselves.

I cannot estimate how much our children speak with their parents; I don't know whether it happens more or less often than outside the kibbutz. But I do know that kibbutz parents have a conscience — they want to devote special hours to each and every one of their children. Somehow, they find the time for it — in the middle of the day, perhaps, because not everyone works the same hours.

There is a fascinating area of discussion that we have not touched on so far, which is relevant to the adolescents of this discussion, as well as to other age levels. This is the relationship between the distribution of the time spent together and the total amount of such time. In terms of amount, the time that parents and children spend together here is often greater than it is in the culture from which we come. But there is also another factor — how is the time *distributed?*

The *quality* of the interactions between children and parents, when their time together is distributed in one particular pattern, would be different, I believe, from what it would be if the time were distributed in other ways. For example, boarding-school children see their parents on vacations; they are away for a long while, and then they are together with their parents for rather sizable amounts of time. This situation differs from that of children who go to day school, and then see their parents at home — unless they rush right out again! . . . And *that* is different from a planned visit every day, but with sleeping away, as children do here.

Sometimes, meaningful material — intimate matters — is apt to come up at the most unexpected and unplanned-for times. This is so, partly because, if there is emotionally charged conflictual material in a child, the conflict between bringing it out and keeping it back will be resolved by its taking an indirect channel — coming out as something casual, when it is a matter of parents not knowing that they are about to discuss confidential material. Very often it "slides in," in this casual way, during the course of doing something else.

As therapists, we frequently find that when we set aside an hour, or a special time, to be completely at the disposal of some person, he will say absolutely nothing; on the other hand, in the midst of talking about something else, he may say what is the most important thing on his mind. Again, in terms of adolescent protest, this appear as: "I don't want to talk when I am *supposed to* talk, because the very fact that there is an hour set aside for me is an insult to me: it is a *requirement*. I will not conform."

MONI ALON: It has been pointed out that our children are much more intimate with us than our generation was with our parents. If my parents had asked me to spend two hours every day with them, drinking coffee or tea, I am sure I would not have done it. But our children do it, and they are delighted to do it. I am sure that this is not because we are so much better parents than our parents were, but because the situation is different.

What do they seek when they come to the parents' rooms? Mostly, they seek relaxation — relaxation from the group, from what they are *expected* to do. Now there is no special demand on them to do anything. They want to be together with their brothers or sisters, in the atmosphere of the family. They are even more interested in grandparents and aunts and uncles than we are; it is quite curious, in fact, to see how interested they are in these different relationships.

On the other hand, I think there *has* been a certain decrease in intimacy. At a gathering of educators, we asked 230 children, from the sixth grade to the age of eighteen, a lot of questions about matters of sex education. One of the questions was, "Have you spoken to your parents about sex questions?" ". . . to your educators . . . ?" ". . . to your peer group . . . ?" and so on. The children mentioned first their peer group, or a children's society — that is to say, children of their own age, or a year or two older. The educator came next; they all spoke with him. But then there was an interesting difference between the girls and the boys: at least 20 to 30 per cent of the girls spoke to their mothers about intimate questions, but only 3 per cent of the boys spoke to their fathers about such questions. Also, about 20 to 30 per cent of the girls spoke with the metapelet; I am talking about girls of seventeen or eighteen, not about the younger girls. At least in this sphere, girls seem to have better communication with adults than boys have.

What do they speak to their parents *about*? On this, we have no statistics; but I agree that they do not know enough about the troubles of their parents. They know that father or mother may have troubles, but they do not feel the grief or the worry, because in these two hours, father or mother will not show their worries.

The children also have *their* points of reserve. They do not like to talk about things occurring within the group, or about other children in the group. They do not like to "mix with" the adults at all, not even their own parents. They do not speak very openly about failures; at best, they will let you see that they are in a very bad mood, and then wait for you to ask them what is wrong. They are often provocative that way: they do not tell you that this and this occurred yesterday, they make you ask them.

It is not that children who don't speak to their parents about their love affairs don't want their parents to know; on the contrary, they sometimes try to find ways of letting their parents know. This is because they think that their parents would probably approve of their having a love affair; it would mean that they have now entered the realm of the adults.

Mrs. Winsor: In our generation, it was not customary for us to talk with our parents about our private lives — our sex experiences. Probably very few people here confided in their parents, but shared their experiences with their peer groups instead. This was a very sensitive and secretive aspect of life in society as a whole, an area in which there was a great deal of defensive behavior.

Very likely, if you look closely at the sort of things parents feel hesitant about discussing with their children now, you will learn that it is not so much their adolescent loves, but their feelings on the question of entry into the adult society of the kibbutz, how they feel about taking on the role of the loving, giving parents. Perhaps not so much those young people who are headed for exciting, interesting, creative work, but the others, who will have the humdrum, repetitive tasks to perform. This may tell you something, in an indirect way, about the stresses of the kibbutz, and help you to judge whether there may not be in fact better approaches to aiding youngsters at that crucial period of growing up.

Dr. Schouten: Whether intimacy between child and parent (at adolescence) is a burden or not, depends on the quality and intensity of the early attachments (at the prelatency age). In our culture, the adolescent has to ward off intimacy with the parent, because that would arouse anxieties, resulting from the heightened oedipal conflicts that are typical of the developmental stage.

Since, in the kibbutz, the relationships between children and parents are different from those in our society, because of so many different arrangements (among which the most important may be those of sleeping arrangements), that fact alone might have certain consequences for the adolescent stage. Because early attachments in the kibbutz are less conflict-laden, there is no need for adolescents to fear the revival of those early feelings, and consequently, there would seem to be less necessity for them to ward off intimacy with parents.

DR. REDL: There is one issue that I think we have not considered thoroughly enough. We are still drifting, time and again, into talking as though we were back with "just the family, the one child with his parents," forgetting the terrific impact of group psychology at that age. What I am especially trying to draw our attention to is this: there are moments in an adolescent's life when the real point at issue is not one particular parent, teacher or metapelet; it has become, instead, a question of "us kids" versus "those adults."

This was quite clear in camps that I have run for delinquent youngsters. Staff would at first become concerned, when some youngsters didn't want to come in for an interview, fearing that this might mean that the specific youngster did not have *rapport* with the specific adult. In some cases, it soon became clear that that was not the case at all: the youngster just didn't want others in his age group to know that he had talked with an adult; he did not want them to think that he had gotten *too chummy with somebody from the world of adults. . . .* In fact, he would often pretend that there had been a battle between him and his adviser, rather than a confidential chat, for communicating too readily with a member of the adult world might make him *suspect as a reliable member of the teenage gang.*

For us, too, there comes a time when Johnny is not "our kid," but "one of those adolescents" — "and I couldn't possibly allow Youth to talk that way to Adults." In short, from a certain age on, individual children become "youth" to us, even though the issue under discussion may have nothing to do with that. Perhaps when some kids hesitate to discuss matters of sex with adults, it is not so much the sex theme that blocks them, but the fact that it is, in their group code, *improper to let "the adult world" in* on certain matters, or to run to them for shelter and advice. What may block the individual youngster from seeking communication with an individual parent or teacher, may be no more than the hesitation to be seen, as a member of the subgroup of youth, communicating too freely with the "overgroup" of the adult collective.

It does not matter how good the overall relationship of youngsters toward their kibbutz, how realistic is it to assume that there are no other group psychological undercurrents between your youth and the adult collective? In fact, it might even be more important, instead of simply being surprised about communication blocks between youngsters and their educators, as we are wont to do in middle-class Western society, to try to get a closer look at the subgroup codes and mores about communication, between the kid groups on the one hand and the managerial group of the kibbutz, as the larger unit. While this would not obviate what we previously said about problems of delibidinization, it might be a worthwhile way to gain additional understanding.

NECHAMA LEVI: I would like to distinguish between two problems: one is the community life and its pressure on the adolescent; the other is the need of adolescents to be alone with their relatives, to be able to share some intimate feelings — and not only thoughts — with them. The adolescent cannot do this with his friends, when they are together. For example, one girl falls in love, while another doesn't; one girl is more developed than another, one boy more successful than another. When they live together, discussing their problems together becomes difficult because it raises individual problems, even though they are very good friends. There is no doubt that our children really are good friends: they have confidence in each other, and they also have confidence in their teacher or their metapelet. But when they become adolescents, jealousy seems to crop up in some situations, mainly among girls.

On the outside, adolescents move away from their parents. They do not want them to know about what they are doing at night, for example; they only worry about "What will Mama say when I come back late at night?" or "How can I answer, so that my parents will not know how late I came home?" There are certain questions and problems that children cannot discuss in a group, questions which they have to bring to someone else for an intimate talk. In the long run, it depends on the parent, but most of the children seem to find a way for an intimate talk either with the father or the mother at, let us say, teatime when they are together, or when father and mother return from work.

I think it is wise for children to stay with their group all day, and afterwards, to come to their fathers and mothers and stay with them until they go to bed. There is a real family atmosphere in the kibbutz setting; older and younger children, who meet every day in the family house, are together able to keep a balance of those family feelings that bind the children to their parents.

MONI ALON: I am aware that there can be such a thing as "over-consciousness" about educational questions, and that therein is a certain danger. But I wouldn't like you to think that adolescence is an open book before our teachers and parents; many things in it are still obscure, and we really don't know very much about them. I think it is good, in a way, that they are covered: we are certain that the development of our children is going in the essentially right direction; and we must not be concerned with *knowing everything* about them, or having them think that we know everything about them.

After all, our children are, to begin with, not easy speakers. (Generally speaking, I don't think anyone would say that "sabras" are easy speakers.) But this may be a trait of the younger generation throughout the world today; they aren't really interested in speaking with other people in a very intimate way. The generation of the Youth Movement was quite different in that respect. For instance, there are children who keep diaries and nobody knows about them; they are concerned that *nobody should know* about them. That is an interesting trait: they want to have these things *for themselves.* It is their right, and we have to respect these limits with an adolescent.

Parents don't speak with their children about their own daily cares. If something goes wrong in the family itself — if there is a family crisis — children know about it, not from hearing about it, but from feeling it. They become upset long before the crisis comes out into the open. On the other hand, if there is a crisis between the parents and the kibbutz — say, the parents think that they have to leave — sometimes (even more often) the children will say to their parents, "You want to leave? Please, but without us; we'll stay here." In that situation, a child of sixteen or seventeen may often show quite an intense desire to cling to the kibbutz; sometimes the parents stay only because they don't want to leave without their children.

DR. BERNARD: In dealing with the psychology of adolescence, it is generally helpful that there be leeway available for alternatives. Mention has been made of quite different types of intimate matters; similarly, the fact that there is family "closeness" can be either security-giving to an adolescent or somewhat oppressive. It all depends on the play of those subtle and somewhat opposing factors which may be present psychologically within the adolescent.

This explains the characteristic adolescent search — when he feels too close for comfort in any one situation — for someone else to turn to; it also explains why leeway — that is, a sufficient supply of alternatives — can be so very helpful. In this instance, the alternatives seem to be primarily the peer group, the teachers, and the parents, all of whom provide the kibbutz adolescent with a certain opportunity to distribute his confidences. It is very good that there are such alternatives; and it would be desirable, I think, for adults to appreciate that fact, so that they do not respond to their "rivals" by feeling hurt or hostile, or by trying desperately to extract confidences from their children, as proof that they (the parents) are still loved.

There is one element, however, that has not been sufficiently touched on, in the discussions. With regard to the balance that one needs to achieve, psychologically and emotionally, between opposites, we frequently find among insufficiently wanted or rejected young people, a hunger, a longing to be understood by the adult world, to be able to share confidences with them on important and intimate matters. However, we sometimes meet very understanding parents, psychologically progressive, sensitive and loving parents, in relation to whom their own adolescent children feel it to be a severe psychological burden that they are *too well* understood.

DR. REDL: As long as we have in mind the family-bound child — the situation we usually have to deal with back home in the United States — then I think that, by and large, the closer children come to adolescence, the easier it is for a "stranger," who has not been part of their family neurosis and early childhood life, to become an object for communication with regard to issues that the adolescent considers "intimate." This, by the way, is also troubling many of the parents in our culture; as a matter of fact, they get quite upset about it. "What is happening between me and my children?" they ask. "They don't confide in me anymore. Anybody else they will talk to, but not to me!"

Thus, the parents become worried that this may be a sign that their children are "losing their relationship" with them — when, as we know, in most cases exactly the opposite is true. The very intensity of the reawakened oedipal struggle makes it harder for the material of which we are speaking to be communicated to somebody from their intimate childhood-family scene, than to somebody who is safely outside of it all, as a "stranger."

On the other hand, if *your* children, by virtue of the fact that they live away from home so much, and so long, and by virtue of the multiple attachments already mentioned, do not have such intimate ties, in terms of the reawakened sexualization of child-parent relationships, then one might postulate that, with them, the problem would not be as great. However, in order to decide this, we have to ask ourselves first: "Is it really true that living in children's houses part of the time, as contrasted to the Western family style, reduces or thins out the extent of early libidinous ties, and therefore also reduces their reawakening during the pubertal phase?"

Now, it seems to me that statements on that question, made during this conference, have sometimes been contradictory. Much of what you have told us about the normal living of the children does suggest that it is different, and obviously so; on the other hand, some of the clinical material makes one suspect that some things may not be quite as different as one would wish them to be (or is supposed to assume that they are) — that some of the basic emotional events are in fact very much the same. It would be really difficult to know until we got a clearer picture of how much of your clinical material is true only for those situations in which some kind of crisis has emerged, and how far it also has significance for what happens on the larger scale — although perhaps not so noticeably — in the *normal living of all children.*

My suggestion would be that we ask ourselves, "What is the *actual* experience with these adolescents so far?" For instance, if adolescents in your culture do have problems with the sexual component of their boy-girl relationships, to whom do they feel free to turn? If they should say that they do not feel like turning to their teachers or metaplot, we would then have to start speculating: Is this because they *naturally* would not feel like doing that? Is it primarily because the *specific teachers or metaplot* in question are not well trained in this area, and therefore would not tend to encourage confidences? Is there some other, *special reason?* Similarly, if it turned out that there are large numbers of adolescents who feel quite comfortable talking to their parents, we would again have to ask: Is it because those particular parents happen to be more than usually skillful and emotionally comfortable in handling it all; or is it actually because the customary psychosexual blocks do not even arise, for reasons of a general nature?

There is one other issue in all this: I think that when we talk about the communication of "intimate material," we need to differentiate much more carefully just what "material" we are really thinking about. Our general assumption that the communication of intimate material is of itself evidence for a special relationship of confidence is, I am certain, unwarranted. It seems to be regarded as less significant that the *type of issue* that is ready for such communication may vary considerably with the communicant, even though the level of basic relationship and confidence remains the same. If I meet some old friends, there are some things I would immediately talk about with them, while it would never dawn on me to talk about other things — and *not* because I wouldn't "trust" them, but because the nature of our relationship would place a priority on certain subjects of communication.

The whole question of whom adolescents have "communication" with must be looked at from this angle. If your adolescents have, let us say, lesser degrees of conflict about issues of sex and dating when they are talking with their parents, primarily because of the lack of libidinous childhood involvement, that fact would of course be interesting to note. On the other hand, in the kibbutz, the parent is also generally the representative of the collective at large; he represents not only parental authority, but also the highly cathected value demands of the "overgroup" — namely, the kibbutz. In that case, while we might expect less inhibition in communicating with parents about dating and sex, one should expect *more* inhibition in the area of decisions about vocational choice, or concerning their conflict over staying in the kibbutz or leaving it, or about the question, "What kind of person should I become?"

It is quite possible that while sexual concerns would be minimized, issues having to do with the overall value system of the kibbutz society might be more heavily laden with anxiety and guilt or conflict, and therefore more taboo in terms of communicating about them with those who represent authority. In short, I think the question of whether we get more or less confidential communication between adolescents and parents, in kibbutz society, should be preceded by the question of just what the communication channels and areas are to be used for.

The Role of Parents

MR. ALT: I am very much concerned with the general attitude toward strengthening the parental role and defining it. How far has the effort been made to maximize the role of the parents, to give it status, importance? The strong parent will, of course, remain a strong person in the eyes of his children, but I can see the weak one simply abdicating. It is very important, I think, to give some thought to the parental role and how those other professional parents — or, if you like, those who play a parental role — can strengthen it. What things should a parent do that will make him more important in the eyes of the child, as opposed to transferring parental responsibilities to the professional — who, presumably, is *more competent* to discharge the responsibility?

While I would draw on professional help, it is the parent who must remain the source of authority and the symbol of protection.

DR. HIMMELWEIT: If you want to get some material for yourself about adolescents, pick out different people, perhaps from a number of different kibbutzim. They don't necessarily have to be educated — simply people whom you feel to be warm-hearted and sensitive, who can really just listen and get other people to talk. Then let them talk, not only with the age group you are concerned with, but also the slightly older group, who will of course be speaking retrospectively. We have found that when you speak to an older group, and get from them retrospectively what their stresses and experiences were, at a particular age, you get some hints as to the kind of questions you might then ask of the children of that age.

When you do talk to the children, there are two ways in which one might go about it. One is to talk to them as a group, and to say, "Look, every generation falls out of touch with the generation that follows," and so on — inviting them to be your consultants, but, in the most genuine way, assuring them that they have something to teach you. Most of them, I think, will bring out a great deal of material under these circumstances — material which you can then follow up individually. Since you already know so much about the children, you can pick out, for further individual discussion, those about whom you are worried — that is to say, your "weak people," who may, in fact, have quite different sets of problems. One could do this in a number of different kibbutzim, after finding out about the parents, what worries them, where they feel particularly insecure.

It has been mentioned that the children are protected from the worries of the parents. A lot of parents in our society, too — and especially middle-class parents — tend to hide many of their worries, and to deal only with their "respectable" concerns — those that have economic reasons — rather than their own personal failures. They use *each other* very much as supports, in that respect.

RACHEL MANOR: When Dr. Himmelweit said that you have to

learn how to *listen*, how to *consult* the youth, she set a very difficult task for us. Many of us do not really know how to listen.

I would like to hear more about the kinds of work that our
visitors do — not, in this instance, with disturbed children, but
with normal children, and normal parents. How do you carry on
parent education? We have tried to form a parents' group around
the youth group; I am sure we will be able to do it, if only we
can learn how. We have so many opportunities, and we still know
so little about how to use them.

MRS. IRVINE: I sometimes get the feeling that there is a strong
tendency in the kibbutz movement to pull up by the roots a child
who is growing quite well, just to make sure that it *is* growing
quite well. I wonder whether this may not be the reflection of an
excessive desire to be *conscious of everything* that is going on in
the families, and in this society, which is something like an extended family. I am a parent too, and I have come to the conclusion that it would be better if I were to renounce my longing
to know everything going on inside my son; it is better for him
that I should *not* know everything going on inside him.

I feel somewhat uneasy about the suggestion for parent education and parent groups, because I am afraid that such groups
might foster a sort of collective anxiety, and thus interfere with
parental spontaneity. If a problem arises in the group, then it
might be very useful for the educators and the parents to get together, in order to try to work out something. But when things
are going well, there may be some danger in holding regular
group meetings for self-evaluation. I would not like to see parent-
hood "professionalized" in that way, because spontaneity with
children is very important both in family life and in social life.

DR. REDL: When we started this discussion, we were all very
concerned about strengthening the family, and guaranteeing
plenty of contacts between kids and their families, for that purpose. During our discussion, it has struck me that perhaps your
kids need a lot of family contact, not only because of what I have
mentioned, but also because the family can give them a *healthy
vacation from their other groups*. With such an intensive "group
life" going on all day, can it be that your kids need a chance to

escape from it for a while? Why should we then be so eager to load on to the few family contacts that the kids do have, the additional burdens of "confidences" and what not, rather than giving them what they may need most — a *respite* from their group involvedness?

If this is so, by the way, then it constitutes a very interesting reversal of our situation in the States. *Our* kids, during their adolescence, want to have group activities and plenty of them, one reason being that it is normal for them to need and enjoy such activities. However, isn't another reason the fact that it is one way of *getting away from their families?* With your kids, the situation seems to be the reverse: for their emotional and mental health, they need to *relax in family situations,* in order to recover from the constant involvement with their groups. What is implied in my thinking is this: Why talk all the time as though the only reason for the presence of your kids with their parents is the preservation of family strength? Wouldn't it be just as good a reason if, on the contrary, it was the family that gave the children the chance to recover from the group-psychological strain of the rest of the day?

Now, educationally speaking, this may seem to be a somewhat low-status reason. From the mental-health point of view, however, it is not a low-status reason at all; on the contrary, it may be one of the greatest strengths you can offer your children during their adolescent years. It hasn't sounded at all necessary to me for you to insist that kids and adults be "strengthening family ties" every minute they have a chance to be together. In fact, it seems to me that you have remarkably little trouble with family ties at all.

SHIMON STERN: In our very small communities, we have a very outspoken channel of the evaluation of every member — one that is constantly functioning, either consciously or unconsciously. The adolescent child will gradually come to know it too; he will know what places his mother and father occupy in this sociometry. Sometimes he'll hear remarks about it; if not, he'll gradually come to know it and feel it. Perhaps more than in any other society, this influences the relations between adolescents and parents. It may even take the form of a seventeen-year-old boy attending a General Assembly at which his father or mother, or both, are the subject of discussion, either favorable or otherwise.

Sometimes this proves to be a major problem. For example, if his parents are at either end of this ladder of evaluation, he may have cause to be ashamed — or proud — of their *social merits*. Either way, it is very problematical for him. If they are very prominent, for example, there may be the situation (known outside the kibbutz, too) of the child's having to live in the shadow of his parents' prominence. This may explain why some youngsters choose to go to another kibbutz — to a younger kibbutz — in order to be able to stand on their own two feet.

The Shadow of the Parent

DR. REDL: We have been faced with a very specific question here, which I think we have an obligation to examine closely — namely, what to do when a youngster's status in his group, and his reactions to his own self-image, become heavily dependent on the parent's image in the rest of the community. This, by the way, is a problem with which we are also somewhat familiar, except that it does not hit us quite as strongly, unless the children live in a residential or boarding-school setting. If the children go to a day school, the chance to erect a screen between their home life and what they say when they are with the other kids is much easier.

As to the problem we are dealing with here, these are some of the suggestions I would offer:

1. One of the most important questions is just how the *adult* reacts who is in a responsible position at the time. While you have indicated that your teacher is primarily taught to *teach,* while the overall *educational responsibility* lies with the metapelet, I would still insist that the teacher can also use some special training in how to handle delicate situations of this sort. Skill in helping kids cope with "self-image" problems does not necessarily come with training in the skills of teaching specific subject-matter, and some of these issues *cannot* be postponed until after school.

For instance, I can see a number of well-meaning teachers

responding to such problems with what would seem to be the most logical method — namely, "Let's discuss this." Yet, sometimes this may be precisely the *last,* and not the first thing, that ought to happen. Therefore, if the task of detaching from the child the image that the adult community has about his parent or parents is an important one, then teachers certainly should have special training in handling issues such as these.

2. It may also be necessary to take a look at the *adult value system* which produces conflicts like these. It may be that it is the adult community that needs to learn how to avoid stereotyping people's role images, to the point where it crushes out all other aspects of their personalities, and so leads to that very aura which created our problem. In short, if what has been presented is an issue of such great significance in the child's life, the chances are that some form of repair is in order in the thinking of the adults themselves.

The Individual and the Group

Needs of the Individual

DR. EISENBERG: The question of individualization has come up in terms of the overcrowded schedule of the adolescent and the consequent lack of sufficient differentiation.

I think that insufficient effort has been devoted to encouraging individualization in the children's room and the children's corner. In the children's houses, even those of the younger children, every bed looked like every other bed; there were no toys, and apparently, no personal possessions in the corner. It seems to me that as an early *anlage* of the individualization we would like to see taking place among adolescents, every child should be encouraged to have some personal possession or possessions in his corner; that each child's bed should look different from the other beds in his room — not for identification, as with the little ones, but just so he will know that it's *his.*

One can learn, from the differences in physical possessions, to accept the fact that while we live together and belong together, I am one person and you are another, and we are *expected to be different.* Within practical limits, one is permitted — I would rather say "guaranteed" — *choice* in this.

MORDECHAI KAFFMAN: Individualization *is* one of our concerns; I think everyone would agree to that. But the problem is not whether or not to *give* each child an individual corner, an individual bed, or whatever — because that is not the sort of thing we really lack.

We once asked a group of adolescents to choose specific clothing — and, whatever the reasons, it turned out to be a group selection. The majority of these girls or boys wanted one specific color. I think this may give you an idea of the problems we are facing. What we are trying to do, in different ways, is to convey to these adolescents that sense of *individual choice,* which is, in our view, desirable.

DR. EISENBERG: Perhaps one might say that the kibbutz can judge its success in meeting this problem, during the early years, by whether or not there were, at that time, differences in choices. If there were not, then you would have to regard their absence as among the results produced by the educational method.

MISS WILLIAMS: To my mind, children should not only have their individual toys; they should also have facilities for *safeguarding* these as their own, as something that one *does not have to share* with anybody else, if he doesn't want to. During the preschool years, we work with children towards their accepting the idea of sharing; but children must *have* before they can *share.*

You accept as one of your basic beliefs the idea that children should be encouraged to use their own individual initiative, to do things differently from other people, and yet you find that children seem to want *what others want.* If somebody is wearing some particular item of clothing, then other children want to wear the same thing. Can you, in some way — within the framework of your in-service education program for your teachers and nurses and metaplot — explain how to encourage children, or to motivate them, in such a way that they will have the conviction to feel *"I am a person;* my needs are *not always the same* as somebody else's needs; I *can* change, I *can* be different."

JUDIT GILAN: It may be true that we have not done enough, up till now, about the child's individual corner, and the possibility for every child to have his own place. But I want to make two brief remarks about this:

I have visited many children's homes in Europe, and in them I saw the private belongings that each child had around his bed or table, or on the walls. All of them — I observed this very closely — *all of them* were signs of homesickness: pictures of relatives . . . something from home. Our children, who are at home, do not need a corner of that sort.

The second thing is: whatever we may think of their earliest years, when our children grow up, they know and appreciate individuality very much.

MISS WILLIAMS: In visiting your schools, I noticed that you have encouraged the children — you have, in fact, done this very well — to make things with their hands. I wonder whether the things they make can be brought back into their living quarters, thereby carrying this evidence of their individuality into their rooms. Whatever it may be — a chair, a painting, a clay object — it is the child's. They are making this sort of thing, but it is just not to be seen in their rooms. Why?

JUDIT GILAN: That is right — but the conclusion is not: There are other aspects to this question. The children want to do these things — but for their parents, for the whole community. I have the impression that in adolescence this is not as *important* to them.

I have sometimes asked children of that age: "If you had the opportunity to live one in a room, would you want that?" And they don't want it. One, no; two, perhaps. They tell me, "Three is the minimum. In a threesome, we feel good." (Yet it is not like that afterwards.)

DR. HIMMELWEIT: Yet your rooms look like those of our traditional English public schools — dreary and uniform. I should like to see you adopting the technique of the progressive schools, assigning each child one of those boards, above his bed, on which he can pin drawings he has made, or anything that interests him. And then, why not a chest of drawers for his belongings, since he does in fact have some?

Some of you have mentioned that the children want to dress alike, want to live with other children. This may very well be true, but what we are considering here is that area in which the child *can* express his individuality. And I should like to see some part of each day left open for his being alone — free to do *as he likes,* and to do it *on his own,* if he so wishes.

JUDIT GILAN: We have such hours. But what we are doing with regard to the problem of individualization in the learning process seems to me to be more significant. We have developed teaching methods which permit each child to recognize his own individual personality — and that is, perhaps, more important than their having their own individual plastic object.

MONI ALON: I think we are all agreed in wanting each child to have the feeling of being a particular person, to have individuality.

I do not deny that our children sometimes say (although it is really the grownups who do so, more often), "We are all like each other, of the same 'stands'." If you know the children, however, you know that that is not so. They are in fact very, very different from one another.

Especially at the tender age, we help to create a lot of individualization. First of all, there are differences among children's houses, not connected with movements, but with the personality of the metapelet. I know of children's houses where there are differences in very small things — perhaps in the pictures, which the children chose themselves, or in the corners, with all sorts of different things in them. All this is quite dependent on the personality of the metapelet.

Also we try to create opportunities for thinking connected with fantasy. For example, if you look at the children's drawings — those of the younger children, especially — I think you will find a lot of individuality. And we encourage it, not only in their drawings, but also in the different ways they mould things, and so on.

Our teaching methods try to open a vast field of initiative to the individual child — different levels, different tasks. Finally, at the higher level of the secondary school, we strive for differentiation by letting the child himself decide what he wants to learn, which individual tasks he will take upon himself.

I think that in this sphere we have done a lot; I am not altogether sure we could have done any more. However, I would add that there are some spheres which we have neglected and, as we can see from our discussion, it is clear that they have more importance than we thought earlier. First, about personal belongings. Is this merely a question of belongings? After all, we are not speaking about the tender age, when, perhaps, the toy is a symbol, or the child wants the teddy-bear on the bed as a symbol of security, and so on. When we are speaking about the older child, I don't think that the question of "belongings" is the deciding factor.

Somebody has spoken about clothes. If you had come to a kibbutz ten years ago, you would have seen that our children all wore the same clothes. The pedagogic reason we gave then was that children *ought not to think too much* about clothing; we were eager *not to create envy* amongst the children on those grounds. Today we think about this question in a different way: we understand, for instance, that one has to come to grips with the question of narcissism. There is the possibility, and there should be the possibility, of individuality in how one dresses, as well as in how one does other things.

SHMUEL NAGLER: In reviewing the material on adolescence, we have become conscious of the following: girls — during adolescence, and sometimes even during preadolescence — as well as some sensitive introvert boys, suffer from the fact that their daily lives are *too fully* organized. They have a feeling of being constantly "with the crowd," without having any opportunity to do the things *they* like, or, now and then, just to do *nothing* — all of which makes the search for their identity more difficult. This is particularly true in the case of the "nice" neurotic types that we treat.

MENAHEM GERSON: That is one problem we really have to *deal with* — that is, we have to give up merely *observing* this problem, and take some practical steps towards its solution. The question of the lack of free time has been talked about — in our movement and, I assume, in all the movements — for years now, but we really haven't done anything about it. As difficult as this is to do, I believe that we must become more energetic in this respect: we have to tell the public that the present situation is bad. And then we ourselves have to find, among the present components of our educational structure, the opportunity for more free time — perhaps in the area of work.

MRS. IRVINE: We were concerned earlier with the child's having special possessions and special places in the children's houses. This didn't seem to me quite so important as it did to some of the other people from the West, because the child, after all, has a divided living-space. He has his public space — the children's house and the schoolroom — in which he leads a collective life and has collective possessions; but he also has a private space in the family room, and it seems that this is where he would want to have his private possessions. If he makes something himself, he doesn't take it to the children's house; instead he keeps it in the parents' room.

It now seems clear to me that it is "space in time," rather than "space in place," that is essential. An adult in the kibbutz works his eight hours; after that, he can play music, paint or do what he likes. But the child who wants to read more than his fellows seems to have very little time in which to do that, because his program is so full of extracurricular activities. By the time he has completed his lessons, his work, his meetings, and his sports, there is very little time left for an activity of his own choosing.

CHAVAH SHAMIR: As educators, we sometimes feel the way a mountain-climber must feel, when he has finished climbing up a lower peak and wants to climb up a higher one, in order to reach a still higher point. When we reach one point, or peak, in the socialization of our children, then we see for the first time many other problems, which we hadn't seen before we got to that point. We have solved many problems of group living, we think — for example, the problem of stealing, and so on. On the other hand, we feel that the child gets too much encouragement towards group living — particularly at an age when there is such a strong tendency, to begin with, to live in a group.

Even though we encourage our parents to develop in their children a certain individual interest, in reading and so on, we see that the children tend very much to live in their groups. Although we encourage and even direct the children and their parents to get out from the groups a little, in order to find their own private corner, we still have this problem. While our curriculum is arranged to give the children opportunities for individuality, these opportunities must be more and more highlighted, precisely because of the set situation the children live in.

MORDECHAI KAFFMAN: Children devise several different ways of escaping from group life; when they are really in need of developing their individuality outside of the group, they will succeed in finding some way to do so. Perhaps Dr. Redl is right when he says that one of the components of our family life is precisely this need to escape from group life.

In talking about the sibling relationship, we sometimes forget that there are also developments in the subgroups; when the subgroup becomes narrowed, we have the couple. This is very interesting to observe, even at the school age. It is very important for the child to have *his friend;* later on, at adolescence, we shall see — particularly amongst girls — some of the intimacy which in the kibbutz is distributed among different circles: sometimes to the parents, sometimes to the educators, sometimes to their special group, sometimes to one particular friend.

DR. BERNARD: The kibbutz child appears to be observed on what amounts to a twenty-four-hour, round-the-clock basis. This has been spoken of as a desirable thing: he doesn't have to take exams, he doesn't have to do this or that; why? Well, everybody *knows* him. I am afraid that for some adolescents, this can be a form of deprivation, a form of what I shall call *invasion* of psychological privacy, for all that it grows out of the good things that are being done in the way of understanding.

That is why, perhaps, some of us have spoken about the desirability of somewhere providing for more free time, more opportunity for the adolescent to wander off, to seemingly be doing nothing — while psychologically, within himself, he may be doing a kind of inner growing that is truly important, even though it may not appear as such from the outside. There is this kind of compensatory psychological need to get away from being *too fully understood*. It does not matter that it is a benevolent understanding; it nevertheless can feel like a kind of oppression from which one needs to make some sort of escape, if only that of having secrets.

The real meaning of a secret is something we must understand: sometimes it may indeed be something repressed, something shameful, a source of great discomfort to the child; it would be very good if there were encouragement and resources that could help him to share it, to bring it out and thus reintegrate. That kind of "splinter" of psychological difficulty within him, which he has to carry alone — that we are all too familiar with. But I want to stress this seeming paradox — that at a given moment, secrets may actually be his only way, emotionally, to enjoy some of the healthy self-assertion we have been talking about.

MONI ALON: The relationship inside our groups is that of a "brotherhood." There is sympathy and a strong desire to cling together; but there is also competition and anti-sympathy. The youth who come back from the army — for some years afterwards, perhaps five or six years — form a sort of subgroup inside the kibbutz. Afterwards that subgroup breaks up, of course; but it maintains a very deeply rooted interconnection, not only at the time of schooling, but even after it.

DR. EISENBERG: What some of us are concerned about is that group controls may become dangerous if they are used to excess. The threat they wield, in a sense, is that of losing *everything*. The child who lives in a more differentiated society, with all its other problems, has the family, the school, the teacher, this one and that one. He is not bound up in the same way; he can divide his feelings. Fritz Redl's example in our informal discussion was of a Boy Scout troop. If the Scout leader constantly measures the behavior of the youngsters as acceptable or unacceptable in the light of the Scout oath and the Scout principles, the kids will say, "Enough of that — I'm getting out." In other words, instead of surrounding them all the time with the possibility that they may be violating the very *precepts* of the organization, it might be better if sometimes the educator — or the Scout leader — were free to say "No — because I *say* no!" In that way, it wouldn't always be the whole group that encompassed you, that closed in on you, that sat on top of you!

DR. REDL: It sometimes seems difficult for a child to change the image he has produced in the rest of his group or in the community at large. The more cohesive the group, the more difficult it is to change in it the image that one is stuck with. Especially cohesive peer groups are very hesitant, may even become downright hostile, if any one individual wants to put them to the discomfort of altering or modifying the stereotype they have developed about him. This becomes an additional educational challenge to the teacher or metapelet, in fact to the community as such.

There are ways in which we can help the child to react more adaptively to the false image, taking care not to do those things that would feed the group's desire to hang on to it. There are also ways in which we can help, sometimes persuade or even force, the rest of the group to accept the fact that they really do have to give up some of their fun, because it is detrimental to one of them. The most obvious ways of doing this are frequently the most destructive, and may even have exactly the opposite effect.

However, all this falls into the area of group leadership techniques; that is to say, it belongs in the category of things that can be taught and learned. The task of helping a peer group to extricate itself from a mess it has got itself into, but which it is not fully aware of and cannot handle by itself, seems to me to be a very important responsibility of collective life.

DR. EISENBERG: How should a teacher deal with a group in which there is a child who is a pariah?

DR. REDL: That is an issue, the proper handling of which would take more time than we have available. Without any pretense of doing justice to the complexity of the issue, here are some of my thoughts:

I would try to see for which of the youngsters that situation was most important. While we usually say in these cases that it is "the group" that reacts in such a way, this is rarely to be taken literally. Usually, it is one or another youngster's strong need to act in a certain way that sets the tone; then it is picked up by the others. There may be one or two who need to work off their own anxieties or tensions by picking on this victim. I would try to "spot" those one or two. Sometimes youngsters have to hit other kids hard, primarily because they themselves are deeply unhappy, or because some specific needs of their own have been neglected. In that case, I would try to help them with their own position in their own group, which would more or less automatically knock the props out from under their destructive behavior.

Finally, as I suggested earlier, the question itself may have arisen as the *result*, not the cause of a group discussion. The whole issue may have been handled clumsily, with the result that the atmosphere of confusion, or even irritation, which was left hanging in the air, finally descended on the head of our poor victim.

In short, while the varieties of ways to handle this are by no means endless, they are manifold indeed, and each one would require a different course of action. Such questions cannot be answered out of thin air, so to speak. They can be answered reasonably well, however, if enough specific data about the situation and the people involved in it are put before us.

DR. EISENBERG: One might say, then, that within the educational institution — I don't know how much of this is offered at Oranim now — the study of group dynamic methods, with case discussions, and drawing on people who have acquired some technique and background, would be one specific thing to give more time to in the curriculum, even if it is already present. This is a relatively new development, and not yet very strongly emphasized in many of our own schools.

The Individual and the Outside World

JEHUDA MESSINGER: The idea that the adolescent is the problematic part of education is both true and untrue! He is problematic to us only in the sense that it is with him that outside society has its strongest advantage. Actually, our technique of education with adolescents has been quite successful. If there is a lack, or some deprivation, in early childhood, they seem to catch up very well. Where? In latency, of course, but even more so in adolescence. The fact is that the children who come out of the kibbutz and go into *general* society are physically healthy; they look well, and it's good to talk with them. When they go into the Army, or into jobs and activities among the general population, they come out in the topmost group—probably the best proof that our technique has succeeded.

Although the kibbutz population is only 4½ per cent of the

total population, the proportion of the kibbutzim youth in the Officer Corps of the Israeli Army is a number of times higher than that. There are also certain branches of the Army that need a better type of man — not just physically or intellectually, but in qualities of personality. One of these is the Air Force: learning how to manipulate modern airplanes apparently calls for a tremendously healthy personality in all respects. Practically a majority of those who are doing these most important Air Force jobs are kibbutz people; there has even developed a tremendous pressure from the Army on the kibbutzim, to supply more of their men. Finally, there are fields that are more dangerous, and involve more personal risk; these could probably tell us something about the personality qualities of the kibbutz men in them.

The kibbutz kid is not an adventurous type by nature, who would just like to do terrible things, as we sometimes see among people entering these services. Volunteering for these specific courses and branches does not give you any special benefit; it is not even given recognition, because it is under cover. Yet the volunteering of our kibbutz children is tremendously high, and I believe that it is particularly true of adolescents.

SHIMON STERN: There may be a crisis when our children enter the Army, but I don't think it arises from the fact that they are meeting another set of values. Some of them, perhaps many of them, when they step out of the kibbutz for the first time, for a period of two or two and one-half years, only then really start to appreciate the kibbutz. You hear very often that they are homesick. But this is very natural and not a special phenomenon of kibbutz youth.

On the other hand, it is also a fact that we sometimes try to find ways for them to get to know another way of living different from the one they know inside the kibbutz. For instance, we have them living in one of the towns as wage-workers, or in a *moshav,* so that they can compare the kibbutz with other forms and other surroundings.

DR. HIMMELWEIT: Considering that your young people go into the Army, or into the "open society" with its diverse value systems, at a very crucial time in the development of their own value system, you should be immensely pleased that as many as

80 or 90 per cent wish to return to the kibbutz. I should like to propose that one examine what in the organizational set-up of the kibbutz *aids* the perpetuation of the appropriate value system, and what, without anyone's wishing it so, sets up *counter-pressures*.

Several of you have mentioned that the children are proud of the work their fathers do — especially if they are tractor-drivers, or have some job that carries prestige. This is, of course, exactly as it is in the world outside; certain careers carry status, and children are proud when their fathers have such careers. (It is interesting, by the way, that in this sex-egalitarian society, no one has yet spoken of children being proud of their mother's work!)

MRS. IRVINE: I wonder whether the essence of the kibbutz can be preserved only through daily contact. It seems to me that by the time someone has grown up in kibbutz life, his identification with it should be strong enough to withstand much longer absences.

Reference has been made to kibbutz members who are now working outside in the community, but the only people specified were members of the so-called "first generation." I wonder how many are members of "this generation." One of the needs of healthy, dynamic young people is to *change* something: to have an area in which they can *build something new*. At the same time, this area of change can be in different geographic locations. Since the kibbutz itself is a small society within a somewhat alien world, I would doubt that it could endure constant change at too rapid a rate.

JUDIT GILAN: There are children who can find self-identification only by leaving the kibbutz. It is not enough for them to rebel within the framework of the kibbutz, their place of living; they need physically to go away. Because we want to defend ourselves, however, we are not tolerant in this business of leaving the kibbutz. This place, which should be home for every child, becomes strange to him if he goes away for a time.

One solution is for young members to go and live in a very young kibbutz, or to begin a new kibbutz. That is a revolution, sometimes; but few of the children who leave do so because they don't like this life, or cannot live here, or don't want to live here, but only because *they cannot find themselves without going away* once in their lives. Can we be tolerant of this or can we not? How long can the parents themselves stay in the kibbutz when they cannot feel that they have given a home to their children, who *are* going away?

MENAHEM GERSON: A few years ago, we had Margaret Mead with us. I showed her a few kibbutzim, and after she had listened patiently for a long time, she made one comment which, although this happened a few years ago, still sticks in my mind. She said: "You know, I have never seen such a dynamic village as yours. But there is one point that you are not at all dynamic about: you expect every child to come back to this small community that he came from. I would feel much more certain about the future of the kibbutz if you let your more restless characters found new kibbutzim — or join them."

Now this has been a demographic problem. For quite a time, the very idea was taboo, because it would have done demographic damage to the kibbutzim. But now, kibbutzim — at least, some of the more established kibbutzim — can consider the possibility without shuddering, so to speak. I really believe that we are approaching the time when that sort of advice can be put into practice. As a matter of fact, in one of the kibbutz movements, this has been discussed at great length, but it has been postponed as far as I know . . . (*Interjection:* It has been started already . . .) It has started? Good! In our movement there has been a discussion about it, but no decision taken. When we reach the stage of decision — and we certainly shall reach it soon — this will be one of the best and most important ways of giving our young adults the feeling that there is something they can start anew, something through which they can become individuals.

JEHUDA MESSINGER: I would like to make one remark about the necessity of our relating the kibbutz more to the outside world, and giving more opportunities to the youngsters. We are becoming much more conscious of this than we have been in the past. I think of the problem as a case of discrepancy between function and essence. The essence of kibbutz living is *living together in a community and maintaining the community spirit.* At the founding of the kibbutz, this essence was congruous with the kibbutz's actual function in the society: just being a kibbutz, settling, doing things was enough. Now, there is starting to be a discrepancy, and if we have a new function in the kibbutz, it is probably along the lines that have been indicated: education, welfare, the outside world.

Conformity and Rebellion

DR. HIMMELWEIT: There seems to be a great deal of concern over whether the kibbutz adolescents are being sufficiently provided with occasions and outlets for "adolescent rebellion"; the concern is about the consequences, for later personality growth, of the absence of opportunity for such rebellion.

The term "adolescent rebellion" was adopted at a time when disagreement with parental views often meant severance of ties with the family. What it conceals, however, is the perfectly natural course of growth: that, at times of maximum growth (physical, intellectual and emotional), the young person — and equally the adult who deals with the young person — experiences strain. Further, every human being who is born into a society at a later period than those who initiated and developed it, looks at it, during the course of his growing up, with new eyes — not taking things for granted, but instead wondering why certain things *are* the way they are, and what might be done to change them. The young people in the kibbutz (as anywhere else in the world) also experience this *need to reevaluate,* and *to change* things.

JUDIT GILAN: Everyone understands that in kibbutz life we have high ideals, and that we would like our children to identify with these ideals. But that becomes very difficult when the children identify with the realities of our life, rather than with our ideals. We ourselves remember these ideals, because they were the ideals of our youth and we want to see them again in the children. When we don't see them, there is a feeling of disappointment with the adolescent.

The fact is that it is the same everywhere and for every adolescent — the same sense of disappointment among the grown-ups. Outside the kibbutz, however, most people do not have such high ideals of life, although they may have their own personal ideals, which they try to transfer to their sons. Here the feeling is stronger because it has to do with a whole social structure. Thus, our disappointment, I think *is* a problem — if not with regard to all of our youth, then surely for some of them.

The second problem is the question of ideological education. Every adolescent rebels against the things that are important to his parents. Everyday problems, however, are not that important in the life of our society; the one thing that is very important — and we feel it and say it — is that we all have the same ideology. We have had an *ideal* of parents and children living together in peace in kibbutz life. But I think that while we must say to our children: "You see, this is how we want to live," when we say, "It's right," we must remember that we are at that very moment giving them an object for their rebellion.

DR. KRIS: I think that the adolescent revolt may have taken some different form from the one that the older generation had envisaged, in line with the way their own revolt had gone. In principle, this revolt may very well be the same — unless, as some seem to believe, it is simply not there at all. Some of the likes and dislikes that have been mentioned — such as the fact that the children do not want to become teachers (a position we may look upon as substitute fathers) — may express this kind of revolt. They may thereby be saying, "We do not want to do what you so much want us to do — namely, to choose an intellectual field."

One of the members who showed us around the kibbutz that we visited mentioned that their adolescents seem to show so much less interest in politics than they, the older ones, had shown in their youth — and still do, at present. "The young people like to farm, but they do not like politics" — this was the impression, and it was shared by other mothers and fathers in that kibbutz. The remark was accompanied by evidence of the pained feeling that the subject obviously aroused in this mother, who spoke at the same time about the lack of revolutionary spirit among the adolescents. My own unexpressed thought, as I put these elements together in my mind, was that this may be one of the forms that adolescent revolt can take — just being uninterested in what the parents have been especially interested in — in this instance, politics.

MRS. IRVINE: Discussion of adolescent rebellion revolves around a basically philosophical question. As I understand the socialist philosophy, social progress takes place through the confrontation of thesis and antithesis, out of which there then emerges a new synthesis.

We have been asking ourselves whether the kibbutz adolescents rebel, and if they should. Do they rebel too much, we ask, or too little? I think that what we are really asking is what to do about the antithesis. Where will you find that antithesis, which — in your own thinking — you need in order to progress? When you do find it, will you welcome it or be afraid of it? Can the kibbutz contain its own antithesis, through which to move on to a new synthesis? Or to what extent does the antithesis consist of leaving the kibbutz along with the rest who do leave — in which case you may continue, perhaps indefinitely, to have the thesis *inside the kibbutz* and the antithesis *outside*? But then the synthesis will not be a *kibbutz synthesis*; it will be something that has arisen *between the kibbutz and the world outside.*

CHAVAH SHAMIR: We try very much to encourage critical thinking among the children, perhaps more so than in any other schools, because we are aware of the fact that our children probably don't have a wide variety of stimuli for thinking, they don't see different patterns of life, as do children in New York, for instance. And then, our children probably *identify very strongly* with the pattern of the life in which they are living: usually, they *like* their teachers, they *like* their parents; they don't have reasons, when they are young, to oppose them. In short, our children don't have too many stimuli — either positive or negative — to think critically about the pattern of the life they are living.

Let's take, for instance, fifth-grade kids. If we were really *afraid* of their seeing other patterns of life and of becoming critical, then we wouldn't take them out to a *moshav* as we do, for instance, and leave them there (where there is another way of life), saying: "Well, you come back and describe their life to us as you saw it, and then we'll discuss it. We'll see what their sorrows and their joys are, and how these compare with what you see in our way of life." "When I say our," I tell them, "I really mean your parents, and you yourself, as a child of ten," and so on.

And we have been really amazed by the observations that the children have brought in about the things they have seen.

What I feel to be the problem, as a teacher and as a supervisor of teachers, is that the children cling too much to the patterns that their group has worked out as their own way of life. They conform so much, and for so long, to the thoughts and beliefs of the other children, that there is really no age at which the child is truly critical of the life he leads. Of course, that may be because he is not mature enough — emotionally, that is — to detach himself from his way of life. If he were to do that, he would lose the sense of belonging that is so important to him.

MISS WILLIAMS: Usually the more alert people in any society today speak badly about it. The individual, in order to live in society, uses as the outlet for his discontent all kinds of derogatory remarks or ideas. People who go outside the city talk about their city — how badly it's run, how the Mayor is doing all the wrong things, and so on.

When the individual cannot fully agree with his society, he thus verbalizes that disagreement in all sorts of critical remarks. But that's *all* he does about it — more or less. Oh, he may work for some party, perhaps; but up to "the revolution," people usually live in that very society which they are all the time criticizing.

A society that lives within the framework of another society must direct its criticism, if it does not want to dissolve, against *the outer society*. This means, in simple terms, that we say to our kids, "The outside society is terrible, we have a much better society." That is why, in our society, there is less aggression directed towards the society itself: the group directs it *outward*.

JEHUDA MESSINGER: Criticism, in so far as it exists among us, is directed against the outside society — *but it is also against the specific kibbutz*. It is *not* directed against the kibbutz movement.

What happens, for example? You hear from the kids, the parents, that in our kibbutz, the kitchen — this, that and the other thing — is "terrible." As a matter of fact, this is one of our major educational problems. Everybody talks about what's wrong with "our kibbutz" — not *the* kibbutz, but "our kibbutz." Why isn't it nicer? why don't they cook better? why didn't they put this girl in that place, and the other one here? That is what they say, every day, about the environment in which they are closed up. Yet the same people, when they go to visit outside, or come here to this Institute, say all the good things about their society that they do not say inside the group.

I was telling Dr. Himmelweit just yesterday about some of the Diamond studies, and how he came to the conclusion that people in the kibbutz are extremely unhappy: he just took bits and pieces out of the paper published in the kibbutz. What is written in that paper? It is full of criticisms; it says: "What happened yesterday could only have happened here. . . ." and things of that sort.

One of my teachers, when he was talking about the Prophets, used to explain to us: "If you read the Prophets, you get the impression that the Israeli society of two thousand years ago was really terrible. How they cry out against social injustice! Now, was the Israeli society of that time worse than the Egyptian society, in which people were being killed every day, in which there was *no social justice at all, no law at all?* No, there was a *tremendous sensitivity* on the question of justice in Israel, and it found expression in the Prophets. That's why they wrote."

What happens in the daily experience of the kibbutz — the day-to-day expressions of dissatisfaction, so to speak — reflects a dissatisfaction that stems from that very social sensitivity, so much more deep-rooted than it is in general society. There, dissatisfaction is directed towards the general society; in the kibbutz, it is directed to the specific, local place, still leaving open the possibility both of identification with the kibbutz movement in general, and of opposition to the society which surrounds the kibbutz.

As to individualization, one also has to differentiate between individualization in the area of opinions, and individualization of personality. (This has been one of our most basic, profound recognitions; it is really the foundation for our success.)

Every single kibbutz — whatever the way it operates — gets its people to think in favor of, and to vote for, the opinions that it advocates. Let us take the movement of "collective ideology." In their case, there is actually very little possibility of the expression of different ideas; this is how they create very good members.

Another movement, on the other hand, will lay great emphasis on presenting *different* opinions: different speakers and the spokesmen for different parties are brought before the children; they are given books to read on the different philosophies; they meet with different people. The outcome is the same: this movement also has very good members. This seems to show, does it not, that one can go about the collectivizing of opinion by quite different means. Sometimes, the means can even lie outside the framework of intellectual pursuits.

However, I want to make this distinction — the collectivization of opinion is a completely different problem from the individualization of personality; and I believe that as the result of the way we have worked, there has been a tremendous individualization of the personality of the kibbutz child. It expresses itself in a very simple way. I have worked for years as an educator outside the kibbutz, and I know that if you place children in most social situations, you will see that they readily follow the leader. Yet kids of the same age, who belong to the kibbutz, will not follow the leader. They have their own personal opinions; they oppose the opinions of others; they even get into all kinds of scrapes with the law.

German society provided a terrible example of the opposite behavior. And I know about how things are in American society, with which I have also had some experience. I would say that the kibbutz children in Israel are in fact the most individualistic group you can find — if you wish to compare groups as to the total *personalities,* and not the specific opinions, of their members.

MENAHEM GERSON: There is a great need for our adolescents to develop their own opinions and beliefs. You see it when they return from the Army — sometimes before, but it's especially noticeable when they come back from the Army. Then you often get the phenomenon of their insistence on living *in their own room,* for a certain period at least.

It is very difficult to encourage intellectual individualization, and not only because they live three or four in a room — there are weightier reasons. First of all, we're living in a small community. I wouldn't say that we are farmers; still, it is a farm world. In this rural environment, there is less stimulation, for instance, with regard to clashes of opinion. An urban child will see the announcements of quite a number of different parties, especially during pre-election periods; our children do not see that kind of thing. Every child in town has the chance to meet quite different political opinions — I mean, theoretically — but our children don't have that. (In practice, to be sure, they often do have it because, in spite of our "ideological collectivism," we still have all shades of opinion. Not all the parents are "orthodox," even if we must assume that the teachers are.) Still, it is not easy to make them individuals, in the political field. I am often reminded of one of the books which made a deep impression on me — a book by Rokeach, *The Open and the Closed Mind*. We can be quite sure that we won't have the kibbutz we want, if our achievement is a bunch of closed minds!

What can one do about it? First of all, I believe that we have to *face* the problem. I would not venture to say that this problem has been recognized everywhere in our movement. There still remains a great concern, especially on the part of our political leadership, that our children should "toe the line," should have the "right" opinions about matters. I believe that this approach is deadly to political alertness. We have to fight it, and we have to change it — precisely *in the name of real political loyalty.*

The things we can do educationally in this respect — to make people think and to make them individualized — are quite limited. I think the most important thing we can do is to have the sort of political education that places the problems squarely and does not stress the point of view of only one particular party. It is most important, in my opinion, to make our adolescents *think,* to make them *see things from various aspects, and not only from one.*

SHIMON STERN: We have to find — I think we have found, in many ways — how to help the development of our children's criticism. When they come to the age of thirteen or fourteen, they start to criticize many things that they never commented on before: things about every aspect of the kibbutz — the Secretary (or the Secretariat), democracy in the kibbutz, the management of the kitchen, every place where they walk and live. And it's the task of the educators not to silence this criticism; on the contrary, we have to *listen with understanding* and discuss these things.

In most kibbutzim, there is a free discussion nearly every evening, between the educator and his group. I know that there are kibbutzim that stop this at the age of fourteen or so, but I think it's very important to keep it going down to the end of school. If there is a framework the children are used to — say, meeting every evening with the educator, in order to bring up any topic from the day before, or from the paper — and if they continue this very freely up to the age of eighteen, then you do have a means for criticism.

From the age of sixteen, in most kibbutzim, the children take part, or at least they are present, in the General Assembly. (From the age of seven, when they come to school, we start to tell them at least once a week what was on the agenda and what was decided in the Assembly; from the age of sixteen, they are present themselves.) This brings me to the last point. You are the target of criticism wherever you educate, I am sure; but it's much easier to just go to school, meet your pupils from 8 o'clock in the morning until noon, and then not see them any more. In that case, they won't hear you speak (say, in the General Assembly), and they won't meet the people who know you very well, and who sometimes, of course, will speak about you. That makes the educator's very complicated position somewhat less complicated; but it may also cut the heart out of that position. . . .

MONI ALON: There should be greater freedom of criticism — criticism in discussion. If we are to apply any pressure at all in the direction of conformism, then we should see to it that there is also the possibility of examining the other point of view, the other side of the coin. And this would not be because we were becoming liberal, or that we now felt neutral about the outcome. We are quite involved, as we have always been, and we want to educate our children to live in the kibbutz — but we also want them to *come to their own conclusions,* so that they will be able to stand up to a crisis, sure that *they themselves* want what is decided on.

Today we understand that there should be more opportunities

for discussing things. I can't say that we are yet doing this properly, but how to do it in a better way is a question to which I cannot yet give a definite answer. This is, as Dr. Redl has suggested, a technical question, rather than an ideological question.

There is a personal need on the part of the individual to know that he will leave his own individual *impact on society,* even though he accepts its basic rules. To begin with, there are great differences between the two generations, and thus there are *possibilities of discovery and change* in a democratic society like a kibbutz, a society which knows that there are some problems for which the solution hasn't yet been found — problems such as the position of women, or the tasks of industrialization. One cannot yet say whether the second generation has discovered exactly what is the special task inside the kibbutz movement, but I think it is in the process of finding out.

Our young people have quite a difficult problem discovering how to be true to themselves, how to be constructive and yet fulfill their responsibilities. I can't say that they have already found the answers to these questions, nor can I say that we, the older generation, are making their task, at every point, an easy one.

CHAVAH SHAMIR: It is very likely true that we don't have adequate techniques for achieving our educational goals, in spite of the fact that they are very definite. We need much help in this area. Whenever we get literature from America about the things they have done, that always enriches our methods of doing things. For instance, one sentence read: "As long as the child can't express his own problems in his own words, then he only repeats the values that he has heard from the older people, and you don't really have a situation in which you can educate him." We have to find out all those areas in which the child *really* has problems and then try to help him with the answers: *finding the answers with him,* and not letting him simply repeat the values that he has actually taken over from the grownups.

We now feel that sometimes, when a child *seems to be identifying* with the values which we have wanted him to take up from us, he is only repeating them; he has not had a problem of his own that he has used them to solve. When you have found how to solve such a problem together, then you can really assimilate a value very profoundly — you can truly *believe in it* — because it has provided the answers for something you really need. Yet, it is only lately that we have learned this difference between repeating a value and believing in it deeply.

MRS. WINSOR: The really big question, I think, is not whether the children have the opportunity to think critically about your society, this society of the kibbutz that you have planned and built. I should like to pose a quite different question: How are the values or the ideology of your society transmitted? For many of us, a head-on approach to this process of transmission creates some problems, in terms of the developmental processes of the middle years and adolescence. An approach through content — the stuff that makes up their school experience, their learning and their life — offers quite different possibilities.

MISS WILLIAMS: In trying to reach the youth, I feel, the administrators would first have to go to the people who work directly with the children, the staff members themselves, who, in turn, should go to the children to *find out from them* how they conceive the world around them, what they are thinking, what they feel needs to be changed. I'm not thinking now in terms of research; I have in mind simply such things as group discussions, or any other way we can devise to find out from them what their ideas are.

Now, after we have gone to the children themselves, we must bring all this back to the administrative fathers and have it in some way incorporated into the in-service educational program. That program must find room for the things that the children themselves feel they need, because they are "the generation" now, they are the people who need, in some way, to be *helped to plan their own lives.*

DR. EISENBERG: There is a custom — at least in one kibbutz, I gather — in which they have, on occasion, called together groups of high school graduates from a number of different schools for prolonged discussion. They distribute questionnaires to be returned unsigned, in an effort to find out what young people think; I am not sure, however, that they have found out any more than we have about what young people are like.

I was struck by the fact that a very fruitful discussion with one group of teachers was started off by a girl who had just come back from the army and discussed what her army life had been like after her high school experience in the kitchen, and so on. This provided a framework within which teachers and youngsters together were able to discuss some of these problems. It seems to me a very useful way of finding out what young people think: to *ask them, instead of speaking for them,* as is so often the case.

DR. HIMMELWEIT: We have raised the question of whether educators might not be specifically encouraged to help the children verbalize their negative feelings about kibbutz life. There must be some such feelings — this isn't a paradise, we have been told. Even if the children themselves hesitated to do so spontaneously, it should be encouraged as an educational task. This is not a question of getting them to say: "No; this is terrible; we want to leave," but of encouraging them to be free to say something critical, without expecting the world to come to an end for them — and equally of being confident that, after they have said it, the society itself will not disappear.

RACHEL MANOR: A child in our society should know that he can express, verbally, his discontent and his anger, and that, in so doing, he is not a bad child, a deviant from his group. There is a *fear* of being different — precisely because *the group is the chief punisher.* In informal discussion, Fritz Redl said to us: "The children love their groups; they want to conform to them." That is the point: they don't want to be different, they don't want to be deviant; and yet they *do* have hostility, they *do* have aggressive feelings.

Sometimes it would be better that the educator said "No!" and not the group. Then they could be angry with the educator, and not with the group. The group *throttles* them! I remember a meeting of young parents who had themselves been kibbutz children; the expression "We were throttled" was repeated several times. I think we have to take heed of that.

Someone said, during lunch: "Has a child ever said to you, 'Kibbutz life is no good?'" Our children don't say it; they are afraid to say it, because they feel we won't allow them to say it. And I think we don't permit them to say it because *we* are afraid.

(*Interjection*: Perhaps they haven't much reason to say it.) But they *have to be able to* say it sometimes! Only then will they be acting spontaneously; only then, I feel, will they be able to make changes within the older kibbutzim! We say: "You have to make changes, you have to give your opinions on things . . . " But they don't dare to do it; we say it to them in such a way that they don't dare to do it.

We have to work more with our educators, and at deeper levels. I don't think that we have to reach a more intellectual level, to explain more to them about the ideologies of other parties, and so on; that's not the point. We have to work so that they feel we are *tolerant,* that we are not afraid they will leave if they are, for some time and on some questions, very different.

I want to bridge the gap that clearly exists between our personal feelings and attitudes and our declarations. I feel that gap in the adults, and especially in the educators. And we have to work on that question with parents, too. This is a very important aspect of the problem of individualization.

MRS. IRVINE: The suggestion has been made that teachers should stimulate children to express themselves more aggressively, to be freer in their criticism — not to be "yes-men," as we say. It seems to me that one cannot give this sort of task to the educators because, first of all, it is a question of how much internal criticism the kibbutz itself can stand, how much it feels it can stand. We've just been hearing how much anxiety there is in the kibbutz about internal criticism, how important it is that criticism should be directed outward, against the external world, so as not to disrupt the movement. As long as the kibbutzniks feel that way, how can the educator be asked to encourage the children to criticize more freely?

If children start saying "the kibbutz life is no good" (as somebody here suggested), or even making much more specific criticisms, I think that their educator will probably be regarded as a failure or a danger. This is a problem for the kibbutz as a whole to solve, if it is to be solved at all, and not just the educators.

MRS. WINSOR: One needs to differentiate between the kibbutz and the kibbutz movement. There is a qualitative difference, in that there is a role and a life process for *this* generation in its *own* kibbutz. (Let me say, parenthetically, that to itself, every generation is *this generation*. Only retrospectively or prospectively does one look to the preceding generation or the next.) This generation can play an important role in the development of the new nation; the young people today have a role to play significantly different from the social role played by their predecessors. Moreover, the kibbutz movement as a whole may have an important contribution to make to the changing world in which we live, as well as to the new state of Israel.

MRS. IRVINE: I respect the anxieties that have been expressed: the desire that there should be some change, some improvement — *but not too much!* I can see a society like the kibbutz developing in phases, with a certain rhythm: a phase of change and development, and then a phase of consolidation. At a time when you are in the midst of a phase in which you want to consolidate, there are still plenty of opportunities for change and dynamic impact in the world around you — outside, yet not too far away.

The historic task of the first generation was not only to conquer the soil, to establish productivity, and so on; it was also, as Golan and Levi have pointed out, the "absorption of Jewish immigrants in Israel, and facilitating the productivization of members of the petty bourgeoisie." These tasks are perhaps even more urgent now than the expansion of agricultural productivity. This generation in Israel is confronted by the challenge of assimilating the tremendous influx of disparate elements from all over the world — a task that presents real problems, which, from your own accounts, have proven to be extraordinarily difficult. I know that there has been an attempt to bring these immigrants inside the kibbutz society, and that this proved to be unworkable in many cases. So there is a real need — an intellectual as well as a practical need — to experiment, to find the forms in which one can communicate some of the kibbutz ideals to all these people, with their tremendously different backgrounds.

If any substantial proportion of "this generation" of the kibbutz were to become actively involved in such an activity, that very fact would help solve the question of whether they are accepting their ideology passively, or choosing it. One becomes much more actively conscious of one's values when one attempts to impart them to other people. In this way, the kibbutz would at one and the same time be meeting a need of the whole community (by helping to assimilate new members to the existing value system), as well as some of the needs of "this generation" — by putting their values through a testing fire, which will enable them to hold these values in a more active and choosing way.

DR. HIMMELWEIT: The big problem you have is how to kindle, in children who have had such a happy and secure upbringing, that desire to *change* society which will alone bring forth those same extraordinary qualities that made *you* capable of overcoming the great hardships you experienced while founding the kibbutzim. A second problem is how to reorganize the power structure within the kibbutz, so that it is actually the young people who *do the changing themselves, not they through you.*

They should be asked for their advice as to what part the kibbutz could play in the wider society of Israel. To offer them, as an alternative, the opportunity of developing a new young kibbutz is too limited. Your young generation would, I expect, be able to tackle, as effectively as you tackled it, the problem of grappling with the soil, or those problems that are most pressing for Israel today — the social and educational problems. Here the kibbutzim could do so much, not through youth movements attached to the kibbutz, but by helping in whatever form help is needed, without expecting in return that the people helped will accept the kibbutz way of life.

In the past you were faced with the problem of having to make your land bear fruit; there were too few for the task. Today you have a similar problem; to achieve these goals may require reorganizing the kibbutzim so as to save manpower. If this were done, and if members of the kibbutzim could work throughout Israel, then that would provide diverse outlets for the young members, and, at the same time, offer more varied job opportunities for women. Above all, it would show that kibbutz society, unlike many previous communal societies which failed to survive, can survive because *it can adapt to the needs, not of its own community, but of the larger society of which it is a part.*

Problems of Sexuality and Aggression

SHMUEL NAGLER: Kibbutz teenagers who come for help put much less stress on their sexual troubles than do non-kibbutz teenagers, especially during the first interview. They are more worried about problems of social adjustment — such as lack of popularity, inhibitions in their social contacts, or difficulties in learning and work. When asked during the interview about their sex life, they are seldom — on the surface, at least — embarrassed or surprised; they display a calm, matter-of-fact attitude, with expressions such as these: "There's nothing to it, everything is natural"; "Our teachers made everything clear to us."

We were not surprised to unveil, quite frequently, strong defense mechanisms at work in these cases. We assume that the sharing of bedrooms by adolescent boys and girls causes this mechanism to be very strong. It is an interesting fact that love relations seldom develop between girls and boys who have grown up in the same kvutzah, as is also true of clan exogamy.

NECHAMA LEVI: We have to deal very seriously with the problem of early sexual life and early marriage. How wise is it to keep sleeping adolescents, boys and girls together, till eighteen in one room? If it is true that these adolescents can live together in one room and not have sexual relationships, then I say, without being a psychiatrist, that they are *not normal*. As for young people of eighteen who are normal and are sleeping in one room, it is a very natural thing for them to feel a desire for each other. Perhaps we can say that they don't have any desire for each other; but the question is, do we *want* them not to have any feelings of desire? Do we *want* them not to want to be one with another? Perhaps if we were to come to the conclusion that that is very good, then I could say to myself, about my daughters and my son, "That is how they will live." But I am a little afraid: I want my daughter to love somebody, and to have a relationship with him when they are together.

The other thing that bothers me is boys and girls showering together. If that is no longer catching on, then I take it as one of those experiments that we once made in various fields of our life, where we did make mistakes. Why did we make mistakes? Because there were no books that told you how to create a kibbutz, how to rear children on a kibbutz. I was a teacher for many years, and I made many mistakes.

I don't think we can make the definitive statement about how long the children should shower or sleep together; that statement will be made by the children themselves. But I do think that we have to make our rules more flexible, better adapted to the development of the adolescent.

Dr. Fritz Redl: Frankly, at the beginning, I was starting to wonder why we cannot be as specific in raising those issues about adolescence that must be bothering you, as we were with regard to issues concerning the younger children. The moment we talk about adolescents, we seem to get into big issues of overall philosophy, ideology, and so forth, and we tend to drift away from the practical issues of daily life — of which, I am sure, there must be plenty.

One of the problems under discussion is the question of sex. The interesting thing about this is that what we learn by experience sometimes turns out to be the reverse of what we originally expected. In the discussion about mixed showering and sleeping arrangements, for instance, this seems to me to have been the case. Originally, you suggested a very permissive arrangement, because you felt that this would be contributory to making kids more comfortable with sex and more happy and mature in their adult lives. Then you find out that, in some age ranges, what looks like a "liberating" procedure is actually more "inhibiting" in the long run. What would be wrong, then, with changing arrangements to take that experience into account? This has nothing to do with your overall philosophy about sex; it is a simple issue, to be decided in terms of procedural mental-health appropriateness. You obviously would do well, therefore, to detach it from your articles of faith.

Dr. Schouten: It has been pointed out that all sorts of pathological manifestations appear outside the kibbutz. But nothing has been said about "acting-out," which is, in our society, a very common manifestation of emotional disturbance. I have been asking around about the existence of delinquency here, and so far I have received various answers. One is that there is no delinquency because there are no police, or because some antisocial acts are not labeled as such, and are therefore not interfered with — at least, not in the way we would.

I should like to know how you do deal with certain antisocial actions. I've heard, for example, about lemons or other things being stolen from another kibbutz; or about young people taking the tractor from the kibbutz and going out on it. How do you deal with such situations? That would tell us whether you are allowing yourselves to be more or less aggressive, so that the children may feel that they can be aggressive towards you.

When children have been educated in an atmosphere of love — with no aggression at all — for eighteen years, it is astonishing that on going into the Army, these same children seem to be the people who take on the most dangerous and most aggressive jobs. Can it be that there is a *repression of aggression* up to a certain age, and that later on, in the Army, this aggression comes to the fore, but in the context, and with permission of the ideology?

SHIMON STERN: I'm sure that there is some connection between this lack of aggression up to the age of military service and the fact that our kibbutz youth are known as good soldiers. But there is another question: what will our *girls* do with this aggression? (*Interjection*: They go into the Army too . . .) Yes, but they don't get these jobs.

I can give you one example of the reaction of kibbutz society to an act such as has been mentioned — for instance: taking a tractor or a car without permission. I know of one case where the boys and girls of a number of kibbutzim spent about a month together at a seminar near Tel Aviv. After a week, a few boys took a jeep, and went off in it to Tel Aviv. They were sent home, being no longer permitted to take part in the Seminar. (I know that there were boys who said: "These fellows are not very upset about that; the Seminar is not important for them"; in any case, that is one example of how that sort of act was handled.)

In our kibbutz, we have the problem of riding bicycles on narrow pathways — which can be dangerous at night. Two boys who did this were brought to the Secretary. In a special meeting, the Secretariat decided that the boys should not ride their bicycles for two months. It's questionable whether or not this was a hard punishment, but these boys regarded it as very hard, and so did many members of the kibbutz. After a month or so, there were members who started to approach the educators or the Secretary to ask whether it couldn't be a shorter period. I don't remember now whether or not they curtailed the period.

Sometimes, by the way, such questions arise with regard to adult members. For instance, if a driver in a kibbutz goes too fast, or if somebody in the kibbutz does something against the law — not the law of the kibbutz, but the law of the State — the usual thing has been for the Secretary of the kibbutz to turn to the Police or the law court, and there to try to defend the member. In any case, it has never come to imprisonment, but has always been settled with the payment of a certain fine. Still, there are members of the kibbutz who say: "That's not the right way. People would be more careful if they would sit in prison for a month or so."

MONI ALON: I think there is "acting out." If there is an emotional disturbance, it is acted out. These people are referred for help; they are worked with and helped. We have early therapeutic treatment — much earlier than in a regular society — and many things don't reach the degree of acting out that would be dangerous. Perhaps that is why, when it does take place, it is in a much lower key; but the phenomenon itself exists, just as it exists everywhere else.

NECHAMA LEVI: Aggression can take place in different ways: sometimes it may not be the noisy sort, but still it can be seen. Our society is arranged in such a way that everything is seen; if someone is really "acting out," that, I think, is more difficult for us to see than somebody who is aggressive and a bed-wetter, or who stutters. The question is: *How* is aggression acted out among us — is it with noise, as in general society, or is there a different way?

MORDECHAI KAFFMAN: It is quite certain that we do have aggression, and we probably have the same amount of it as any other society. Our children of preschool age know how to fight; they will snatch a toy, or express their aggression in different ways. At different ages, they have different ways — not only the displaced ways of expressing aggression previously referred to, but such direct ways as criticizing the leaders, the group, the teacher, and so forth. There are verbal expressions of aggression, and there are also all kinds of acting out — but *according to the social values of the group*.

A great deal of imitation can be found in the acting-out of the gangs in general society; here, they have *their own ways* of acting out antisocial behavior. Thus, they do something like taking the tractor — which is very dangerous and, besides, antisocial. Sometimes, some do steal; but it is not called "stealing" in the kibbutz society — because if you take some toy, or something belonging to another child, another term is used to describe it. Still, we do have these problems in the kibbutz society, and I am a little surprised to hear some people say that we are not expressing our aggression, that we have to encourage its expression! We don't need to encourage it because *we have it!*

One of the most important ways of handling this problem is the group decision. The group meets to discuss the problem; first, the deviant child with some kind of antisocial behavior talks about his problem; then the other children give their opinion; and then they assign the punishment. They say something like: "You will do this or that; or you will be deprived of this or that privilege. . . ." Even if there is only a discussion, that is sometimes punishment enough.

CHAVAH SHAMIR: We don't have gangs, in the sense in which you know them, because our children have what I suppose you could call "legal gangs." They have no need for the antisocial gang that is so characteristic of American society. Instead, they have their little groups within the large groups, and these are offered a great variety of activities, and also encouraged to find objectives for their own activities. This probably uses up the energy that would otherwise go into an antisocial direction.

RACHEL MANOR: I think we have to differentiate. Of course, we have disturbed children, with behavior disorders; they act out, as they do everywhere else. But what about the healthy children, who are the majority? We have to think about *them*. I am of the opinion that there is not enough *verbalizing* of aggressive feelings; it is because of this that they have to criticize, because of this that they have to do all kinds of things . . . (*Interjection*: But that's the same thing. . . .) No, it's *not* the same! That is just what I'm trying to get at! If we will only recognize this difference, we will have fewer behavior disorders and less acting out . . . yes, and less criticizing . . . and we will have much more spontaneity and initiative. That is the issue!

"Teacher" and "Educator"

SHMUEL NAGLER: We do not have enough material on adolescence, and I think that we should be aware of the reason for this. It is not merely a problem of our policy on referrals. I feel that educators in the secondary schools are less aware of emotional problems than are the kindergarten teachers; they are first and foremost *teachers,* and not educators.

MRS. WINSOR: As an educator who is also a teacher, I am a bit confused about the semantic difference between an educator and a teacher. Someone who teaches physics is also an educator, as I see it. There has been so much talk about the "educator" and the "teacher," that one would think they are two different people; but it seems to me that the same person fulfills these two roles, which are essentially inseparable.

DR. EISENBERG: Suppose we define a teacher as someone who teaches physics, and an educator as someone who, at the same time that he teaches physics, also raises children to *a higher level of personal development.* The latter is the fuller role.

MONI ALON: I agree that we want a teacher of adolescents to be an educator. We are not always sure that he is one, but that is what we want him to be. Sometimes he simply retires into teaching. I call it "retiring" because, after all, it is easier to be a classroom teacher than to form contacts with children. It is not only a question of creating good teachers, and then setting them to work; we also have to find the ways to help them *during the time they are working,* and not only during the two years when they are receiving lectures in the Seminar at Oranim. We have been thinking about how to set up informal groups of six or seven teachers, working in the same age group, not from the same kibbutz, but from the same district, and have them meet, say once in two or three weeks, to discuss the sort of problems they all have.

MENAHEM GERSON: It is certainly our intention to regard our teachers as mainly educators; but, just as everywhere else (so far as I know), the more important the teaching material, the less you can win over the educator to the sort of approach that does not emphasize the teaching material so much as it emphasizes education. I remember a study by Dr. Himmelweit along these lines.

We do have to lay more stress on our training of educators. But please understand that this is not only a question of quantity, of "doing more." For instance, at Oranim today, I am quite sure we are already achieving a greater awareness of educational problems or psychological problems with our "metaplot" than we are with our high-school teachers. It is not a matter of our intention only; it is a matter of the emphasis placed by these people themselves.

(*Interjection*: And by the people who send them. . . .)

MRS. WINSOR: There is a variety of roles to be played in any given classroom; it is not necessarily the task of the "teacher" to build the totality of an interpersonal relationship with the student. We have been so concerned with the *climate* of learning, during these last decades, that we have not been nearly enough concerned with its content.

In adolescence, it seems to me, there is a deep respect, even love, that goes out from the children to the teacher, for the very reason that the teacher is giving of the fullness of his knowledge and discipline, and is showing the youngster his respect for their common goal of learning. It is in this sense that the teacher at this level does not always need to be — in addition — what we have so lovingly called an "educator."

We need to take a somewhat more specific look at the role of knowledge and how it is transmitted, and how the adolescent, in particular, looks upon the worth of that knowledge to himself as a growing individual. In that light, we need to consider; what specialization does the teacher need? what skills? what bodies of knowledge? I am not denying the need for a satisfactory relationship as supportive of the learning process. But we can also respect a teacher for *what* he is offering, as a teacher; and the young person, I believe, has a very profound — I will even say, emotional — response to that offering, because *that* is among the things he so profoundly needs at this stage of his development.

I want to place this clearly at the secondary-school level, however; if we were talking of the middle years, I would have a different comment to make, and if we were talking about nursery education, I would have still a third outlook.

DR. EISENBERG: In what Mrs. Winsor has just said — for those of you who may not be fully aware of this — there is the reflection of a considerable controversy now going on in America about content versus process orientation in teaching. You are, I gather, less interested in the acquisition of specialized skills — except those necessary for survival — and more in the production of a certain kind of man. Some of us feel that you may end up "short-changing" the man — if I may use a colloquial expression — by not having provided more content orientation during his formal educational period.

RACHEL MANOR: It is true that we do not have to try to know everything about every child; but, on the other hand, I know adolescents who come to our clinics and say: "They (the teachers) don't know me; they don't talk to me; they don't even know who I am." That is a fact. There are teachers whom I know very well — and they are all considered good teachers — who have said about the same girl: "She is a very dull girl"; "She is average"; "She has an I.Q. of about 130"; "She is brilliant but she is depressed, afraid." Nobody, it seems, really knows her — not her group, and even less so, the teacher.

I'm not so sure that a teacher who is really able only to give good lessons in physics will be able to *know* the children (and they surely will not know the children if they have only strong emotional ties with them). Our teachers have to be educators in a dual sense: they have to *know* the children; but they also really have to *teach* them. I think there has to be a continuous and rather intensive training for teachers, to enable them to be sensitive to the educational aspect of their work, and at the same time, to recognize the limits of emotional involvement in the educational process.

DR. REDL: We have so far used the term "teacher" and "educator" on two entirely different levels. One level is meant as a *job description*: you call the people who live with your children "educators," and the people who teach them in classes "teachers." At the same time, in both these areas of operation, you obviously need a mixture of skills, which may have to be distributed rather differently from the manner which the job-description label might lead you to expect.

Now, this is where our problem sets in: When you talk about "teaching" the older children in your schools, it is obvious that in order to get them to learn something, you must, to begin with, be equipped with a wide array of knowledge, attitudes, experiences and skills, related to "teaching" in the usual meaning of the term. On the other hand, you are not only *teaching* them something, you are even more interested that they *learn;* and this means that there is a lot you have to know, not only about the subject matter you teach, but about the *learning process,* as it goes on in living adolescents in groups.

There is also a third dimension which is too often forgotten the moment we begin dealing with a classroom teacher. There is a great deal of skill involved in the leadership of groups of children who are collectively engaged in a learning process, and yet have their bodies, minds and personal lives somewhere out on the fringe of that process. Even the simplest "teaching of subject matter" therefore implies some skill in making it possible for groups of children to engage without needless stress in this collective learning process. It means being able to handle a group that is "scapegoating" somebody, or pampering somebody else into a spoiled "mascot," to his and everybody else's detriment; it means being able to help a group to deal with collective examination panic or post-classroom exuberance. In short, there are many — among them, group-managerial — issues involved, in being a classroom teacher.

As far as I know, we have no terminology, in any language, which appropriately separates these two — or three — facets of teaching and education, and then puts them together once again in special packages, as they may be needed. We tend to call "education" those things that are not directly related to any given subject matter, and we call those things that happen while children are engaged in the learning of some specific subject matter "teaching," even though neither of these processes actually belongs wholly in one or the other of these categories.

DR. HIMMELWEIT: I recognize that there is an enormous emphasis among our Israeli colleagues on *training*; but I think that it is much more important that these people be *happy in themselves*. The research that we have done in England on teachers' attitudes and accomplishments has shown that the basic thing was whether or not they *enjoyed* teaching, whether or not they thought the children were "teachable," whether they found the parents difficult or easy.

There is a very great danger — which we are facing in England at the present moment — of making teachers jittery about all these different roles. Among us, everybody teaches; those who do more "looking after" the children in the school, simply teach a little less, or have different subjects.

If you follow up this idea (and I think it is a very good one) of having teachers of different kibbutzim come together, I would be against their coming together for a fortnight, intensively. I would instead recommend that they come together, from time to time, for a day, or for a week-end — but *often*; and that there be time for them to just chat or go swimming . . . I sometimes get the feeling that everybody is so much burdened by thought and worry and concern, that it all becomes a bit heavy.

SUMMARY OF DISCUSSION

DR. BIBER: Before we began our discussion on adolescence, ideas about adolescence and its relation to the kibbutz way of life had already been raised in our joint sessions. I would like briefly to review some of the concepts and questions that had been presented.

A high degree of importance had been placed upon the need for a greater differentiation of educational opportunity, especially at the secondary level, to provide for differences of inclination and ability among the children. Our Israeli colleagues are experimenting with ways of accomplishing this differentiation, without thereby turning the child society at adolescence into a "class-structured" society, on the basis of differences in ability — a trend that would violate the kibbutz ideal of the proper educational atmosphere.

We also had to familiarize ourselves with the educational goals of the kibbutz. The goal here is full intellectual development, a rich cultural background, love of learning and the life of the mind — all without consideration of any gain therefrom. This is, of course, altogether different from the sort of preparation of young people with which we outsiders are familiar — directed toward careers or the fulfillment of career-ambitions. The latter are here regarded as atypical, and although they are sometimes accepted, are generally regarded as deviant. For some adolescents, by the way, this may very well become an important life problem.

We learned that some of the kibbutz adolescents — girls to a greater extent than boys, and along with them the less extrovert among the boys — feel that they lack adequate opportunity for self-realization. One very interesting contribution dealt with the special problems of adolescent girls in forming ideals for themselves as women. Their mother created a feminine image that fitted the mood and the needs of the early pioneering days. Now these girls see their mothers dissatisfied with their roles in kibbutz society. It is therefore natural that they should seek identification in the realities of the contemporary scene rather than with their mother's earlier ideals. For the boys, another sort of ambivalence is created when they shift from idealization of the father, during their earlier years, to looking upon their fathers as "ordinary mortals," as the boys take their places as members of the kibbutz, and become daily partners with their fathers in the kibbutz's work and decision-making activities.

We learned too, that in those kibbutzim in which collective ideals had gone through considerable adaptation — in which, to be exact, their implementation had become lenient — there was a higher incidence of younger people becoming disaffected, and using their disaffection as the basis for their decision to leave the kibbutz. This does not mean the overt denial of "kibbutz ideals," but rather a decision that no longer considers their continuing to live in the kibbutz to be the only way to fulfiill these ideals. Where choices of that character are accepted as valid, their very existence contributes to the natural ferment of adolescent society.

It is surprising that we did not spend more time than we did on the question of sex mores in childhood and adolescence. The arrangements in one kibbutz, although not representative of all, are strikingly different from what we have been accustomed to — boys and girls sleeping in the same rooms up to the age of eighteen years, and developing attitudes close to that of clan exogamy. The clinical people pointed out that kibbutz adolescents seem to be more troubled about questions such as lack of popularity, and learning or work difficulties, than about sex matters, We did hear, however, about subsequent sexual inhibition, and one of the clinicians made the comment that this calmness about sex matters, in conversation or interview, may well signify strong defenses rather than the absence of conflict.

The importance of group identity for the kibbutz adolescent rests on the potency of the group during the latency period. The problems associated with group pressures were discussed rather fully in terms of overemphasis on uniformity, etc. We heard about the emergence of certain anti-group feelings, in the form of a wish to "get way," to have more time alone, to be less regulated in schedule and in activities. The weight of group organization seems to be most burdensome for the girls and the more sensitive boys; perhaps not all children can equally benefit from, or enjoy, so much merging with the group.

Our discussion then developed a pattern which was unintended, perhaps, but commanding. Its design was rather that of a series of concentric circles than of parallel lines in ordered sequence, with clear beginnings and endings. At the core were certain basic questions of prime concern to all of us, as parents, teachers, child therapists, whether from the kibbutz or from Western society. They revolved around the wishes of the older generation that the younger shall sustain what has been good and replace what has failed. Here in the kibbutzim, the older generation has accomplished a mammoth human task of the reconstruction of ideals, against every kind of obstacle, and within the span of a single lifetime. Out of that sort of life experience, as was pointed out, come high hopes for what the children will be and what they will do with the world they have inherited as the fruit of their parents' struggle and heroism. But the question was then placed squarely before us: granted that it was wonderful that one generation produced so many heroes, is it realistic to assume that heroes produce heroes?

There is a dual wish on the part of the older generation: to bring each child to his own fullest realization as an individual, and at the same time, to insure the perpetuation of humanist values for the future of society. I am aware that the humanist and socialist systems of values are not identical; with respect to child-rearing and education, however, they share common ground. Indoctrination — either moral or intellectual — we deem to be contradictory to our psychological ideal of the autonomous personality who has integrated his values out of his experience. By contrast, we both seek to refine the techniques of independent problem-solving and to gain a deeper understanding of those processes of identification through which our children will be able to develop themselves as individuals, and at the same time to serve as the carriers of the human and social values we cherish.

On one point, however, our views were divergent: the basic principle, held by members of the kibbutz, that *that particular social form,* that particular way of embodying socialist ideals, must be maintained *intact* and re-established by the next generation. Until we were able to grasp this principle as basic and to discipline our thinking within it, we visitors were only partially communicating with our Israeli *chaverim.*

We had the benefit of some strikingly clear descriptions of parent-child and teacher-child relations during adolescence, as well as the clarification of some key issues currently in the forefront of kibbutz thinking. It was impressive to learn of the methods being used — *and* constantly analyzed and improved — methods which we recognized as optimal ways of bringing children to the honest, autonomous resolution of developmental challenges, whether on matters of learning, adaptation, or sex, or on questions of their interest in communal affairs. But we also discovered a realistic awareness of, and concern over, the issue of the final choice — whether or not to stay in the kibbutz as an adult.

We were told that among the adolescents, especially the most serious-minded, there was no feeling that they were *choosing* this way of life; it had already been established before and for them. The converse appeared in the parents' attitude: they want the children to *choose* to stay in the kibbutz, but not because they, the elders, wish it. Although the question was raised as to what experiences, what teaching methods could be developed to help the children feel that this final choice was deeply their own, I don't seem to recall any very helpful suggestions.

Perhaps the subsequent discusion took the only direction it could towards clarification. It was Dr. Stern, I think, who called for a closer look at the gap that may exist between ideology as it is verbalized and taught to the children, and the realities of life as they see it being lived. His point — that youth is very sensitive to these incongruencies, when they do exist — sounded a familiar note for any of us who have ever been in close contact with adolescents. He pleaded for less reliance on verbalization and more attention to the influence of the total life atmosphere, including the opportunity for adolescents to have adult models other than the parents for identification.

I would not venture to say whether this is a peculiarly kibbutz problem, or one that belongs more universally in the realm of personality, especially when one remembers that the overactive verbalization of ideals all too frequently serves as a defense against the inability to live by them. But to me, it has often seemed to be the Achilles' Heel of the parents' position during their childrens' adolescence. It was noted that what the parents want their children to do is to carry out the *ideals* of their own youth; the children, on the other hand, identify with the *real people* in their lives. The content of adolescent rebellion turns out to be, ironically enough, exactly those ideals that were once most important to the parents. The parents of those children who leave the kibbutz thus have deeper than ordinary feelings of rejection to handle, and their anticipation of the problem is naturally all the more threatening.

We then turned to another topic: the intellectual experiences through which opinions and viewpoints have to take shape. Here it was stressed that criticism is openly expressed by the adolescents; that it is listened to by the adults, with understanding; that opportunities for discussion, among the young people themselves and between them and their teachers, are institutionalized through regular meetings, attendance at assembly, etc. When the question arose, however, as to whether the children should have a more extended exposure to non-kibbutz forms of living, perhaps by living in town or in a *moshav* for given periods, there was less unanimity of opinion among the kibbutz people, some of them apparently feeling that such a move might constitute a threat to the final adoption by the children of the kibbutz way of life.

It obviously became necessary for us to get a clearer picture of what constituted a threat, in this sense, and on the strength of that, to define what remained open as orbits of possible change. In that connection, we had the benefit of several clarifying statements — for example, that there are articles of faith which set the boundary lines, and that question-raising and critical thinking were useful only to the extent that they took place within these boundary lines, that is, without violating the basic articles of faith. It was realized, however, that there is a danger of a sort of "ossification" in a society based on faith (I am quoting here), and that the usefulness of critical thinking lies precisely in the fact that it prevents such stultification. One of our group, Dr. Redl, ventured to suggest several issues that might represent both "safe" and important points for change.

The position was put forward that what we had been told about adolescent reactions should be seen not as a rebellion at all, but as the expression of the natural developmental impulse to take *one's own view* of what it is all about. It was suggested that knowledge in depth was needed in order to arrive at an understanding of the children — their self-feelings, the directions of their identifications, the status assessments they make within the democratic community of the kibbutz, the sources of their contentment and their conflicts. Research, organized along the lines of longitudinal studies, and conducted cooperatively by the three movements, might yield essential information about the inner feelings of children in relation to this socializing process. These suggestions for study, made by Dr. Himmelweit, are in keeping with our optimistic belief that greater knowledge of the individual's socialization process can be a key to the resolution of some kinds of social problems.

On this matter of research, Dr. Bernard put several rather serious questions before us. Would it not be necessary to engage in some fundamental thinking about how compatible research is as a method to the frame of reference within which we agreed to contain our thinking? Would there truly be an open field for the utilization of our findings? Might it not create difficulties, if research of this kind were undertaken within a small, all-known-to-each-other and all-involved-with-each-other community of human beings? Such questions made us realize how difficult and yet how imperative it is for us to move our thinking out of our own social context, and into this quite different social complex. This became, in fact, a pervasive feeling; suggestions tended to be made somewhat hesitantly and tentatively, precisely because of our growing awareness of how much "translation" has to take place, before ideas that have been developed in one social context can become meaningful or adaptable in another.

In the interest of coming to grips with a few specific questions, we concentrated, for a while, on the question of individualization. As a start, our chairman offered his impression, gained from his kibbutz visit, that there was a lack of differentiation, of personalization in the life environment of the very young children. In their response, our kibbutz colleagues first made it very plain to us how important the concept of individualization is to them as a theoretical value, and then went on to show how advanced, by any standards, are their methods of implementing this principle.

By way of illustration, they told us of their use of the sort of play materials that encourage original use, as contrasted with the mechanical kind; of the differences in the settings and atmosphere of the children's houses, as they reflect the personalities of the metaplot; of the use of learning methods that encourage individual initiative at all levels; of the assignment of such learning tasks as call for independent pursuit; of the differentiation and free choice of clothing, in contrast to what was customary in early kibbutz days, etc. There is evidence that these methods "take" — on a projective level, in the drawings the children produce; on a more realistic level, in the wide range of differences among the children as children.

The problems that emerged during the discussion were salient ones, to judge from the extent to which they drew the kibbutz members into an active, sometimes controversial, exchange of opinions among themselves. This was among the times when I felt that we, as outsiders, were more useful as catalysts than as "experts."

On one point there seemed to be general agreement: the adolescents are living too over-scheduled lives; they should have more time for their own private pursuits or just to be alone. One kibbutz colleague was most interested in bringing about a change of climate in order to permit the freer expression of hostile, critical or aggressive feelings, on the grounds that such feelings are part of a developmental process, one aspect of self-assertion. She took the position familiar to us who had come from outside that, without adequate leeway for emotional release of this kind, there will be a serious sacrifice of spontaneity and initiative.

We also discussed the extent to which the children are exposed to a wide range of differences of opinion — experiences through which they will, to quote, "individuate as minds." Some found it a problem that the kibbutz children, although they are encouraged to think critically, are exposed to a relatively narrow range of experience to think critically about. For others, there is a grave question of how much critical thinking about kibbutz society the kibbutz can tolerate, in the light of its position as a society within another society with which it is not congruent. One of our group made the point that a certain objectivity might be gained if critical thinking about social systems — kibbutz, Israeli, and others — were to be developed through the channels of curriculum and school studies, and distinguished, more than we had in our discussion, from expressions of resistance or aggression.

Another aspect of the question of individualization is the central value of the group process in kibbutz society. In the discussion, the advantage of relieving the individual child of the pressure of a single dominating authority figure, by investing the entire group with authority, was weighed against the possible disadvantage of having group controls and sanctions become so strong and effective that the processes of individualization are thereby weakened. It was further recognized that group pressures at the child level gain in potency when the adult society tends to idealize (perhaps even to over-idealize) the group process as a universal form for making decisions and exerting sanctions. Many of us have been involved in efforts to maximize peer group processes and to diffuse the investment of authority, as ways of improving, psychologically, the socialization of our children. I am sure I do not speak for myself alone when I say that open, mutual consideration of this question, set in a different context from that of our previous efforts, has offered refreshing stimulation in an area in which we visitors have needed it.

At our final meeting, we dealt particularly with the quality and content of communication between parents and adolescents. What is discussed differs, as we would expect, in different families: in some, questions of sex are discussed freely; for others, such questions are shifted to the educator. In general, adolescents are less likely to bring their doubts about kibbutz life to their parents. It is scarcely surprising that communication should be blocked in this area, since it is the most highly charged question in the relations between parents and children.

The principle of the revival of oedipal conflict cannot, by itself, explain this problem; there are other brakes on the level of intimacy that can be attained. Parents hesitate to talk about aspects of their work that involve other people (all of whom are known to the children) — a kind of communication that could easily degenerate into cross-generation gossip. It may seem to the children, however, that they are being excluded from matters vital to their parents; they retaliate by excluding their parents in turn — a mechanism that is familiar to all of us.

We were asked to distinguish between intimacy and familiarity: the adolescents are looking for familiarity and the relaxation of family life, while at the same time, they turn away from intimacy. In the kibbutz situation, they find other adults with whom to work out their intimate concerns. It was pointed out that this may prove to be highly advantageous for adolescents, developmentally; how well this worked out would depend on what alternate figures are realistically available to the children and also on how truly accepting were those adults — especially the parents — from whom the child withdrew his intimacy. Several other considerations were brought to our attention: being too deeply known and understood can be psychologically burdensome to some adolescents, creating in them a feeling of loss of privacy; further, intimate communication is a delicate matter, for which a particular "golden" moment is essential — often to be caught "on the fly." The closely scheduled life of both children and parents does not seem to favor this kind of unplanned interchange.

We raised some questions, in our turn, that could only be answered by the systematic gathering of information about how children are prepared for their adult roles; parent education was considered as a forward step. In both instances, concern was indicated for what is involved in taking such steps; in the one case, the difficulty of finding researchers sufficiently identified with kibbutz life not to be rejected as "outsiders," nor, on the other hand, so intimately involved in the life of the kibbutz as to be unable to follow the canons of scientific study. With regard to parent education, doubt was expressed about the consequences of the intensification of self-consciousness on the part of the parents, a development not regarded as necessarily favorable. The further development of teachers came in for quick but serious consideration, bringing to the fore such issues as the multiple role of the teacher, as both leader of a group and guide for intellectual development; the need for training and the dangers of over-training, with its attendant loss of relaxation and naturalness, etc.

Out of our conscientious attention to concrete questions, a general orientation was developing. From clinical evidence, we had learned that there were no distinctly kibbutz-associated pathological syndromes, and that for about eight per cent of the children, problems could be understood in terms of oedipal conflicts. In other words, we learned that certain mechanisms appear to be universal, even under these substantially different conditions of growth and maturity. But one question could *only be asked,* not answered: Are these same interpretive principles also explanatory of the children who have not developed conflicts at the clinical level?

There are many issues of adolescence — and these were the concern of the greater part of our discussion — that involve us in the primary questions of the social-cultural impact on development. We were trying to view these adolescents and their problems within the context of the basic theory of instinctual processes, but without losing sight of the image of these adolescents as a sub-culture of youth — which is a particular subculture of the kibbutz culture, itself a subculture of the larger culture of Israel.

Two comments by kibbutz colleagues brought us back to the issues to which I referred earlier as being the core of our discussions. Dr. Gerson said, at one point, that while the second generation feels at home in the kibbutz, it is not ideologically *invested;* unless there is some way to imbue them with the idealism of kib-butz life, the future will see not a kibbutz, but a village. Dr. Stern, on the other hand, raised this challenging question: Are the problems that have been raised really the problems of adoles-cents, or are they kibbutz problems projected on to adolescence, and reflecting the older generation's anxiety as to whether or not the youth will perpetuate the kibbutz form?

Toward the end of our session, the discussion in our group took a new turn. Up to that point, we had adhered to the injunc-tion that there would be little relevance to our considerations, once we stepped outside the boundaries of the "articles of faith." We had abided by this position, even though our chairman had asked us not to be bound in this way. The paradox was pointed out, of a large human investment in bringing up autonomous, individualized personalities, with independent minds, who, in their youth — the age of decision — find themselves confronting a restricted range of choices of life-patterns and vocations, a re-striction predetermined by an earlier generation.

One of our members was not satisfied to leave this problem at the level of a paradox. She threw out this daring question to the group: Is it not time for the contemporary generation of youth to take on the responsibility of rethinking how the true goals and ideals of kibbutz society can best be realized, and to consider the possibility of the development of *new* forms and ac-tivities, through which the concepts of collective living might be *extended outward* into the society of the larger culture, which is Israel?

Chapter V

FAMILY LIFE AND THE
ROLE OF WOMEN

FAMILY PROBLEMS IN THE KIBBUTZ

Menahem Gerson

Some writers have sought to deny the very existence of a family in the kibbutz. They have arrived at this erroneous conception either through misleading information, or on purely terminological grounds. The fact is that the family is a very significant social and educational force in kibbutz life, and the cohesion between the different generations of a family (which may, by now, very often include three generations) is a very strong one.

Main Features of the Kibbutz Family

The family in the kibbutz is a marked example of what has been called the "companionship family." The emphasis in such family life rests on its emotional contents, rather than on the fulfillment of objective tasks; emotional ties (the sexual ones, the need for dependency and intimacy, the education of children) are the main contents of the kibbutz family. This is also true, in part, among modern families in Europe and the United States but, in the case of the kibbutz, the primacy given to the subjective content of family life is even more firmly rooted.

Two features are typical of the kibbutz family:

1. The kibbutz family does not form a distinct economic unit, with its own economic interest, the interconnections among its members stemming primarily from a common economic struggle. Since husband and wife have equal status with each other, and with all other members of the kibbutz, they have no specific economic task to fulfill as a separate unit. They are each part of a larger economic unit, and their eco-

nomic interests are basically *identical with the interests of the larger group.* This is an important determinant for a socio-logical definition of the kibbutz; socially speaking, it is bound up with its very essence.

2. Families outside the kibbutz also share their educational responsibilities with professional education, at least from the nursery-school age onwards. In the kibbutz, however, this sharing of educational responsibility starts at that all-important tender age. Most parents outside the kibbutz do not have a partner in the education of their children at this age. Furthermore, since the educators are members of the same kibbutz, and since school or kindergarten embraces the whole lives of the children (not only a few hours in the morning), there is a much greater emotional involvement governing the relations between parents and educators.

The Reappearance of Familistic Trends

At the beginning of the kibbutz movement, there existed a clear-cut opposition to any familistic trend. However, after a short time, a certain balance was achieved in the division of functions between the kibbutz and the single family. The "classic" kibbutz family did not impede the strengthening of the family as an institution. The number of children grew larger; today one very often finds three generations spending their free time together on the family lawn, or in the home, where the living space for the family has been gradually enlarged.

These demographic and ecological phenomena are not, however, what we have in mind when we talk about the reappearance of familistic tendencies. Instead, what we find is a tendency to move towards a change in the division of functions and authority existing up to now, which has not left decision-making about the child (in regard to health matters, the choice of work, the selection of educators, and so on) in the hands of the child's own family.

The familistic trends that have appeared recently seek to ensure for the family a position of greater authority in educational matters, and to restore family influence in the choice of work. Research carried out by Talmon-Gerber has shown that at the root of these trends lies a fundamental discontent with communal education, as well as a basic criticism of its strong "ideological indoctrination."

What are the reasons for the reappearance of such trends, after a long period of generally accepted equilibrium in the kibbutz?

1. Charges that the share of parents in communal education was insignificant. (Yet experience has shown that the influence of parents on the child's character and value-orientation has remained decisive.)

2. Doubts concerning the well-being of children of tender age in communal education.

3. Complaints about the impoverishment of family life in the kibbutz. (This does not take into account the changes that have developed in the life of the modern family everywhere. A comparison is made, perhaps unconsciously, with the traditional form of Jewish family life, which in fact is no longer in existence, even for most Israeli families outside the kibbutz.)

4. Slowness in establishing proper training for the large number of children's nurses needed, and in eliminating frequent changes among them. Such training and continuity are certainly necessary in order not to harm the young child. This year, for the first time, a full year's course for nurses working with the tender age was started at Seminar Kibbutzim.

5. Widespread dissatisfaction of women in the kibbutz with their work, which leads them to look for satisfaction in having their children at home. This is probably the most difficult single problem facing the kibbutz. The choice of work for women in the kibbutz is narrower than it is for men. Many women are working in education and can find satisfaction there; a very high percentage is working in the domestic services. But their share in agriculture is comparatively small, and when we recall that, during the early days of kibbutz life, agricultural work was alone regarded as productive, an additional psychological factor can be recognized as intensifying the existing problem.

6. A certain weakening of identification with kibbutz

values, brought about by recent developments in Israeli society. During the period of the establishment of statehood and the normalization of living conditions, the goals of the kibbutz seem, to a large section of public opinion, to have become somewhat restricted. It has not, for example, absorbed any considerable part of the large immigration of oriental Jews.

The kibbutz has never formed more than seven per cent of the Israeli population (that peak was reached before mass immigration began). Today the kibbutz movement forms four to six per cent of the population — quite an achievement, if we take into account the tremendous growth of Israeli society during this short period. Yet there are doubts in the minds of many Israelis concerning the future of the kibbutz, and these doubts have had a psychological impact on people inside the kibbutz. The general problem of the chances for survival of a socialist cell within a capitalist body is the ultimate basis for all these clashes of values and opinions.

Prospects of the Familistic Trends

This is a cardinal problem we are facing: Is the revival of these trends a reflection of the revolt of "human nature" against artificially imposed solutions to a vital problem, or are they part of the birth-pangs of a new social system? We certainly do not accept one "natural" norm for all social phenomena; some of us have learned from Marx to be rather cautious in that respect, while others have learned this same caution from the findings of modern anthropology.

On the other hand, we do not want to deny our ideological involvement in this respect. Research has shown that there exists a negative correlation between the strength of familistic trends and the strength of social and national values in kibbutz life. Futhermore, a positive correlation has been demonstrated between the strength of familistic trends and the growth in a kibbutz of a "private-consumption" approach, or of the striving for a raising of the standard of living *for the individual family*. Knowing these things, we are not prepared to surrender to those familistic trends. We reject the proposal to restore the rearing of children to their mothers' homes simply in order to overcome the latter's dissatisfaction; in the light of the tasks of the kibbutz movement, we must regard this as a regressive tendency.

There are undoubtedly some people who expect the kibbutz to become just a normal, "natural" village. However, we know from history that no cell of communal life has failed to decay if it was not actively connected with the society around it, and did not exert an active influence on that society. We regard the kibbutz as a cell of a new socialistic society in Israel, and as such, it is bound to strive for influence in the shaping of Israel's dynamic society. We do not envisage the kibbutz as a "happy island," whose supreme law is private satisfaction, "normality" in the life of its members. In that light, we feel that the further strengthening of the familistic trends in the kibbutz would inevitably lead to upsetting its chief values. A kibbutz that has lost its revolutionary impetus could be of little consequence to socialism. And we want to emphasize once again that the kibbutz family is fully capable of carrying out a twofold task — both in the education of the children, and as an intimate cell that provides support to the marriage partners.

DISCUSSION ON FAMILY LIFE

JEHUDA MESSINGER: The new kibbutz family is nothing like the old family: we have healthier, closer, warmer personal relations. We started together as a group, in order to achieve a better life. When we started, we were living in tents — but none of us felt that we ought to *preserve* these conditions. Some of the kibbutzim now have refrigerators, and some people feel that "this is the end. . . ."

The community has always taken care of the children; even when there was a terrible security situation. The first concrete houses we built were for the children. A rise in the standard of living does not always have to be viewed as a regression. The kibbutz society made possible the establishment of very healthy relations with the children, and what we see happening today is the giving up of antifamilistic trends. Can the kibbutz stop such a development? It cannot.

SHMUEL NAGLER: There are changes taking place at all times;

that is true. It has also been said that these changes are necessary; yet some of them seem to me to endanger the principles of the kibbutz. In this regard, we have quite different opinions here. Nobody doubts today that the family has its rightful place in the kibbutz. Nevertheless, family life is in conflict with practices of communal education. This is a matter of formal conflict, on which I don't think that we have really reached agreement. There are similar differences of opinion in the kibbutz movement, where the state of the movement is kept up by the strength of its youth.

RACHEL MANOR: There are really two positions here. We have to face the fact that there is a clash of interests between the desire to strengthen family ties and the striving for a *generally* higher standard of living. When a kibbutz decides upon its budget, for example, those kibbutzniks who are more committed to the goals of collective life and the values of the kibbutz will vote for a dining-room; those who seek higher standards of living will vote for a refrigerator or a ventilator for their own rooms. Similarly, as to child-rearing, those families that are integrated into the very system of the kibbutz and identify with it, educate their children so that they too can identify with it. Erikson has said that frustrated children are not the *cause* for neurosis, frustrating them is; when the parents themselves do not identify with those values of the society, then the *child* becomes neurotic. That is the point I want to make about families which see as their ideals their own higher standards of living, and fail to identify with the values of the kibbutz. Even with regard to leaving the kibbutz, it is not by chance that kibbutzim that are *stricter* in their values have *fewer* youth leaving, than do those that are freer, allow more "individualism," etc.

PROFESSOR WINNIK: There is this basic ideological difference between two types of kibbutz: one stays as it was from the beginning; the other shows new and different trends. That is quite clear. Furthermore, why must one use "regressive" in such a derogatory way? Regressiveness is bad, sometimes; but a revolt — *even in reverse* — is sometimes needed to bring about progress, and the demand to go back to family life does not mean the end of the kibbutz. I do not see why these two concepts should be brought together.

MORDECHAI KAFFMAN: In every phase of kibbutz life, we have had to confront new situations and new kinds of relations. There is no contradiction between intensification of family life and identification with kibbutz values; this is merely one aspect of the phenomenon of change. Family life, it is true, was not the same twenty or thirty years ago as it is now. But we are not a closed society, uninfluenced by outside conditions; and those conditions are changing. I cannot accept the conclusion that those who are striving for an improvement in the standard of living are reflecting any weakening of kibbutz ideals and kibbutz ways of life. The whole system in Israel is changing in that direction: both inside and outside the kibbutz, everyone is working to raise the standard of living. Kibbutz members are no exception.

Changes of this sort are really the clue to understanding why feelings about family life have become intensified during this most recent period. If the kibbutz member is striving (and there are reasons why he is) for a more intense family life, and we try to stop this, then I am sure we will create a very serious and real conflict. But we can understand and accept the intensification of family life without taking it as a weakening *per se* of identification with the general aims of the kibbutz.

DISCUSSION ON WOMEN'S ROLE

JUDITH GILAN: Kibbutz society has kept women in the position of a minority; it is first and foremost a society of men. Most of the first generation in the kibbutz came from eastern Europe, and Jewish life there was not given, as you know, to a strong sense of manhood. It was here that they became very strong and masculine — so much so, that masculine women were at first much more readily accepted than feminine women. Femininity was declared an "ideal"; motherhood along with work was not enough; women had feelings of ambition.

I teach the young daughters of the kibbutz, and I have the impression that what they feel is: "I do not want to be like my mother; I want to be something else." The main problem is that the women are not satisfied, however, because their motherhood instinct is so strong.

RACHEL MANOR: In the beginning, it is true, we women did

not let ourselves be satisfied with "motherhood." Our younger generation, of course, wants to be beautiful; they want to be loved, to have the satisfaction of giving love. But, as pioneers, we had to deny to ourselves the satisfactions of being womanly, of motherhood, of educating our children — because we had to be partisans and builders. We were living in hard times, then; now we have better conditions, and we must find new ways of preparing our children for life's problems. Perhaps we have to change something in *our* ways so as to be able to strengthen *them,* and not to fail them when they go out into the wider world from our closed one.

EMI HURWITZ: Fifty, even thirty years ago, women took pride in doing productive manual work like men, and participated in building and farming. At that time, they fully approved the family pattern of the kibbutz, and its educational system. But now their work is restricted mainly to the services: education, health, kitchen, dining-room, and so on. In the outside world, these services may have come to be recognized as very important for the well-being of man; in the kibbutz, however, they have not yet won such prestige — they do not have the status of "professions." And, apart from education and health, we have not yet found the forms for proper training in these fields.

In my opinion, the role of women as mothers was too restricted in the past; now the emphasis has shifted to the opposite extreme. However, there can be no doubt that the satisfactory integration of women in the kibbutz will be based on striking the proper balance between the woman's role as mother and her satisfaction in work. In fact, women in the kibbutz are most satisfied with their motherhood when they are most satisfied in their work or in their hobbies (mainly the arts) ; but this balance is not easy to achieve.

DR. BIBER: To me, it seems rather futile to talk about the problem of the working woman, her conflicts or satisfactions, as though this were a unit problem. In each situation, it turns out to be a complex of social and psychological problems. In the kibbutzim, it has a special history: *The working woman does not now derive the status satisfaction from her working role that she*

once did. Were it not for this, would it be felt as a loss by some
that they have given up the full role of mothering?

In our society, the problems are quite different. The working-
class woman, who works because her family needs her earnings,
may feel poorly used by her husband or by society. This is in
contrast to the woman who is working simply because taking her
place in the world's work outside the home is part of feeling herself a complete self.

Often, the professional woman faces her most difficult
moments when her children are young: the deficit of substitute
care for the children, and the loss of the full depth of mothering
experience for the woman. After a few years, however, when the
children become adolescents and college-going youths, the mother
who works and derives direct satisfaction from her work may be
at an advantage in the parent-child relationship. The growing
independence of the children is not as threatening to this mother;
on the other hand, leaving the mother is not as potentially guilt-
arousing in the children.

MRS. WINSOR: I also want to distinguish the working-class
mother quite sharply from the professional woman, in terms of
her goals and aspirations. Is the major motivation in going into
the labor market economic necessity, or is it self-fulfillment? One
must also consider the sharp differences in child-care facilities
available to the working-class woman and the professional woman.
Without adequate facilities, neither would be able to move; but
the price that the children are paying in some of these facilities is
also a matter for deep concern.

In my work with teachers in areas of deprivation, where the
mothers are working-class women, it seems to me that there are
two sorts of facilities. One is the very simple and old-fashioned
"extended family:" the school-age children of the working-class
mother are cared for by the grandmother, the aunt, or some other
adult, often a poor mother substitute, who resides in the home.
Another form of child-care provision in our large cities — particularly designed for the working-class mother — is an all-day program
for the child, from the age of three (sometimes two-and-a-half),
until he is old enough to go to school or kindergarten, at the age

of five or six. There are even some "around-the-clock" care programs — a before-school and after-school arrangement.

In actuality, these children spend almost all their waking hours, five days out of every week, in the care of non-family figures. What has interested me, as we have talked about kibbutz life, is that we have dealt with it *as though it alone had two orbits*, without sufficient awareness that this is becoming essentially *the pattern of child life in a good many American communities*, and I dare say in all industrialized countries in the world.

In many of our communities — I speak mainly of New York, because I know it best — the child is delivered to the child-care center at eight o'clock in the morning or even earlier, and is taken over by the "metapelet" (the "teacher," or whatever you wish to call her), to be cared for during the rest of the day by a rotating system of professional personnel. Working-class mothers use this form of child-care facility so that they can remain at work. But such facilities are very limited; there are enormous waiting lists for each of the centers.

By contrast, the professional woman turns to the nursery school, which is quite expensive, full household coverage being a rare phenomenon and altogether exorbitant in cost, even for the professional woman. Whether or not this solves the problem of the care of the children involved, we then have a very different approach to professional life. In my own professional work, the return of the young mother to a professional career and/or to new training is a very common phenomenon. In our small training institution for graduate students in education, a growing number of our students, each year, who come for full-time training are these young mothers, with children old enough for nursery school. It is easy enough to say: have your children and then go to work; but if you are seeking professional status, you have your children, rear them, and *then* turn to professional training. *You end up being forty before you can even so much as get to work,* unless you are able at one and the same time to get your professional training, rear your children, and work. These are very difficult problems, and they are rarely solved to everyone's satisfaction.

RACHEL MANOR: I would like to hear some discussion about the *timing* of childbirth. There are trends on that question — and we are giving thought to it. We would consider it a kind of solution for girls to marry early, have all their children very close, one after the other, and then have their professional careers, let us say, from thirty years on. I know that that happens in the States today.

MRS. KARPE: I want to discuss another facility, which is becoming more and more prominent among our social agencies, and especially children's agencies, in the United States — the day foster-home. I have worked in a children's agency, where, for a period of about five or six years, this was really the chief way in which working mothers were helped in the care of their children. Since these were young children, it was felt that they would not do as well as others in these large institution-like setups; instead, they were placed — one, or two, at the most three — in foster-homes, where the foster-mother is paid for taking care of them, but is also given professional help. All this is done under the supervision of social workers. I think it is increasing in the United States.

Another way in which this problem is being handled in my special field — social work — is that there are now many more part-time jobs available. I think that the agencies were very reluctant to do this a few years ago, when it was almost impossible to get a part-time job. Now, the agencies are offering these jobs very freely, because they need the workers, and there are so many openings that they do have to take on part-time people. In the clinic where I work, there are about ten professional people; only one of them, the head social worker, is full-time; everybody else is part-time — including psychologists, teachers, and so on.

I would like to add one more impression of the status of the woman in kibbutz society. I remember that in the Youth Movement, when the original pioneer generation was planning this kind of life, the idea was that women and men should have completely equal status. About eight years ago, when I was last here, I felt that this had been accomplished to a certain degree. Now I have the feeling that women have slipped back into the "kitchen-children" role, a status which could be just as high, but for some reason is not. *While outside society has developed, and women have become more equal, apparently the kibbutz has either stood still or gone backwards.* This, I think, is a real problem for you.

DR. EISENBERG: It is probably correct to say that even in the social-work field (which has traditionally been a female sphere), now that men have entered it, a much higher proportion of men than of women rise to the top positions in agencies.

MRS. ALT: That may be true, but this is chiefly due to bias on the part of some of the administrators of the social agencies.

DR. EISENBERG: That is precisely what I meant to imply: even in such a situation, a male has much wider opportunities.

In my experience, it is the rare professional woman in our society who is not struggling very hard with conflicts about her role, despite the advantages we have in the mechanization of household work, and so on. I see women who are troubled, sometimes about their role as a mother, at other times about their role as a professional. They adopt a variety of solutions: some drop out of professional life altogether, until their children are six or more years old; others, within a very short period after childbirth, return to work, assigning the responsibility of child-rearing to a nursemaid.

In any case, it is clear that this issue is not at all resolved: it remains a very active problem for the married professional woman within our society, despite their apparent abundance of choices. The working-class mother, who works because she has to, rather than because she chooses to, has still other issues to face, of course, including difficulty in getting help, and the inadequacy of the existing alternatives for the children.

MRS. ALT: I agree with my American colleagues that the situation of the American professional woman has changed considerably during the last decade. There are more opportunities for part-time work in the educational field, and also in the social-work field. Many special arrangements are being made for the woman who has had some professional training, has then stayed home for a time and had her children, and now wants to return to professional life. A number of schools of social work have developed special training programs. One of the problems that remains, however, is that in our country, help to women is not generally available towards obtaining contraception information, or towards having abortions legally sanctioned. One outcome of this is a very direct effect on the timing of childbirth, so that it may frequently interrupt a young woman's educational career or professional training.

Speaking for that population of working women with whom I am best acquainted — that is, the large underprivileged group in an urban area like New York City — I must say that while we have made many attempts to provide services for them, these still remain far from complete. We are struggling with this all the time, for we do have a complex problem when it comes to providing care for young children whose mothers must work, and for those families — of which we have a high proportion — in which the fathers are simply not present.

DR. WOLFF: We professional women are in a rather special position: we are members of a relatively privileged class — which makes all the difference in how one deals with this question. When one can, first of all, afford to take up the intellectual opportunities and at the same time afford enough child-care help so that you can really choose what you want to do, one is already in a position to solve this problem. That is why our personal experience does not have too much bearing on the problem as a whole.

I have noted that among my friends, however, those who are housewives are often dissatisfied. They went to college, but have since stopped their education in order to bring up their children; now, in their early thirties, they face the problem of what to do. Their studies while in college do not lead them directly to practical work; often further education is necessary for a satisfying job experience. *What they are able to do depends very much on their economic position.* Those from middle-class families can still take up professions, but others will have to do with much more limited opportunities. Satisfaction will then depend to a much greater degree on the flexibility of their personality.

DR. GOLDBERGER: Conflict in this area is quite common, of course, among working mothers in the United States; yet, even with an optimal economic situation, such conflict is likely to exist. While reading a report on my college classmates, and their lives since graduation, I was struck by the amount of guilt displayed in their comments, both on the part of full-time mothers, who feel that they are wasting their college education, and on the part of those with careers, who feel unable to meet the many demands on their time.

DR. WOLFF: Well, there are some plans that are actually being carried through now. For instance, Radcliffe College has a program in which they give special scholarships to gifted young women with families, so that they can do intellectual work on a half-time or quarter-time basis, which would otherwise be impossible — partly because of the way universities are set up, and partly for financial reasons.

The program is devised specifically for the young intellectual mother who does not have much time or much money, but is bright and creative. It permits her to apportion her time in terms of her family's needs, to have money for baby sitters, and to still go on with her education. This movement has already been very successful at Radcliffe; it is beginning in other universities as well.

MISS WITMER: The solution to this — in fact, the problem itself — does not have to do with the issue of the mother's working or not working outside the home. The central problem is probably related to the major values in our society, among which success (as measured in money) assumes especial importance. *This* is what is really esteemed. Therefore, the role of the child-rearing housewife is not likely to be highly regarded, or at least highly enough regarded to allow large numbers of women to feel confident of *attaining success* through these roles.

Society is rapidly moving towards what we in my college generation often dreamed of — people marrying earlier, having their children earlier ("get that over with," many women say), becoming career women later. Without any planning whatsoever, this has happened. The average age of marriage is now nineteen for girls; it may even be eighteen. And since this is an average, that means many marry even earlier. (For a man, I believe the average age is about twenty-one.) The average age for the completion of childbearing is now about twenty-seven.

In a book called *Womanpower* (put out by Columbia University), there are a great many statistics on this question. The authors have come to the conclusion that there has been a real revolution in the use of womanpower: during previous years, the curve of women's ages, for their entering and leaving the labor market, went up to a peak and then rapidly went down; now the curve goes up sharply after sixteen, and *stays up until sixty*. Almost as many women aged sixty are entering the labor market for the first time today, as women of forty, thirty-five, and so on.

This is, of course, a temporary phenomenon; we haven't solved anything yet, in this area, even though we do have a Presidential Commission on Women.

Chapter VI

SPECIAL SESSION

INTRODUCTION

JEHUDA MESSINGER: This special session of the Institute is being held on what you might call "home grounds." This is Oranim, where we train all our educators — and then try to undo, later on, the bad things they do, in the Child Guidance Clinic. This is where some of the people you are now working with in this Institute come from.

Mordechai Segal, whom you have already met (the Israelis certainly know him), was one of the founders and the first Director of the Oranim School. He has been in charge of the kibbutz teachers' college during all the years of its existence.

MORDECHAI SEGAL: Welcome to the open and unconditioned air of Oranim.

Oranim is a part of Seminar Hakibbutzim, which came into existence twenty-four years ago. Founded in Tel Aviv by three movements, it then spread out to Oranim. The result of a split, the teachers' college was founded thirteen years later. Happily, we have since reunited — a rather infrequent occurrence in Israeli affairs — and the Institute in which the three movements are discussing these problems together, in harmony with our esteemed guests, is the outcome of work that we have done together, both before and after the split, in this Seminar Hakibbutzim.

The Seminar's purpose has been to shape the core of our kibbutz education, to define it in sociological, educational and psychological terms, by way of the actual work of our educators. Seminar Hakibbutzim has also drawn, and is drawing, many hundreds every year, from people outside the kibbutz. It now stands for the principles of progressive education in general.

As far as the kibbutz itself is concerned, Seminar Hakibbutzim

248

upholds an *integral* concept of education. It is, to begin with, training in one institution teachers *at all levels of education,* from the baby-house to the secondary school, as well as the "marginal educators": art teachers, English teachers, special educators, and so on.

Further, the integral concept means that an educator — no matter what the age he is working with; no matter what his special subject, if he has one — is *first of all an educator.* He is trained to view the child as a *whole individual,* and to relate his own partial work to the wholeness of the child's life. It is not a very easy task and is rarely fulfilled in education. We would not boast that it has been achieved everywhere in kibbutz education, but that is what this institution is striving for, and we have achieved something, at least.

It is also integral in that it gives every educator the feeling of belonging to a richly-endowed network of educational workers throughout the kibbutz movement. (Of course, this sense of belonging lies at the base of kibbutz life in general.) We had to build our organization from the very beginning. In fact, it's much more than merely an "organization," it is a uniting of the thoughts and efforts of people working in education in the kibbutzim.

JEHUDA MESSINGER: The business for this evening is the general question of pathogenic factors in modern society. We have invited to this session Israeli guests and friends who have been working with us — colleagues in the fields of education, psychology, psychiatry. We have also invited members of kibbutz educational organizations and committees, who were not able to participate with us in other sessions, because we wanted the Institute to be a much smaller meeting, in which a real dialogue would be possible. In this open session we felt that we should discuss a topic in which the problems of our society touch the problems of society in general.

At one time, it was believed that mental disorders, delinquency, and social disorders had their origin in genetic or organic roots. Since Freud and his *Civilization and Its Discontents,* however, the idea that quite a number of the factors responsible for disturbances in personality are actually located in society itself, has become more and more a part of modern therapy and education. Here we meet on common ground, because the kibbutz itself is in essence an attempt to change some of society's values so as to make it saner and better for future generations. So far, we cannot prove that this has happened; but I don't think we have to prove that. To began with, only one generation has actually been raised *in the kibbutz;* the parent generation came out of that very society which we consider to be beset with a number of pathogenic factors.

Modern society still affects us; it impinges strongly on our kibbutz society. That is another task of this session, perhaps, for the more we understand the pathogenic factors in the society around us, the more we will understand the ways and means of helping to overcome these things, while still maintaining our specific form of society within the larger framework.

CHILDREN AND YOUTH IN THE UNITED STATES
HELEN WITMER

I have been asked to give you a brief glimpse into the situation of children and youth in the United States of America, in so far as they are influenced by socially pathogenic factors. This is, of course, a large order; furthermore, the very topic implies a cause-and-effect relationship, which may not be entirely true.

With regard to these psycho-pathogenic social factors, it seems to me that there are three ways in which they can be classified. We can look at them as *symptoms:* what is there about children in the United States today that makes us believe that there must be such factors? Or we can look at them from the point of view of those *services* that are provided to deal with problems — the assumption being that since there are services, there must be problems that need to be dealt with. Or, finally, we can look at some of the factors themselves rather more closely.

The belief that the existence of symptoms in children is indicative of the existence of pathogenic factors in society is based on the assumption that if all were well in our society, children and youth would neither have nor create any problems. This may be a somewhat dubious assumption. We can suspect the existence of pathogenic social factors in the United States, however, because we have (as I am sure you are only too well aware) quite a lot of delinquency. Lately, people have been getting especially concerned about the fact that there is too much drinking on the part of the youth. Then, too, drug addiction is not unknown, its latest variant being "glue sniffing." Finally, there is, as always, "immorality" — if by immorality you mean producing children out of wedlock, or even going through acts that *might* produce such children. All this is quite bad, many people think. They then add to this the fact that we see too many children (about one third of them) leaving school before they should — that is, they leave as soon as the law allows them to leave (which is usually at the age of sixteen) — instead of going on to complete high school.

To comment on any of these symptoms would take us into a great deal of detail, but I must make one brief observation about our much-publicized delinquency. A great deal of this "delinquency" is quite minor. In counting delinquents, we usually include *every offense* that has brought a child before a policeman or a court. But *two thirds of these children never turn up in court again, and the rate of serious offenses has not perceptibly increased in recent years.*

From the service angle, we see, first, a mounting number of children receiving financial support under the Aid-to-Dependent-Children provisions, and we are terribly concerned about that. Our concern centers chiefly on those without fathers — which introduces the problem of illegitimacy. Second, there has been an increase in the number of children receiving social services because they are neglected or abused. (Actually, we don't know for certain whether there has been a real increase in the number of such cases; what we do know is that there are more of them coming to the attention of social agencies and medical centers.)

Serious questions are being raised about what we ought to be doing to improve matters along both these lines. Should unmarried mothers stay at home with their children and bring them up? Or should they go out to work, while someone else takes care of their children? As to abused and neglected children and those who, for whatever other reasons, do not have good homes, we have much the same questions. We are not so sure that even adoption works out as well as we once thought it did, and we are not as sure as we once were that removing children from their homes is the best solution, even in the desperate cases. Once we do take the children away, what do we do with them? How do we handle the problem best? This conference has given me much food for thought, for in your shared child-rearing plan there may be much that we can learn for our use.

As to the pathogenic factors themselves, there are, of course, a great many such factors; those I have in mind are pathogenic in the sense that they *help to create problems,* rather than because they are inherently pathogenic themselves. With regard to these, I think you will find that we have much in common with you and with all the other countries of the world — both the new ones just coming into industrialism, and the old ones, which thought they had seen all the problems but are suddenly faced with a great many new ones.

They are factors of three different sorts; in their coming together at a single time, they have created a really great problem for us. To begin with, during the last two decades or so, we have had a tremendous increase in our birth rate, so that we now have a lot more people than we ever expected to have. Furthermore, tremendous technological advances are rapidly changing the character of industry — with the result that we don't need nearly as many people doing the kinds of jobs they did before. Even agriculture has become highly mechanized, and requires a smaller and smaller proportion of our people for work on the farms. Finally, as one result of this, there has been a tremendous migration of rural people (and, especially, rural poor people) into our big cities.

The combination of these three facts has already presented us with terrific problems — and there are worse ones to come, unless we can rapidly do something about it. Most youngsters must simply be better educated than they are now. As many as 40 per cent of them are not finishing high school, at the very time when we have a rapidly diminishing need for unskilled labor. Furthermore, we cannot ignore the kind of culture that most such youngsters come from. It is probably not as diverse as you people are having to deal with (a sizable proportion of your immigrants come from even more divergent backgrounds), but it is a serious problem for us.

All this raises the question of how early in their life we have to begin our educational efforts to fit these culturally deprived children for the kind of schooling they will need in order to carry on well in the highly industrialized, automated world that they are going to come into as adults. Some of the newer approaches stress that it obviously isn't worthwhile starting this in high school. I would be exaggerating if I said that it isn't at all worthwhile, but certainly high school is not the most suitable place to start giving these young people extra help. Perhaps even the first grade is already too late, some people are saying, at least for some of the most deprived youngsters.

To summarize, it is in this combination of factors that our major problem lies. The pathogenic effects of these factors — their influence on delinquency and similar aspects of children's behavior — are all too obvious; the necessity of taking effective action as soon as we can is equally obvious. And for this we must learn — as I have learned here — whatever we can.

DELINQUENCY IN HOLLAND
J. A. M. SCHOUTEN

Perhaps I can tell you very briefly about the problem of rising delinquency in Holland. Some people are inclined to believe that this is the result of American influence. I don't think it is fair to say that, although there are, of course, Americans who have visited Holland and, I hope, have profited from their visit. It is true that in Holland people are much inclined nowadays toward Anglo-American culture. Twenty or thirty years ago, they were more inclined toward our Eastern neighbors.

I work with delinquent adolescents of a special type — not the type that we see especially in New York, where I think delinquency is more of a sociological problem, but comparatively incidental cases of boys from families which, to a great extent, are discontented with their own situation.

With regard to these families, two aspects may be related to problems we have talked about; they may even reflect the opposite of what is important in a kibbutz. Most of the families in question are living in a very isolated way, feeling the impact of, or projecting hostile elements from, the life outside toward their own very close-knit circle. This is a pathogenic factor that we find quite often among middle-class families in Holland — parents and children living closely and intensely with each other, with all the estrangements and isolations that come with that sort of arrangement.

Secondly, while the typical kibbutz family is not an economic unit, among the families of the boys I treat, one reason we encounter so much discomfort and tension is that these families have to keep up their economic and social status. The fact that the fathers are in a constant competitive struggle to maintain the social and financial status of their family is quite a pathogenic factor, with a real effect on the children. They constantly try to push the boys into all kinds of achievements that they are not equipped for.

THE EPIDEMIOLOGY OF PSYCHOPATHIC BEHAVIOR

Leon Eisenberg

I would like to raise one theoretical caution, which all of us might bear in mind, and especially our psychiatric colleagues. When one takes a system and theory of psychopathology, built up on the basis of studies on patients raised in traditional Western families, and then attempts to apply this as a standard to the special situation of the kibbutz (or to any other group with a modified family) it is quite possible that some of the findings of similarity are in fact artifacts. This is due to the restrictions imposed by the nature of the exploratory therapeutic process which, after all, was standardized elsewhere. It is not that the facts as such are false, but that essential information may be *missing* because of the nature of the individual exploration.

I thus find it very difficult on theoretical grounds to accept the conclusion put forward here earlier in our institute that the amount, nature, and type of psychopathology is the same for kibbutz and non-kibbutz society. There is at least the possibility that if group analytic methods had been used, somewhat different conclusions might have been arrived at. If we were to study the behavior of *groups* of kibbutz children as compared with *groups* of our children, we might discover differences that would be very significant and far more important that the similarities we have found. Unfortunately, the psychopathologist tends to find what he looks for — which is a methodological problem in psychiatric and psychological investigation.

As has been stressed in all of the psychological work that has been done with conditioning, it is important to recognize the extraordinary malleability of human communication, in response to systems of less than conscious reward and discouragement, in a psychotherapeutic process. Some of the theoretical issues that are of extreme concern to us — quite apart from the kibbutz, but rather from the standpoint of "understanding human nature" — have yet to be explored, because we have yet to evolve the methods for doing so. Thought might be given by the professionals in our midst to finding ways of divorcing themselves, as far as they can, from their traditions, and to look at these things with a fresh eye. This is one of the research areas that needs to be explored.

We visitors know, in fact, relatively less than you kibbutz folk do about the epidemiology of psychopathology in *our* population. We get a kind of skewed referral system; you are more likely to have available to you a uniform range. When we use, for example, teacher referrals, as has been done in several studies, strangely contradictory results come out. In one study made in Baltimore, teachers and doctors examined a number of children; very cursorily, I'm afraid, they agreed that "roughly 30 per cent of the children" had problems. Unfortunately, only 10 per cent of their choices were the same: 20 per cent of those the doctors had picked out the teachers had not, and 20 per cent of those the teachers had picked out the doctors had not. There are a lot of fundamental methodological problems that make it necessary for us to be particularly cautious when we are making comparisons.

PSYCHOPATHOLOGY AMONG KIBBUTZ CHILDREN
Shmuel Nagler

The idea that the proportion of disturbed children in the kibbutz is not much lower than that for other societies would have caused considerable disappointment to leading kibbutz educators fifteen years ago. They had hoped that the transfer of motherly care and socialization from the emotion-packed atmosphere of the family, i.e., removing the child from the parents' room to the children's house, and shifting some previously parental educational functions to objective, professionally trained people, would eliminate essentially pathogenic factors.

It remains a fact, however that there is a certain percentage of disturbed children (about 10 per cent) in kibbutz society. If we seek to distinguish between the etiological factors present in the children's house and those in the parents' home, we may say that the factors in the parents' room outweigh by far, in their significance, those in the children's house. This, in my opinion, proves that parents, even in the kibbutz structure, remain parents, with all the conflicts present in the parent-child relationship, conflicts that naturally can occur only within a framework of strong emotional ties.

We find, in the kibbutz family, all sorts of pathogenic factors such as are generally encountered in child-psychiatric practice. There are kibbutz parents with deep personality problems — for example, the schizoid mother with shallow feelings, or unconscious hatred toward the child, or (as the result of marriage conflicts) overprotectiveness, etc. There is also the problem of an unwanted pregnancy, which has interfered with other plans, or of the child not being of the desired sex, and so on.

The following are among the examples of pathogenic factors that we have found associated with the children's house: the frequent change of nurses in early childhood; the practice of not permitting mothers to serve the food to their own infants, when they lacked mothers' milk. (These mothers, in addition to their disappointment at being deprived of their natural motherly function, were also deprived of any sort of warm contact with the child in the nursing situation.) That practice has since been discontinued, and these mothers, too, are now tending their infants.

An additional pathogenic factor was revealed when mothers, during clinical interviews, voiced their complaints about the noisy conditions in the infant's home at nursing time, when there was the usual gossiping, as the other mothers and fathers came in to "take a look" — a state of affairs that ultimately leads to interruptions in the nursing activity, and to an obstruction of the intimate relationship between the mother and her infant.

Other pathogenic factors connected with the children's house are primarily caused, as we have come to realize, not by organizational shortcomings, but rather by human limitations in the educator's personality. There are pedantic metaplot with definite anal character trends; in their groups enuresis appears as a group phenomenon, even though the children come from different family backgrounds.

A metapelet whose devotion to those in her care has been generally acclaimed suddenly encounters tense relations with mothers. Particularly young mothers, who happen to have an abundance of milk and are eager to feed their infants, complain that they feel unwanted in the infants' house. They feel that they are urged not to lend the breast at all mealtimes, to wean as soon as possible, and not to indulge in playing with their children. In the course of our investigation, the metapelet recalls that during the many years of her own marriage, her strong desire for a pregnancy had been ungratified, and that after having finally undergone a complicated pregnancy and delivery, she had been unable to nurse her infant with her own milk. It soon becomes obvious to her that these unfortunate events had influenced negatively her relations with more fortunate and more successful mothers.

The kibbutz structure, in embracing two emotional centers, provides an excellent opportunity for parents to project both their incapacity for loving and their resulting guilt-feelings on to the staff of educators in the children's house. Outside the kibbutz, such possibilities of projection are not so available to parents, since the educational institutions are of lesser emotional significance. One specific problem in kibbutz society, in this connection, is the absence of "distance" between educators and parents: educators are not paid employees of the kibbutz.

Hence, the relations between educators and parents may be distorted by interpersonal relations which lie in ranges of conflict outside of and beyond educational matters. Objections raised by parents against the institution of the children's house may, of course, be based upon real anxieties: there *are* metaplot whose personality is not suited to their profession. But there may also be instances of neurotic anxieties. Particularly in the latter case, the basic security of the child — the balance of trust versus mistrust — is liable to be affected adversely.

Five-year-old Roni shows separation fears and nightmares. There are always heartbreaking scenes when he has to return to the children's house after having spent some time at his parents'. What is most disturbing to the parents, as well as to the educators, is that this young boy escapes from the children's house on stormy nights, and seeks refuge in his parents' room at such a late hour that it is impossible for the parents to send him back. The metapelet is particularly upset by the fact that the mother rushes into the children's house countless times a day just to make sure that nothing has happened to her Roni. (The metapelet confirms the fact that Roni stumbles more often than other children do, and hurts himself, too, quite frequently.) When the mother rushes to his rescue, he starts crying in heartbreaking fashion, and does not stop until the mother shelters him in her arms.

The metapelet is irritated by these interventions on the part of the mother. She charges the mother with having spoiled the boy, on the one hand, and on the other, showing gross selfishness in leaving the child behind, while she is traveling around the country. (She accumulates several rest days, on which other parents devote their time entirely to their children, so that she may be able to undertake her travels.) Apart from that, it is the metapelet's conviction that on those days when the mother is away, her child definitely feels more relaxed. (It may be assumed that the metapelet also feels more relieved, since she does not have to fear the frequent calls of the mother at the children's house.)

The mother too, has strong feelings against the metapelet. Yet the picture of the metapelet, as drawn by the mother, is very much in contrast with the metapelet's generally good reputation. During the course of treatment, the mother recalled being strongly affected by her parents' divorce, which took place when she was nine years old. She was sent to a very expensive children's home, whereas her younger brother, who was not going to school yet, was allowed to stay with her mother. She tells of a governess who punished her by depriving her of meals, and sometimes even by applying corporal punishment. "On the surface, everything looked smooth, but it was lamentable for children once they got in there." When she immigrated into Israel, and subsequently when she married and became a mother, she made up her mind that she would ensure a better fate for her own child.

She now became aware that she had identified the children's house in the kibbutz with the children's home of her own childhood, and the metapelet with both the uncaring, "runaway" mother and the punishing governess. Her own child, whom she identified with her more favored little brother, she had to leave frequently (to remain in the children's house while she herself was away), in the same manner as that had been done to her. At the same time, she felt compelled to protect him (out of a defense against aggressive tendencies) against her own bad fate, which she unconsciously wished him to experience, too. Thus, here was an example of the psychic development of the child being impaired by deep neurotic mechanisms in the mother.

These problems of complicated interpersonal relations between parents and educators now take up the major part of our attention, as far as our taking case histories, treatment and supervising activities is concerned. And let us not forget, in all this, the problem of the educators' own children, who may suffer from the fact that they have to watch with their own eyes how their parents' devotion is being assigned to other parents' children.

We have been concentrating on pathological phenomena, but we must remember that there are certain positive aspects to a child's life in the children's house — for instance, the opportunity for corrective experience. In cases where mothers are suffering from severe psychic disturbances, such as depressive disorders, the nurse may turn into a genuine mother substitute ("Ersatzmutter").

Another form of corrective experience may take place in the case of an overprotective or overpossessive mother, through the medium of a metapelet who loves the child without being emotionally involved to such a great extent. Positive and lasting results of this corrective experience can only be achieved if the metapelet is able to muster all the tact necessary to avoid arousing in the mother feelings of competition, guilt, hatred, antagonism against the possibly more successful "Ersatzmutter." Clinical assistance to both metaplot and mothers is sometimes required, in order to ensure a balanced relationship.

In nurseries charged with the care of age groups one to three, which usually consist of five or six children each, apart from the possible personality disturbances in educators, such as have just been outlined, there also exists the danger of the lack of close contact with grownups during daytime. I am not certain whether there exists an "instinct of following," but these toddlers are generally at the heels of an adult, and I am quite convinced that *the group is unable to provide for the equivalent of an adult's support.*

As far as the oedipal period is concerned, we find no pathogenic factors that show the influence of the kibbutz structure. The early pioneers of collective education had very "optimistic" ideas: they hoped that the removal of the child from the parents' room would cut the ground from under the oedipus complex. These ideas were in line with the opinions of social anthropologists and the followers of the neo-Freudian school. But these expectations have not come true, as far as we can see from our experience.

Even within the kibbutz structure, the parents of disturbed children definitely remain the basic and main object of the child's sexual and aggressive impulses, and its first object of identification. Marriage problems, such as the lack of sexual or emotional gratification, confusion of roles within the family constellation — phallic mothers or passive, weak fathers — bring about a heightening of the child's sexual and aggressive drives, anxieties, guilt feelings, and confusion in sex identification. All these make the termination of the oedipal conflict a much more arduous task.

When families break up because of the death of one parent, there is a relatively good possibility of finding a father-substitute. In cases of divorce (of which there are a great many in our clinical material), the child tends to be confused, feeling deprived and deserted, either among the father's or the mother's other children. This is especially so when both parents stay in the kibbutz after the divorce, remarry and have more children.

A sixteen-year-old girl (let us call her Elisheva) was referred to our clinic because of learning difficulties and lack of concentration. There were very sharp ups-and-downs, and instances of insolent behavior toward her mother and educators. Elisheva had a boy friend one year her minor, and their relationship was also causing great concern to the boy's parents, as well as to his educators. They were worried by the fact that the girl seemed to have taken complete possession of the boy's mind and activities. In a short time, Elisheva had gained full control over his daily routine, keeping him away from outdoor sports, study, and any contact with his peers.

During treatment, it was revealed that Elisheva had been subjected to seeing her parents divorced when she was only eleven years old. Her father had brought into her family two children from a previous marriage. Both her father and her mother remarried. The father's third wife happened also to be a divorced woman, with one child, who was a member in Elisheva's group. Her mother's brother also had previously divorced his wife. Elisheva spoke very emotionally of her disgust when she had to be seated at a festive Passover *"Seder"* (dinner), amongst all the various partners and ex-partners who had, amazingly, decided to spend this evening together. She had come to the conclusion that the practice of divorce must be a family characteristic, and had therefore decided to bind her own partner with the strongest ties, so that she might escape divorce.

Divorce generally hurts children; in the cities, at least, children and their divorced parents are not forced to see each other constantly and therefore have a chance to recover from the family upheaval.

COMPARATIVE PSYCHOPATHOLOGY
OF KIBBUTZ AND URBAN CHILDREN
Mordechai Kaffmann

The kibbutz is one of the few places in the world in which accurate etiological figures on mental health can be obtained without an overly complicated set-up. The characteristics and problems of kibbutz children can be traced rather accurately from infancy to youth, through recorded observations of metaplot and teachers, parents' cooperation, medical records and additional available data. In this respect, the high rate of population stability in the average kibbutz constitutes a supplementary asset.

I have had the opportunity to follow closely for several years the total child population of different kibbutzim. A strikingly constant annual figure of children "in need of help because of emotional disturbance" has been observed — the rate being 12 to 15 per cent of the total sample. This figure embraces all kinds of diagnostic situations, from minor reactive behavior problems to severe internalized emotional disorders, at all age levels (a more marked pressure is felt from six to twelve). For instance, last year, we received at the Oranim Child Guidance Clinic 338 referrals.

The sex distribution shows a preponderance of boys, about two to one in relation to the number of girls; but we can observe that this proportion differs at various age levels. At the preschool age, we have a three-to-one ratio of boys to girls; at the primary school, two-to-one, and at the high school (adolescence) it is almost one-to-one (there is a slight preponderance of boys over girls, but the figures are very close). This 20 per cent of referrals of children at the high-school level may not adequately express the reality. Dr. Nagler has already mentioned several reasons why we do not get so many children at that age; there is another specific reason. Most of our facilities for screening children with emotional problems are in some way concentrated at the preschool or primary-school age, and we really lack such facilities at the high-school level.

A combination of factors seems to me to explain the apparently high figure for referrals of emotionally disturbed kibbutz children. First, the possibility of early detection is increased by the constant observation and evaluation of the child. That is quite obvious. Everyone — the metapelet, an outside observer, the parents — can observe the child, as compared with so-called *standard* children in a group; if there is a deviant child, the deviance is generally capable of being observed quite early.

Second, advisory and clinical agencies have been established in order to help the emotionally disabled kibbutz child. It would take a long time to explain all the facilities that the kibbutz has set up in order to screen, to diagnose, to find out who is emotionally disturbed. We have, first of all, in most of the kibbutzim, a so-called "special" educator (*Mem Mem*) — the person in a kibbutz who is in charge of the screening of these problems. Sometimes teachers and metaplot, when they have such a problem, find that they cannot solve it. This person serves as the link between the kibbutz and the clinic of the kibbutzim. We also have a special committee in each kibbutz, to discuss such cases, as well as a central educational department, with specialized people who have long-standing experience in these problems, and who go from kibbutz to kibbutz, in order to give advice in relation to specific cases. Finally, we have the clinics of the kibbutzim — Oranim is one of them.

The third reason for this apparently high figure for referrals is that advice and therapeutic help are *accessible to all kibbutz children*, without any exception or discrimination on the basis of social status, financial resources or diagnostic categories. Comparative figures of a reliable character are lacking on the percentage and diagnostic distribution of emotional disturbances among Israeli urban children. This absence of comparative data cannot be replaced by clinical impressions, theoretical predictions, or conclusions drawn from psychotherapy in isolated cases. *Until now, no objective evidence has been brought forward to substantiate any assumptions, either of a greater or a lesser incidence of emotional disturbances on the part of kibbutz children at different age levels, as compared with the number of children of those ages in outside groups.*

The search for clinical signs or behavioral characteristics — such as might suggest emotional deprivation, as the direct outcome of the kibbutz system of upbringing — has also failed to produce any positive objective findings. There are papers containing the statement that it was "supposed" that there are some kinds of emotional deprivation at the preschool age; but these are no more than impressions, which up till now have not been based on factual data. Our clinical material simply has not shown any such signs at that age. (We would, of course, be very much interested in discovering them, where they existed, so as to determine the reason and to try to help those children.)

Even if we succeeded in matching two parallel groups — of

kibbutz and of control children — extreme caution would be required before we were ready to draw any definite conclusions. Let us consider one example, extracted from our study of the frequency and intensity of a wide range of behavior problems, among the total children's population of three kibbutzim. The group investigated included all the children of these settlements up to the age of twelve (a total of 403 children), who were followed on a systematic recording basis from their first few days of life. This study showed no evidence that the incidence of behavior problems or of deviant behavioral characteristics is unusual, either in early childhood or at later ages. The incidence of symptoms such as excessive or inhibited aggression, temper tantrums, enuresis, encopresis, rhythmic motor habits, night fears, fits, speech problems, learning problems does not seem to differ substantially from the usual figures, based on samples of unselected groups of children.

It might be interesting to observe that in all these findings, the transfer of toilet training to the metapelet has not reduced the rate of enuresis (encopresis, perhaps; but enuresis has not been reduced), and to say a few words as to why this has happened. It has been suggested here that the transfer of some habit-training to the metapelet reduced elements of conflict between the parents and the child; subsequently, the theoretical implication was formulated that perhaps this could bring about reduction of the rate of, let's say, enuresis. Yet we found that our figures on this are exactly the same as have been observed in other children in Israel or abroad; the number is the same — yet the reasons are absolutely different.

When we analyze our enuretic children — and we do have some experience (I think we have studied about 200 enuretic children) — we have to distinguish two age levels. Up to the age of six, the most important factor is the children's house; this means, I think, a problem of faulty training, or perhaps of faulty training plus inconsistency, on the part of the metapelet. I am not talking here about the emotional problems of the metapelet, although that is very important in some cases: we know that the metapelet may be responsible for as much as 50 per cent of the enuretic children. At this age level, we know that the children's house and the training there plays a very important role, generally, in toilet-training. Later on, we can see the role of the parent-child relationship in the fact that the enuretic child goes on being enuretic, despite the fact that its early toilet-training was performed by a so-called "neutral" person.

In one kibbutz in which I have been working, we have reduced the enuresis from 13 per cent, the usual figure for children after the age of three and one-half, to practically zero. This means that, if the metaplot were given advice, and could treat this problem with some professional know-how, enuresis could easily be reduced throughout the kibbutz.

It should also be noted that a very high incidence was found in relation to thumb-sucking. The figures given for corresponding samples of American children disclose a strikingly lower frequency of thumb-sucking, from *twice to three times less* than the figure of 41 per cent among our kibbutz children at age three to nine. Before one becomes involved in theoretical elaborations, however, on the possible relevance of this finding as an expression of a disturbed object relationship, one has to consider the nature of our child-rearing practices with regard to thumb-sucking. On the whole, thumb-sucking is regarded by most kibbutz educators as a normal expression of oral identification needs, so that children up to the age of nine or ten are permitted to suck their fingers without external interference.

Indeed, I have often seen not only this permissive approach, but even an active, encouraging attitude towards thumb-sucking during the first two years of life. The baby is helped by adults and siblings to enjoy this autoerotic identification. Actually, like other child-rearing practices, this is not regarded as a *necessary attribute* of kibbutz education. There are other kibbutzim in which a less permissive approach has been adopted by educators and parents, and a parallel law of the incidence of thumb-sucking can be observed. One kibbutz, with a population of about 150 children, shows a striking reduction in the rate of thumb-sucking — from 30 per cent to 16 per cent at age three to nine, over a period of five years, apparently in connection with a less indulgent approach towards the habit. Finally, a comparative study was carried out among 108 thumb-suckers, aged one and one-half to eleven, and 225 kibbutz children of the same age who did not show this symptom. *No significant differences were found between the two groups, as to the frequency and intensity of behavior problems.*

Diagnostic and therapeutic work with almost 2000 emotionally disturbed children, referred to the Oranim Child Clinic of the kibbutzim during the past eight years, has failed to reveal any separate clinical entity that could be recognized as a specific or prevalent kibbutz symptom. Diagnostic categories are the usual ones, as tabulated for children raised in Western or traditional families. They include primary behavior disorder, neurotic traits, psychoneurotic conditions, personality disorders, reactions of adolescence, borderline cases, anorexia nervosa, early infantilism, organic childhood psychosis, adult types of schizophrenic reaction, diffuse brain damage, mental deficiency, psychosomatic illness, etc.

By the way, during his recent visit, Bowlby made a prediction. He believes that the separation between children's houses and parents' houses will produce a higher incidence of separation re-action — separation anxiety — that will in turn bring about an increase of depression among kibbutz youngsters. In our experi-ence with hundreds of adolescents, we have found only one clear-cut case of a depressive state; there were also one case of manic-depressive reaction and one case of anorexia nervosa with de-pressive features. For the most part, however, in our clinical material, depression is not one of the outstanding clinical findings.

We have had the opportunity to compare a sample of almost 200 severely disturbed kibbutz children, referred for psychiatric examination at the Oranim Clinic with a group of 100 emotion-ally disturbed urban children. In the parallel diagnostic groups, kibbutz children appear to exhibit more clearly severity of clinical symptoms. It is difficult to determine the factors, isolated and combined, that might explain this finding. In addition to the different systems of upbringing, there are undoubtedly several variables that have to be considered. We should not forget, for instance, that the kibbutz facilities previously referred to, which permit the earlier detection and treatment of children's emotional disorders, are almost wholly absent in the case of Israeli urban children of the middle and working classes.

The issue has already been raised as to whether an increased incidence of separation-anxiety reactions can be observed, as a consequence of the system of separate children's houses and the transfer of the traditional parental functions to educators. Certainly there are some cases, particularly below the age of eight, with obvious clinical manifestations of separation-anxiety — for instance, children who run away from the children's house by day or at nighttime, looking for their parents. However, this is definitely the exception and not the rule. Altogether, school phobia as an expression of separation-anxiety occurs very rarely in the kibbutz experience. Some cases of school avoidance are to be seen among brain-damaged children with feelings of intense anxiety in the school's strained situation, from which the child seeks to protect himself by withdrawing from the school. *In general terms, school avoidance in the kibbutz may be taken to be a sign of severe psychopathology, often a warning symptom of an incipient psychotic reaction.*

Despite the crucial role of metaplot and educators in relation to both quality of task and amount of time spent with the child, the parents nevertheless constitute, in the kibbutz as in the traditional family situation, the most decisive and stable object of emotional attachment. Psychopathic disturbances among kibbutz youngsters provide an illustrative example. This diagnostic category constitutes a rare finding among kibbutz children. Altogether we have diagnosed social or psychopathic disturbances in four instances, all of them boys in the age range of fourteen to eighteen. They show the well-known symptoms of antisocial behavior and impulsiveness, shallow interpersonal relationships, lack of manifest anxiety concerning all reactions, and a tacit disregard for the feelings and needs of others.

Although the sample is too small to warrant any definitive conclusion, we should stress that in all these cases a similar dynamic constellation was observed, emphasizing the parental role in this kind of disturbance: we found an ineffective, submissive or absent father, along with a closed-minded, engulfing and overpermissive mother. There was clear evidence of extreme parental overindulgence, reflected in a constant yielding to the wishes and demands of the child. In three of the four cases, the parents (par-

ticularly the mother) justified and encouraged the child's antisocial behavior as a displaced way of expressing their own dis-
conformity with the kibbutz system of life.

On the other hand, it is also clear that the age group and the
educational framework failed in these cases to help counterbalance the pathogenic child-parent relationship. For a variety of
objective reasons, the group lacked stability in its inner composition, and was affected by unusually frequent changes of nurses
and teachers. As a result, only slim chances remained for possible
identification with a stable, self-assertive father-substitute figure.
Furthermore, the educational handling in all four cases was, for
the most part, lenient and inconsistent, fitting in with the permissive parental approach.

The outside observer may be surprised to hear that all the
different types of child-parent relationship, both normal and abnormal, can be found in the kibbutz family life: overpermissive-
ness, overprotection, inconsistency, perplexity, rejection, neglect,
etc. Though group life involves both direct and indirect pressure
on the deviant parent to conform to kibbutz-approved practices
of child-care, the basic pattern is not easily modified. All degrees
and varieties of parental attitude are present. Therefore, it is
unrealistic to describe some stereotyped kind of parent-child relationship in the kibbutz as helping to shape a stereotyped child
personality. The parent-child relationship, which influences to
such a great extent the emotional life of the child and the crystal-
lization of his personality, covers a wide range of possibilities in
the kibbutz family life, just as it does elsewhere.

It is illusory, in our opinion, to try to describe the kibbutz
Sabra as a type of personality. That is the reason why different
writers have given contradictory descriptions of what they thought
constituted the typical personality structure of the kibbutz Sabra.
We are not too surprised, for instance, that one observer, after
observing a few kibbutz Sabras, found them to be introverted,
notably shy and embarrassed, when interacting both with strangers
and with kibbutz members who are not their age peers, while, at
the opposite extreme, they have also been described as socially
stable and rather extroverted youngsters.

To summarize, our clinical experience shows that *nonorganic child psychopathology in the kibbutz, as elsewhere, depends primarily on the family constellation.* We have not observed serious manifestations of child psychopathology in the presence of a healthy, gratifying child-parent relationship, even in the case of abnormal, stressful conditions at the children's house.

PATHOGENIC FACTORS IN THE MODERN CHILD'S LIFE
Fritz Redl

Let me first say a few things about the concept of "pathogenic factor" itself. It is all too easy to fall into the trap of using that term in an obsolete way. In psychoanalysis, for example, we initially used the term "traumatic experience" too widely and too loosely — forgetting, or perhaps not yet knowing, that short of some obvious and extreme situations, almost anything we do to children *may* or *may not* become "traumatic." Which it will be depends on the nature of the situation, the surrounding culture, and of course, the equipment the child brings to the situation — equipment that may or may not enable him to cope with the experience.

Fortunately, we soon shed our naive use of the term, having become aware that things are not as simple as we had thought they were. There are some situations that are "all set" to be traumatic for the child. However, even these sometimes fail, because *he just won't let them* — or because we give him so much support that he is quite able to cope with them, perhaps even to *turn to his advantage what would throw someone else into a trauma.* In short, we no longer look at "traumatic experiences" as fixed events, which "ought to" make the child sick (if not, maybe there was something wrong with him to begin with?). We have found a lot of children who have some sort of "resilience"; we have also found that in some expectedly traumatic experiences, there are ingredients that help some children to deal with them constructively.

If I had the time, I would like to develop that concept of "ego resilience" here — especially since some adults seem to be of the overconscientious type, just waiting for the chance to feel guilty about what they may have "done wrong" for their children. Such people are likely to underestimate the support that children are able to draw from a situation with supportive elements in it, or how many children turn out well in spite of all the things we have done to them.

Let me instead list some of the things you need to do, if you want to be *sure* to create a pathogenic effect. For there *are* some things that can "mess up" a child — although I don't think that's an easy thing to do: unless nature and society come to our aid, it will sometimes take us eight years or longer to produce a thoroughly maladjusted child. Among the children I have had to deal with in my various projects, the surprise has often been: after what has happened to them, how come they aren't sicker than they are?

If I had to list those factors I would consider to be highly pathogenic — provided they are packed with sufficient intensity into a child's life — I would give priority to these:

HITTING THE CHILD WITH A SLEDGEHAMMER. (Especially on the head, and preferably before you know which bones in the top of their skull have grown together). There are many experiences that are psychologically quite comparable to this. If I were to do no more than list the ones I observe in my work back home every day, it would take all the rest of my allotted time. Just two, by way of illustration: The imposition of cruelty *beyond the child's capacity for endurance;* the production of guilt or shame, condensed into a brief time span, and similarly going *beyond what the organism can absorb.*

VITAMIN DEFICIENCY. A painful degree of pauperization, with regard to those psychological ingredients that are *essential for normal survival and healthy growth.* Even if you didn't do anything especially nasty to children, so long as you kept from them these basic psychological ingredients, you could be pretty certain to make them sick. For example: deprive kids of the age-typical activities they need, of the necessary props for meaningful play, of real opportunities for meaningful work, of the feeling of being imbedded in an atmosphere of acceptance, of the chance for tangible evidence of mastery, of group-code-relevant skills, such as carry weight in the society in which they live. In short, *empty their lives of positive relationships,* and instead expose them to boredom and vague ambiguities. If you kept this up long and consistently enough, you'd have a good chance to succeed.

By the way, some of the consciously benign systems also fall victim to this one, without being aware of it. An institution which takes care to avoid cruel or severe punishments, in its despair (itself more than likely the product of understaffing and miserable financing) , may have recourse to "withdrawal of privileges." When that gets to the point where life becomes essentially empty and meaningless, the effects may be just as disastrous: *you might as well have been nasty to the children, to begin with.*

PUTTING POISON IN THEIR SOUP. This third way takes a relatively short time, is especially neat, and it is also easy to disguise. Nothing is obviously wrong with the soup; in fact, it is an excellent soup, the cook did a perfect job, and no visiting health inspector could find any fault with it. All its ingredients are exactly what the dietitian or the doctor ordered — except that last one: you take a sip of it, and you topple over dead.

There is an institution back home I was called upon to survey. They have a wonderful recreation program: everybody is busy in some kind of "constructive" activity all day long, and it is wonderful to photograph or tape. The trouble is that somebody threw in a really heavy dose of "competitive challenge." The children are busy — but they're scared stiff. *Not* to measure up to top expectations would mean that you were ostracized, which means that you might as well *not be.*

There is thus a constant fear of being outrun by one's competitors: other children are not "pals," they are *racehorses to outrun;* fraternization with them may endanger one's own success curve. The nightmare that they will be found wanting by the adults or will be made to feel the contempt of lusty peers is constantly with these children. It undermines *precisely those values in the name of which the activity program was instituted.*

Another instance: a system of rewards and punishments has been devised by some institution or school. They know that children need to have an awareness of limits; and that after a child has acted wrongly, it *helps* him to be able to "pay," or to make up for what he has done by some sort of penalty — after which, he will be accepted into the graces of the group, collective or otherwise. Only, the type of experience that some people dream up as reward or penalty is *so stupid, cruel, unimaginative, so much out of line with age-typical expectations, that it simply kills the kids.*

EXPOSE THE CHILDREN TO OVERWHELMING BUT OTHERWISE "NORMAL" EXPERIENCES (WITHOUT GIVING THEM THE HELP THEY NEED IN ORDER TO COPE WITH THEM). In other words, *deprive them of "ego support."* The emphasis here is not on the experience itself, but on the child's ability or inability to cope with it.

Some experiences that are potentially pathogenic, we have no power to avoid or to protect the children against. However, we *do* have the power, and to my mind, also the *responsibility*, to support these children in their process of *reacting* to these experiences. For example, you may not be able to avoid submitting a youngster to the unexpected arrival of a new brother or sister, with its potential threat to his position in the family; or there may be a death in the family, or a child may have to move from a small rural community to a large industrial town, and so forth. However, with the exception of some very extreme situations, it makes a lot of difference whether this same youngster is left to his own devices in coping with any of these experiences, or is given the type of "ego-supportive" help with which he may be able to decontaminate the experience of whatever pathogenic effect it might otherwise have had.

What I mean here by "ego support" may be categorized under two heads: one, support that is built into the structure of the very experience itself; two, support that has to be furnished, preferably by somebody with an important role in the child's life. For example, even so "simple" an experience as a children's game has certain "supportive" elements built into its very structure. In a circle tag-game, children *know* that they are *expected* to stay close to the circle, that the chaser is expected to try to catch his partner, that the chased child is expected to give in good-humoredly when caught, that the group is expected to ignore signs of anxiety or lack of skill up to a certain point, so as not to expose any player to ridicule beyond the level of playful banter.

These built-in game rules and behavior expectations operate as supportive elements. They help one child to cope with losing, prevent another from becoming too wild and triumphant in his victory, and keep the rest of the group from acting too cruelly towards the performers who are not doing so well.

Some games, however, do not have enough of such ego support built in; or, for some of the players, in moments of excitement, the built-in supports do not suffice. Then it is the task of the child or adult who is leading the game, to intervene. Thus, the teacher may have to *comfort* a loser, to help him cope with his embarrassment and shame; or he may have to *tone down* the excitement of the winner, to help him stop short of making himself unpopular, and so forth.

There are many situations in which it is the task of the educator to construct the play or work or learning life of the children in such a way that needed ego-supports are *built into the very structure of the experience.* There are others in which our responsibility is to see that the staff in charge of the children is well aware of its obligation *to furnish such supports,* and skilled in doing so. In sum, while some potentially pathogenic experiences cannot be avoided in life, the responsibility for helping children to cope with them remains. The final outcome will depend, not only on the *nature of the experience* with which the kid has to grapple — whether pathogenic or not — but on *the help the child gets* in the process of coping with it.

I have dwelt at somewhat greater length on this illustration because, as kibbutz educators, you should not only be worrying what potentially pathogenic things society does to your children, or whether what you do to them has that effect; you should be giving serious thought to the question: *What do I do to support kids in moments of potentially pathogenic experiences?* Your problem is not only *How can I cleanse their lives of the avoidable ones?* It is also *What can I do to fortify them for coping with those that cannot be helped?*

I was happy to have the chance to observe, in "my kibbutz," one of the most dramatic evidences of the skillful handling of an otherwise pathogenic, or at least conflict-loaded, situation. When Mama turns up to pick up her little girl for a short stroll, and when said little girl returns triumphantly with a cookie in her hand, that does constitute a potentially pathogenic experience for the other kids, or at least it exposes them to emotions and conflicts they may have some trouble coping with. In the scene that I watched, any pathogenic implications were pretty well eliminated by the beautiful orchestration with which mother and metapelet handled the scene. Mother did not just yank her kid out of the group, with a "Never mind, you other kids" expression on her face. She paid attention to all of them. And the metapelet did not make the mistake of catering to Mama when she appeared on the scene, but knew, on the contrary, that right then was when the other children needed her. Finally, when Mama returned with the child holding the cookie, she also had cookies for the rest of them. Thus, a potentially loaded situation was pretty well decontaminated of its possibly pathogenic effects; the kids were well "supported" in the process of handling their own feelings in a very adaptive way.

On issues of the younger generation, it seems to me that public opinion where I live is very sick. Even people who are individually wonderful — brilliant, kind, and very nice in their actual behavior towards their own children, or to those entrusted to their care — seem to take a very peculiar stance when it comes to talking about "The Youth of Our Time." Something strange happens to the best of them: group psychological pathology takes over, and they say, recommend, and do the silliest things, no matter how reasonable and understanding they may remain in their daily lives.

Issue No. 1: Utter Confusion in the Area of Managing Child Behavior

Unfortunately, over the years, a peculiar distortion has developed, partly as the result of the very psychiatric thought that was meant to produce the opposite results. There is a tendency now to regard questions about how to deal with particular instances of child behavior as "very superficial," and to assume that one's "basic attitudes" in these situations are more important than one's "behavior." It doesn't really matter what we do to kids, the argument goes, so long as we love them, don't reject them, have the "right attitude" toward them. Since your emotional relationship is what really counts, whatever else you may do to them can't really do them much harm.

If you put enough arsenic into somebody's food, he will die. It doesn't matter then how much you loved him, that you did it only out of ignorance, or even under the delusional impact of good-will; if you were stupid enough to think it was good for him, that's something for you to consider — but *he* will be dead. There is a cut-off point beyond which our behavior, the experience we expose a child to, *does* make a real difference.

Fortunately, not all of our behavior falls on the other side of that fatal margin. In many instances, our other assumption — namely, that the attitude with which we do something is more important than what we do — still holds. Even more fortunately, healthy children, in generally favorable life situations, have a pretty good ability to deduct from adult behavior what might be pathogenic — provided its basic attitude is all right: "My old man was kind of mad today; boy, he sure blew his top. But he didn't really mean it; I know he likes me. I'd just better watch out next time that I don't tell him about a bad grade right after he has had a bad day at the office. . . ." Nevertheless, beyond a certain point, adult behavior that is hard for a youngster to cope with will result in disturbance, sickness, pathology of some kind or other, even though it may have been, on the adult's side, well-motivated, well-intended, psychiatrically "clean."

Therefore, I am in favor of paying a good deal more of our attention to our "behavior" towards our children, and not limiting our concern solely to our relationship, emotion and feelings toward them. This is not intended to detract from what we have been preaching during the last forty years or so in psychiatry — namely, that "basic attitudes, relationships and emotions" are what count. All I want to establish is that the fact that these are "the most important things" does not mean that what we *do* is altogether negligible.

Now, this is what I am leading to. Leaving aside the befuddled, stupid or hostile adults, I find that in our society even the most brilliant and best-intentioned ones are really quite confused about *how to say a clean yes or a clean no.* By "clean," I mean one without any garbled message attached to it. Where I came from, people have trouble not only with a "clean no" (in which case, they are likely to confuse firmness with anger and hostility) ; they also have trouble with a "clean yes." Many times, when they think they have been too "permissive," they have not been permissive at all, just evasive—which is not the same thing, at all. Suppose you finally give in simply because Junior has worn you down about some special permission he has been pestering you about, and you have thrown up your hands, as if to say: "O.K. Here is your permission; just leave me alone, for heaven's sake; I don't want to hear about that any more." That was no "permission" at all, it was a victory wrung from a tired opponent. No wonder it does not have the effect a real permission would have had. In short, the adults seem to have trouble either saying "no," without becoming hostile, excited, and then punitive about it, or saying "yes," without shoving the responsibility for decisions off their shoulders and on to the "befuddled" kid's. It is my contention that this confusion in thought and action is one of the most "pathogenic factors" in the lives of our youth.

Issue No. II. Estrangement from Youth: Moratorium without Oxygen; the Emergence of a New Prejudicial Stereotype

ESTRANGEMENT FROM THE YOUTH OF OUR TIME. In contrast to our beautiful sentiments about "how important" the young are for us, I find, in our society, a lot of "estrangement" has succeeded in sneaking in between us and the kids we love. Teenagers are uncomfortable with adults, except in intimate friendships and family situations, or in the case of a well-established personal rapport; in general, they don't quite know what to do with us. They'd rather not have us around at their gatherings, while we, in turn, become downright rude when a teenager turns up at ours. Some of this, to be sure, is normal, but I have begun to sense the emergence of a "collective" discomfort of the adults with their young — which is definitely a pathogenic factor in the latter's lives.

MORATORIUM WITHOUT OXYGEN. The term "moratorium" I have borrowed from Erik Erikson. While they are growing up, we allow a certain amount of leeway to our children; we widen the fringe within which they can experiment without having to commit themselves to the "identity" of their later lives. For many of our young people, however, this is a moratorium without oxygen: *what is the good of a leeway to experiment, when there is nothing for them to experiment with?* The urban youngster of my country finds himself in a vehemently infantilized and highly pauperized life-space. His chances for a meaningful work experience, for the opportunity to make a meaningful contribution to society at his own level, are quite poor — and no amount of "recreational facilities" can make up for that fact!

THE EMERGENCE OF A NEW PREJUDICIAL STEREOTYPE. In the United States our prejudices are being taken away from us, collectively speaking. At least, we are becoming more successful in making people embarrassed about their enjoying them. But I really think that as a generation of adults, we are in process of developing a new prejudicial stereotype against the "Youth of Our Time." Teenagers are just "not to be trusted"; they are guilty until proven innocent.

Issue No. III. Financial Stupidity and Financial Arrogance

These two afflictions I consider to be altogether the most pathogenic forces directed against our young. Of them, financial stupidity is perhaps the less harmful of the two, inasmuch as it is still open to cure by teaching and demonstration. Let us assume that I were a physicist engaged in doing some kind of atomic work. Let us also assume that "the powers that be" have had their breaths taken away by the financial estimates of the costs involved — especially by the cost of uranium. They may breathe heavily for a while; they may even decide that they can't afford the whole business just now; but can you imagine one of them ever raising an argument like this one? "Listen, brother, uranium is — well, it's going too far. Why don't you use strawberry juice instead? It's so much cheaper. . . ."

Does that seem fantastic to you? There is an obvious, and all too painful, analogy in the problem of implementing perfectly "realistic" needs in the field of education and mental health. The next step, unfortunately, is even worse, and harder to cure: where financial stupidity is coupled with *financial arrogance,* you really have a "pathogenic factor," compared with which a tendency to incest or rape is a mere nothing.

They invite you as an "expert," and ask you to set up a treatment hospital or institution. "Reconstruct lives? Nothing can be too costly for that!" They give you all the buildings you want (with twice as much plumbing as you need) ; of course, the architecture has to be the latest. When it comes to *staffing,* however, the whole atmosphere changes: then you have to point out, very patiently, that in this specific group, you *can't* have twelve kids, only four, and then explain why. Or, they will build you a beautiful workshop; but then you insist on having two adults for eight kids, because the kids are highly explosive, and whoever handles a kid in that stage of excitement needs to be relaxed, not having to worry about the others at the same time, while *they* in turn need to know that an adult is still related to *them* or *they* will raise the roof. At this point, your committee "blows its top": "Do you think money grows on trees? There are 'reality limits,' you know; or do you? . . ."

The point at issue, by the way, is not the money at all; it is the arrogance displayed by those who own, or (this is usually much worse) who have the power of administration over somebody else's money, and suddenly take upon themselves the prerogative of making decisions about "feasibility" and "advisability" on issues that have nothing at all to do with whatever they may be competent in.

At this point, by the way, I am presenting an illustration that obviously has little direct bearing on your situation, certainly as far as your arrangements for the youngest children are concerned. For here, more than anywhere else, I have been impressed by the exceptional degree of "financial realism" that your collectives display when they make such great sacrifices in manpower as are reflected in your having such good staffing for such small groups.

On the other hand, perhaps what I saw is not as universal as you yourselves might wish; perhaps, as soon as we move up from the toddlers to the older children, some of these struggles are not so far removed from the realities you too have to struggle with, after all. It may be that there are still areas in which you also have trouble conveying to those who have the power of decision over the financial means, that *psychological reality is even more relentless than the reality of their world of financial resources.*

COMMUNITY PSYCHIATRY
VIOLA W. BERNARD

In the United States, among the current developments in psychiatry and related fields there has emerged an increasing interest in community mental health programs for children. It feels a little like "bringing coals to Newcastle" to find myself reporting to those of you who are in the kibbutz movement on certain fundamental aspects of these efforts, which have obviously been so basic to your own approach: acceptance of community responsibility for meeting the mental health needs of all the children in the community; the combination of knowledge and skills from the biological, psychological and social sciences in order to meet this task; and the study of the interrelationships between the individual child's development and his social environment.

The opportunity to learn about the kibbutz experience in child-rearing has, of course, been of special value to us, and we are deeply grateful for it. Naturally, programs cannot be simply transposed, out of context, from the collectives in Israel to the United States — or vice versa — in view of the great differences between the two societies. But we have many problems in common, and it seems altogether feasible and desirable that we should borrow selectively from each other, recognizing the basic principles that underlie specific practices in each case, so that these practices may be modified appropriately for adaptation to different sociocultural settings.

Temporarily reversing the direction of our discourse, I shall sketch very briefly some of the key aspects of Community and Social Psychiatry, and Community Mental Health,* in the United States today, with regard to children.

---

*As used here, the terms Community and Social Psychiatry are interchangeable and refer to a specialized field of psychiatry, which is a medical specialty. Community Mental Health, however, is broader, and encompasses contributions from many disciplines, of which psychiatry is but one.

Community psychiatry may be viewed as an evolutionary stage in the development of psychiatry, extending (not replacing), in theory and in practice, the accumulated knowledge derived from clinical psychiatry and the insights of psychoanalysis. In ecological terms, one may view it as focusing upon those points at which the inner psychobiological processes interact with the impinging networks of the social and physical environments.

This focus is bringing Community and Social Psychiatry research to grips with some hard and pressing problems in the refining of our knowledge about the relationships between sociocultural and psychodynamic data. This, in turn, is of great practical importance towards the improving of our ability to *prevent and relieve* many different kinds of emotional disorder by other than one-to-one clinical methods (these non-clinical methods, to be sure, incorporate and apply clinical understanding). It will help us to identify more precisely, for example, those clusters of circumstances in a given community that may be pathogenic for certain types of children, at particular stages of their development, and to determine by what mechanisms such circumstances produce these effects.

These pathogenic circumstances might then be changed or offset through administrative or legislative action on behalf of the children of that population, thus sparing them the handicap of illness, and conserving our all too meager resources of mental health manpower. The effectiveness of such a preventive approach would stand in sharp contrast with attempts to treat these children individually, *after* they have developed disorders. Therapeutic success at that point would be uncertain at best, and in any event, efforts of that sort would be well-nigh impossible to carry through, because of the scarcity of psychotherapists available in proportion to the number of emotionally disturbed children.

The foregoing illustration of "primary prevention" — a concept derived from the field of public health — helps to demonstrate the composite nature of Community Psychiatry, with its blending of elements from public health and the social sciences with clinical psychiatry.

Primary, secondary, and tertiary prevention are three parts of a continuum of control of mental disorders on a community-wide basis. Each is carried out by a range of differentiated services, involving differently qualified personnel in different settings. The objectives of these three levels of prevention are (1) to diminish the amount of emotional disorder within a given population by preventing its occurrence; (2) to accelerate recovery when it does occur, and (3) to minimize its disabling aftereffects.

For the child population of a community, *attempts to lower the rate of occurrence of mental disorder* ("primary prevention") involve both the reduction of pathogenic influences (early maternal deprivation, for example, or racially segregated schooling), and the strengthening of personality to enable it to withstand and cope with stresses that might otherwise induce pathology. At this level of prevention, the contributions of community child psychiatrists and other community mental health specialists are mainly of an *indirect* and *non-clinical* character. These include consultation with those directly responsible for child care and education, and participation in the program planning, policies and organization of the basic community services for children — health, education and welfare — with special attention to their crucial implications for mental health and mental illness.

Community mental health programs at the level of secondary prevention require the direct services of clinicians in the early diagnosis and treatment of emotionally disturbed children. Here too, the conception of treatment, in its many forms, as a means of *lessening the prevalence of childhood disorder* in a particular population group, entails relating the clinical work to earlier case-findings on the part of those in contact with children in their "normal" settings. It also involves the improvement of referral procedures and the optimal utilization of the appropriate treatment resources, as well as provision for the availability of adequate resources.

Tertiary prevention, with its emphasis on *after-care and rehabilitation*, also requires the coordinated efforts of personnel with diverse skills and knowledge, such as the speech therapist, occupational therapist, remedial teacher and vocational counsellor, among others. Here too, the functions of the community mental health specialists are largely *indirect*, involving the application of psychiatric insights via consultation and administration.

The *concept of comprehensiveness is central* to current thinking about community mental health service programs. In connection with federal legislation which had been set in motion by the late President Kennedy, following the report of the congressionally-sponsored Joint Commission on Mental Health and Illness, each state is now engaged in planning comprehensive community mental health programs. The principle of comprehensiveness is implemented in several ways: the program not only includes the totality of the mental health services and facilities needed by members of the community; it also encompasses *all age levels, all categories of psychopathology, and all socioeconomic and cultural groups within the community.* It also applies to the multiplicity of causal factors to be taken into account. Closely linked to the principle of comprehensiveness are the principles of increased differentiation of services, and improved methods of coordination and collaboration, both interprofessionally — between the mental health and health, education, welfare and correctional professions — and between the general public and governmental officials.

Within the social system of the kibbutz, some of these principles have long been what we would call "standard operating practice," and thus may not strike you as an innovation. For example, your psychological services are *regularly available to the child population as a whole, in terms of individual need.* Channels of communication between all segments of the community are easily available for coordinated effort in behalf of the children. As a planned society, it would seem that you can effect modifications in the conditions of social experience for children quite readily when that seems warranted by convincing psychological data. In our society, however, there have been both unevenness and inequities in the quality of service available to different categories of children.

The comprehensive mental health program is concerned with developing not only new knowledge, methodologies and techniques, but also more effective and more democratic ways of organizing, applying and making available what is already known. All too often, the different children's mental health resources have functioned in piecemeal, autonomous fashion, with a minimum of cooperation. Such separateness can be overcome by the overall unity of the comprehensive program. In a coordinated network of differentiated services, a child should at least be able to move flexibly among different kinds of care, on the basis of clinical indications, with the therapeutic advantage of being able to maintain continuity while shifting, for example, between the in-patient, day hospital and out-patient facilities of the program, during the course of his illness.

Furthermore, because of the close dovetailing between different kinds of community services for children, attempts to improve any one kind of facility depend for their success on improvements in all the others. This point was stressed in a report made recently by a group of us who had studied child psychiatric services in New York City at the request of the Commissioner of Hospitals, in cooperation with the Commissioner of Mental Health Services.* Perhaps the composition and approach of this Committee may help to illustrate some of the professional attributes, roles and functions that are involved in Community Child Psychiatry and Mental Health.

The Committee membership included seventy-five specialists from a broad cross-section of both public and private, medical and non-medical settings related to child mental health. The integration of such significantly different disciplines and orientations in delineating problems and devising recommendations for their solution exemplified the many patterns of interprofessional partnership in community mental health work, which extend far beyond the traditional clinical team that has proven to be of such value in child psychiatry. The Committee recognized, early in its life, that the very act of convening this all-inclusive group was already having an effect upon its individual members. Because the Committee, as set up, cut across public and private agency lines, the increased communication required by our work together helped improve services in and of itself, even before any

---

*At the time these remarks were being delivered, the report had not yet been published. It was published in June 1964, by the New York City Community Mental Health Board: *Report of the Department of Hospitals' Committee on Psychiatric Services for Children to the Commissioner of Hospitals of N.Y.C.* (Co-chairmen: Viola W. Bernard, M.D., and Grace McLean Abbate, M.D.).

recommendations were formulated or could be formally acted upon.

Such interactive processes within this group, which divided itself into six subcommittees and a steering committee, also demonstrated another important content area of Community Psychiatry — that of group dynamics (as distinguished from the clinical treatment technique of group psychotherapy). Perhaps the breadth of the recommendations that this Committee submitted illustrates the community psychiatrist's integrative way of including in his vision both the overall community and the minutiae of the intrapsychic process, in order to establish connections of relevance among seemingly disparate phenomena. To implement some of these recommendations, one needed administrative action, additional funds or legislative changes; for others, one needed changes of attitude, and for still others, much more intensive study.

One of the latter, recommendation #10, came to my mind during this Institute because so many of the children to whom it refers would profit, I believe, if we were able to adapt some of the features of kibbutz child-care for them. The recommendation is:

> The development of residential facilities for adolescents, as well as small group settings for younger children who are ready for discharge from city or state hospitals, but who have no families (or who have unsuitable families) to which to return. These still vulnerable children need a supervised group-living facility, while they receive continued treatment in the community.

In a similar fashion, the Institute has set me to thinking about the dynamics of "supplementary mothering," in terms of its possible adaptation to our patterns of care for several categories of children. Public day-care and nursery-school programs are in process of expansion in many parts of the United States, particularly for children from families with emotional, social or cultural handicaps. Fulfillment of the mental health potential of this promising development will greatly depend on the nature and conditions of adult-child and peer group relationships within these programs. We have much to learn from the kibbutz in this regard, even granting the difficulty of selecting out of the totality here that which is not altogether rooted in the basic kibbutz way of life, value system and ideology.

We have been finding, for example, that "foster homes" — while these do constitute a great advance over the impersonal and oversized congregate institutions of previous years — are not only too scarce to meet the demands of our needy children but, from the mental standpoint, are not satisfactory for many of them. For some, adoption is the plan of choice. We are making encouraging progress in the adoptive placement of older children, of children with physical and psychological handicaps, and of children from ethnic minorities — all of whom were at one time considered "unadoptable." However, we have numerous youngsters without suitable homes of their own, yet for whom neither adoption nor foster-home placement is psychologically indicated. Many of these would thrive, I feel sure, if we had some counterpart of kibbutz life to offer them, with its balance of significant adult and peer relationships, the feeling of group belonging, opportunities and encouragement for satisfying achievement, and a sense of purpose and practical idealism.

In this short summary, I could only outline some of the problems of developments in Community and Social Psychiatry with respect to children in the United States. I have presented Community Psychiatry as essentially integrative in its approach, representing, in a sense, an effort to cope with the dilemma between our need for increased specialization and our progress toward more holistic thinking. The increasing complexity of our knowledge, derived from advances in the human sciences, calls for more and more specialization. Differentiation and specialization, however, inevitably tend to produce narrowing, fragmentation and isolation, which requires new modes of re-integration. That integrative process is a major function of Community Psychiatry.

EDUCATION IN GREAT BRITAIN
Hilde Hummelweit

From my own research, and from the discussions that have been going on at home, touching on the educational and social fields, the thing that we seem to be most concerned with in Britain at the moment is our educational system. It is really so arranged that it maximizes the effects of all the pathogenic factors inherent in the system without providing any of the ego support that would alone make possible growth experience under the circumstances.

The original intention of this system was that no child should be deprived of equal educational opportunity. It was therefore decided — quite rightly — that it must not be the social background of the children that determined the level of their attainment. Therefore, we were to have an intelligence test, because such tests would be least influenced by the social background of the parents, and hence would provide the fairest method for separating children into the various pigeonholes set up for them. All of this was to be told to the parents and to the children, so that they would recognize that they now had "equal opportunity."

We thus have a system which, in its most extreme form, divides children at the age of "eleven-plus" into two types of secondary education. Some 20 per cent go to the grammar school, and from there (again, only perhaps, as we shall see) to the universities. About 80 per cent go to the secondary modern school, which they leave at sixteen. These children tend not to get any further academic training; in fact, they tend not to be inspired very much during their stay in the school system to *seek* any further training for themselves. This is for two reasons: first, because they are given their education at a very slow pace, much slower in fact than is necessary; secondly, because very often the teachers themselves feel, *not that they are responsible for 80 per cent of the youth, but that they have the "failures."* The whole thing rests, remember, on the results of one single test, given on one single day, and taking no account of the child, the parents, or the real situation at all.

For the grammar-school students — evidently because we are not content with the number of hurdles that we have already placed before our youth — we now introduce another one. If a child goes to a grammar school, it is assumed that he is ready for and should benefit from a university education. But we have so few university openings for students that only extremely few children can even hope to get in.

Now begins what I have described as the "provincial tour"

of making your auditions. This comes only after you've passed all the very taxing examinations (and they *are* extremely taxing), and acquired all your right " 'A' level" results — that is, after you have emptied your childhood and your adolescence of anything except the extremely dull and narrowing business of working for examinations, discussing examinations, discussing your "chances." (Teachers have not dared to devote any time to any other activities, because in so doing they might be cutting off the further educational chances of the children; they too are absolutely imprisoned by the system.)

For every single place at the London School of Economics, we get sixteen properly qualified applicants. We now have a well-worked-out system for selecting one out of these sixteen. The others? They go on elsewhere, to try again. (This is also a traumatic experience; you know, I am sure, that one then develops defense mechanisms, how to cope and how to rationalize.) And that is how these poor creatures make their "tour" around all the universities. Some are rejected outright; no one is ever quite clear just why he has been rejected.

The candidate is, by the time he takes his interview, already almost exhausted. He has heard lurid stories of what is required in an interview; he may even have had a pre-interview rehearsal by a headmaster. Our student, aged seventeen or eighteen, now comes in — and three people, who have already seen twelve or fifteen applicants from 9:00 o'clock until 5:00 o'clock (you can see that your chances are infinitely better if you come after coffee than before coffee, in terms of the examiners' sheer fatigue) bear down on this one individual, being exceedingly anxious to find the best in him. After a very, very searching interview (which takes all of ten to twenty minutes) — having seen all these other people before, and not knowing what to ask anyhow — we then make another "final decision."

I am spending time on this, because it is to me a warning of how one can start a system that looks all right — even exceedingly sensible — and then turns out to be probably the most idiotic and barbaric system one could think up, if one tried. I can see no single advantage to it. One not only makes a decision at one point of time; it also matters enormously — ironically enough, in the light of the original aims — where your family lives. For example, if you live in an area near London in which the population is mainly working-class, and you are middle-class and have a child with an I.Q. of 110, you are likely to get that child in, even though the average I.Q. will be around 115 or 120, because the family has really been teaching him study methods and so on, all of which gives him an extra chance. If, however, you have settled in a suburban community, where there are mainly middle-class children, professional people's children, or highly skilled working-class families, the average level of ability needed in order to get into the grammar school may be equal to that which is required to get into a university.

What I would like to point out is that this is the outcome of any system that creates barriers in a situation that should be essentially fluid — and it is fluid as long as one is discussing child development. The whole thing presupposes that there is some particular stage at which you can predict the future of any child. You can, of course — if you make self-fulfilling prophecies: you turn the other children into "less good" children, and you label them from there on like that. In some schools they start this process at the age of six! At that point, you put the child into the "A" stream, or the "B" stream, or the "C" stream. The "A-streams" are the probable eleven-plus successes (whom you have discovered at the age of six, and I'm not joking!). And it is not possible to re-place them, once you have a system of "grading by ability" within the school, because that involves the traumatic decision, which every teacher hesitates to make — to take one child away from some particular stream in order to make room for another.

The teachers simply give up; they take this system as it is and create quite different experiences for the differently grouped children. They have in fact accepted a two-class system — that is to say, "Here are the 'able' children, and here are *all the others*."

Now, all this is something that one pays a price for, curiously enough, in *sheer intellectual achievement*. The moment you have a series of examinations which are going to decide — solely or mainly — whether or not a child can go on to the next phase of education, you are going to discourage any daydreaming, any independent reading, any creative kind of thinking; you are going to create children who will simply acquire an enormous amount of facts, and so look very impressive when you compare them with others. I am sure that such children will score very highly on all kinds of tests, but you are in terrible danger, as we are now finding out, of stamping out all originality and creativity. Above all, you are making it possible for children to feel that it is because of themselves that they are a failure and have been labelled as such, beyond all repair.

If it is true that in Israel there has developed a tendency towards this selective system, then I would urge you to build into it impregnable safeguards. Above all, the teachers have got to fight against this prejudice that it is only with the academically brilliant child that their talents as teachers are going to come to fruition. Many able children will do extremely well with any system, despite their teachers, but I think that one is reducing the whole range of the other children, who could in fact do very much more than we give them credit for. Above all, one is creating an atmosphere of misery, and I think that is an altogether intolerable shape of affairs in any society.

JEHUDA MESSINGER: Israel already has not an eleven-plus but a thirteen-plus examination for all the children, and it is given on one day. It is not as stringent, nor as terrible, and it has, I would say, fewer anxiety-producing outcomes than in Britain; still, there is a significant amount of what Dr. Himmelweit has called "disparity of esteem." There are also a lot of the other outcomes mentioned, but we are fighting against them. We are sustained by the fact that we ourselves have a different sort of school system and are maintaining our influence on the general school system, which I hope will finally succeed in getting rid of that examination.

PROFESSOR KUGELMASS: In almost any society that has a very strong, clear value system, which has been changing at a relatively rapid rate, there will inevitably be difficulties for all those people who have yet to learn how to shift gears.

During the six or seven years that we have had a Psychology Department (and we have a really rugged selection system), there has been a proportionate amount of kibbutz people. They have come with a different way of viewing the world, and different study habits. I think that in some cases they have shown initially a far superior approach to what one might call originality, creativity, real work, the zest for knowledge, etc. But gradually, the kibbutz student has become in some ways far smoother, particularly those who have learned to be much more achievement-oriented.

This provides us with a little background for the problem of adjusting to a very much clearer form of individual-achievement orientation. Those who speak negatively of this orientation call it "careerism"; the more thinking adolescent university students even feel somewhat guilty about it. There is a tremendous internal struggle going on during the time when these people are making their adjustment to the new system of values.

Many of us might say that this struggle is inevitable: "everything is getting more normal," "that is the way it has to be," and so on. But I think that, for a lot of people, it has produced really severe conflicts, and I also think that they have obtained far less help from their teachers and leaders and from the social mechanisms that have been set up, some of which, I feel, are lagging completely. Some mechanisms that used to function well, and were probably quite important for what one might call the mental hygiene of the youth — the youth movements, with the values that they had and the opportunities they gave — seem to have slipped up. I don't know how to improve them, but I think they deserve re-analysis and possibly reorganization.

One could even perhaps generalize. I recall now an International Congress on Phrenology last year. We had to discuss these very same problems with reference to the rapidly developing Asian countries. I think that this experience of very rapid changes can work for *either* the benefit *or* the harm of society: we must always consider the mechanisms we have operating, and whether they, too, do not have to be changed.

Chapter VII

CONCLUDING REMARKS

MR. ALT: I would like to pay tribute to the Conference, and to say something about its meaning to me, as a personal experience. In some ways it has been a return — as it was, undoubtedly, for many others here.

There is, at this moment, a great deal of concern throughout the world, and particularly in the developing countries, about how the child-rearing function should be carried out, and where the responsibility for it should be placed. This usually takes the form of trying to determine the optimum division of responsibility between family and community, or between parent and professional. This meeting, while it has been limited to five days, has already given us many clues as to how other countries and other cultures may be able to discharge this kind of responsibility more effectively than they have been able to.

It is true that the exact forms of child-rearing are not transferable; yet the basic elements in the kibbutz child-rearing process, so well developed in the report by Dr. Anthony, cannot be ignored in planning any arrangements anywhere for the care of children. I think that this Conference has articulated these concepts; if that were all it accomplished, it would have been worthwhile.

But it isn't all. I don't think you wanted us to come together only to make a contribution, important as that may be, to the world at large. I think that you were concerned, properly enough, about your own problems and the help that this Conference might provide towards meeting those problems. I view the meaning of this conference to the kibbutz movement as being centered in the help it has been able to offer to those who participated, and to the others whom they will influence, in guiding change.

There is no question of the present readiness for change; how much change it is hard to assess, yet change is clearly inevitable. No society can ignore what is happening to its human resources; if the kibbutz system is to perpetuate itself — this, I think, has been one of the goals implicit in our work here — then some degree of adaptation to new experiences and new understanding is absolutely requisite.

Guiding change calls for a number of things. I will deal with two: one is knowledge; the other is the intellectual, spiritual, and moral resources of the people who undertake to bring about change or who sanction change.

A great deal has been said here about knowledge and the importance of research. On that question, I would like to make two observations.

First, I think that the Conference should regard the enlargement of understanding in much broader terms than simply organized research. We should draw on *all* sources of increased understanding, many of which may be imperfect, some no more than intuitive, and other merely impressionistic. I say this because the ideal of achieving understanding *solely through research* is completely outside the bounds of realizability.

We can achieve only small fragments of understanding through research; even then, there is no guarantee that those fragments are relevant to the problems we wish to deal with. So, formal research, important as it may be, should not displace other sources of understanding, or become the *only* path to our organized and systematic understanding. Do not overburden research activity; don't place too much stress on it; keep it in focus and in balance.

Furthermore, I feel very strongly that research should remain an instrument *in the hands of those people who shape policy*. It should never be separated from responsibility, and it should never be turned over entirely to people outside the stream of kibbutz life. Of course, this is a relative dictum and needs qualification. It is inevitable that technical help should be utilized; but the basic responsibility for research in education — as well as for life in general in the kibbutz — should remain with those who are responsible for the kibbutz movement (or for the educational phase of it). Never divorce research from responsibility, for if you do, the research may prove valueless.

Finally, with all due respect to the potential value of the use of outsiders, and of the interaction between one group of people and another — and we have seen many values of that sort right here — nonetheless, I believe very firmly that the kibbutz group must find their own solutions, and that they alone can do so. If you use outsiders, use them only in their character as instruments of assistance to yourself, as your *added resources*.

I have one last observation, which is in the nature of a hope as well as a conviction. It is this: to accomplish the many things that we have talked about here calls for the mobilization of a vast body of energy — intellectual, spiritual, and emotional. That energy is now present; it must not be permitted to be dissipated.

Dr. EISENBERG: Expressing strong positive feelings is much more difficult than giving voice to negative sentiments; one is sometimes suspected of being sentimental. . . . On the other hand, critical comments can always be made with great ease. I shall therefore begin with what is easier.

At times, we have been asked for advice here, only to have it become quite apparent that nobody really wanted our advice — at least, about certain things. I think this was partly because we sometimes presumed to offer advice that (a) had not been asked for, (b) was outside the area of our immediate competence, and (c) tended to arouse defensiveness. When somebody said that the children's houses in some places looked a bit vacant, there was an immediate response from a number of people: "Well, that may have been true of the place you were at, but we can show you fifteen others that are better." I don't doubt that you could, but our function was to point out what we felt could be improved.

More important, advice-giving is not really effective in a group as large as this, where there are so many advice-givers that you can readily vitiate the effectiveness of any one comment by determining, in short order, that the givers differ among themselves and, therefore, you need not take too seriously any of the advice offered — particularly if it is unpleasant.

I am a little troubled, as you can see, by what I regard as both a virtue and a vice in the kind of intensity with which you feel what you believe. If you did not have that intensity, there would have been no meeting here, because there would have been no kibbutz movement. On the other hand, one pays a price at times for such intensity, because intensity can very easily turn into a kind of opaqueness to advice, especially when it comes from those who have not shared a common experience. One gets the same feeling, for instance, with people who believe that only those who have been through a war can talk about war experiences.

Now this is a phenomenon known all over the world. You have a closeness, a value, a commitment; you have been "willing to do it." (Someone overheard an interchange, for example, in which one visitor said how nice it was here and how he envied you, and one of your group said, *sotto voce,* "Why don't they come live here?" If you ask that, you will find most of us wanting. Not that it is not a legitimate question, by the way, as a measure of how involved and how convinced we are; but if you were to insist on that degree of commitment, there would be very few people outside your group whom you would find able to be of much use to you.)

I am, furthermore, not yet persuaded that, outside of the sort of people we have in this room, there is sufficient emphasis laid on the importance of *research* in human behavior. Sometimes, it is confused with careerism, with the kind of research that is so very nice in an affluent society, where you can afford, so to speak, to have someone studying the number of legs on butterflies. Ultimately, I suppose, it all fits in, but now it is rather remote from immediate social needs.

But the kind of research we have spoken of here is not remote research. Instead, it seems to me to relate to what is perhaps the central goal of the kibbutz — which is not work for its own sake, but work *as it enhances or changes human values.* This was mentioned earlier in terms of the complex of attitudes that one "wants to produce." Well, how does one produce it? Clearly, you have some of the answers; but, on the other hand, you may be paying a needless price in some necessary areas. It is only by the constant effort to re-examine what you are doing in a careful way that you will be able to answer all such questions.

We have met, among those who took us around the individual kibbutzim, and among those of you here, some of the most extraordinary people. And there must be many more such all around us. As one walked around, one could see the shyness of some of the adults and the comparative lack of color of some of the personalities. However, I would say that on the strength of those we have met — the commitments they have, their interests and their intelligence, and the kind of strength that one feels underneath their gentleness and reasonableness — that one has here, among these people, just those human aspects that have aroused in some of us the feeling that, if this is not paradise, it is, at least, a reasonably close approximation to it.

I am sure that living with this, on the terms you used for your colleagues — your *chaverim* — you understand it perfectly well. But it may not be as apparent to you as it is to us, who come to you from the outside, where we live in a society in which so many people who are intense about their feelings tend to be regarded as a bit mad. Instead of talking about something pleasant and inconsequential, they keep intruding on your consciences with troublesome problems. Perhaps you do trouble each other too much; still, by and large, I think that is a very good thing.

DR. HIMMELWEIT: To me the conference has meant a great deal: the contact with my Israeli colleagues has been extremely valuable; I have learned a lot, and I have been deeply impressed by what I have seen. There has been a noteworthy *atmosphere of trust,* in which we could raise points of criticism, knowing that our colleagues recognized that these were being presented within the context of our admiration for what has been achieved.

You have asked us to raise at this final meeting some of the issues that concern us. That I do gladly, since they are issues which have already been raised by our Israeli colleagues.

The first concerns the "worship of manual labor." All societies have to carry on heavy labor, and it is important to remember that such work is both necessary and worthwhile. This has been established with admirable skill in the whole ideology underlying the kibbutz movement. But society is now changing, and it would seem to me that it has become necessary to consider the price one may be paying for this preoccupation with work on the soil, work with your own hands. I am referring to the fact that lack of mechanization brings with it a lack of opportunity for diversity in work, and, above all, an insufficiency of manpower for the important social work outside the kibbutz.

The second question has to do with research. A society that bases its child rearing on a theory needs to be able to determine how effective that theory has been in guiding the upbringing of children, in achieving the effects intended. Further, all of us (and that includes the members of the kibbutz) need to understand, more than we do now, how far the young people in the kibbutz differ in outlook and values from those living in Israel but outside the kibbutz.

The third has to do with the role of women in the kibbutz. To me it seems that a woman actually has a worse time here than if she were living outside the kibbutz; ouside, at least, the woman has a choice between home and work, or else she can attempt a combination of both activities. You offer no choice, but stress the need for women to work. In the main, however, leaving aside the work of the metapelet and the teacher, women's work is dull and repetitive work in the kitchen and in the laundry. There is need to rethink how to make the work that is regarded as suited to women more varied, by means of different systems and by means of more mechanization.

You ought not to underestimate the unique opportunity you have of teaching the world something about child development and child training. What makes your opportunity unique is the fact that you know so very much about the children and can carry out follow-up studies — e.g., learn about the effect of the growth spurt, the effect of the onset of puberty. All this is extremely important.

I have a suggestion for outlets for the young people's desire to change society — outlets that would build on the quality of kibbutz education and would not threaten its values. I heard recently that a series of factories are being built in the areas between Beerscheva and Eilat. Communities are being developed there with good housing and good medical facilities — but without any cultural life. I cannot think of any people more suited than the young people of the kibbutz to go to these communities in order to develop the cultural and leisure-time life of the families who live there.

This would be useful on three grounds: first, it would be worthwhile and challenging work; second, it is work that is badly needed; and third, it would demonstrate vividly, to the world outside, the capacity of the kibbutz movement to act as innovator and to adjust to changing conditions. It might not be necessary to leave the kibbutz altogether, but to be merely temporarily separated from it; or there might be developed small kibbutzim on the spot, devoted not to agriculture, but to social work. I understand that the government would readily provide the resources. A community without a cultural life, let us remember, is an underprivileged community, and the kibbutz movement has always fought for the underprivileged.

Finally, I would like to make a plea for greater concern on the part of the kibbutz movement for the urgent social problems of Israel itself — above all, for the problem of immigrants who have difficulty integrating into what is still essentially a Western society. I would like to see far more extended youth work being carried out, without any attempt to convince the youth of the kibbutz ideology, but solely for the purpose of enriching the lives of the youth of Israel.

EMI HURWITZ: We have worked here according to the principle of *complementarity*, as Robert Oppenheimer once defined it. We have used different approaches and different methods of our own choosing; we have asked questions, and at times, we have received answers.

Sometimes it was as if we were using a microscope, as we studied small details; at other times, we looked through a telescope, and saw our own kibbutz education as a minute part of the whole world of educational and psychological science. One thing we have not done adequately: we have not studied kibbutz education in the context of the specific Israeli environment — an omission that we Israelis should have avoided making.

I cannot truly assert that I now know more exactly how to deal with our tasks; or that I have found more or better solutions for our problems — even after the several days of discussion with our learned colleagues. But in some spheres of our educational work in the kibbutz, the discussions here have resulted in increasing our confidence and assurance, which will be of invaluable help to us.

Research programs are certainly required, and have to be prepared very carefully. We have to see what can be done to break down our own defenses, as well as those of members of the kibbutzim, who may see themselves as guinea pigs (they may even be approached as guinea pigs, by some research workers) in the study of someone "from the great world of science." Nevertheless, I believe that by studying specific problems and techniques, we will arrive at some truths that will enrich our work, and provide us with a deeper understanding of our educational tasks.

DR. KRIS: I would like to say just a few words to express my feelings. It takes me a little longer than we have had to digest everything; but I know that the food we have received — not the food that we ate, of course, but the food for thought — was excellent.

I think that I have received most understanding of the life of the kibbutz community through the delightful day spent at one of the kibbutzim. I want to express my gratitude to our extraordinary and most intelligent hosts, who showed us such great warmth and devoted so much of their time to acquainting us with the core and the details of kibbutz life. This has taught me, as I mentioned earlier, how careful one has to be in regard to the written literature. Only after the visit to the kibbutz did I realize how much I had misunderstood in the literature that was sent to us.

By now, your second generation has many reasons to be grateful to the kibbutzim. I hope — even though I know that the tasks that face them will be different from those that faced their predecessors — that they will find the way to translate their gratitude into the same sort of enterprise, self-sacrifice and ingenuity that went into making the kibbutzim what they are. Nothing will more certainly insure the survival and further development of the kibbutz.

To come back to my image of food: one becomes eager for more when one has good food; I am happy to find that others feel the same way. I do hope that it is not overly optimistic on our part to have the hope that we will be able to participate, at another time, in such a rewarding situation with such generous people, to function once again as part of a community into which we seem to have grown.

JEHUDA MESSINGER: I'd like to take off from Fritz Redl's comments on how he felt when he came back from his visit to the kibbutz. When we got to the Conference, I also went through three stages. First of all, there was a tremendous uplift: people coming from all over to learn from us — what a wonderful thing! Then I felt: these people, who will soon be expressing all kinds of dissatisfactions and criticism, how can they *tell us*, really; how can *they* know? Mixed a little with our feeling of inferiority was this feeling that, on kibbutz child-rearing, we were tops, even though these were professors. Later on, relaxation finally set in, so that it has turned out that there is actually a lot we can learn, and a lot we can now think out by ourselves, and in both ways, we will really benefit from this tremendous Conference.

There is the problem of too much verbalizing. In a sense, we have become "ideology protectors," at a time when the outside world is becoming so much more concerned with objects and processes. We were greatly helped in this Conference towards getting away from that terrible framework of thought, in which we even endow the little things, the little actions of our lives, with philosophical, ideological meanings (which they probably don't really have) . We may yet be able to get away from the few formulae that we use all the time, and consider a few things in the light of current educational and pedagogical practice.

I'm sorry that there weren't more sociologists and anthropologists here. I believe that the entity of which we have spoken — the wholeness of the kibbutz — can be fully understood only by looking much more at some of the aspects they deal with. The problems that we have to face, the day-to-day problems, are those of social change. We still have to maintain our case in this world.

One thing struck me that hasn't come up too often in this discussion: the fact that in this system, our children live in a loving world, as it was so beautifully expressed by Dr. Biber. There is so much approval, and so much love; but do we not also have to somehow build into our children some of the toughness of the world in which they are going to live, and where they are going to be tossed about — like little ships on the waves — by influences other than their own? (Incidentally, our children are often called by the people in this country the "Children of Tnuva." [Tnuva is the milk distributing co-operative.]) Like any spoiled children, they may not be able to stand up to the reality of man. I think that we have to guard against this.

SHMUEL NAGLER: You probably expect me to tell you about what I have learned, but I am sure you also want me to tell you what I feel. Simultaneously thinking, listening, and formulating, in a language to which I am not accustomed in everyday life, is quite an arduous task. In spite of that, I have to tell you how sorry I am that we must say goodbye to each other.

This meeting was a very important experience for me. During the Second World War, we professional people in Israel were quite isolated; for many years after that, we got no professional journals and no professional books, because of the difficulty in foreign exchange. Now, of course, we have no such problems at all: we get all the journals and books (more than we have time to read). What we really have been in need of is precisely this personal contact with the people who have written these papers and books.

Having taken my university studies in prewar Europe, I am accustomed to the approach in which a professor lectures to a remote audience. I have therefore been very much impressed by the sort of mutual discussion we have had, and the fruitful interchange of ideas that has come from it. We know that we have been limited by the absence of contact with outstanding professional people — which is the price that professional people in this country have had to pay for the privilege of living here.

I regard it as a privilege to live in this country working professionally on behavior problems. It is a special privilege to live in, and work for, kibbutz society, which you too have come to appreciate — especially at a time when, outside the kibbutz society, this country is making such strenuous efforts to absorb and integrate the hundreds of thousands of our people who have survived Eichmann's extermination organization, as well as hundreds of thousands of people coming from the Arab countries, with such different patterns of culture and values.

I would like also to mention the fact that you have brought us release from some of our uneasy feelings and anxieties. My friends in the educational fields — and we, too, who are professional psychologists and psychiatrists — have not felt altogether easy in mind about the problem of child-mother separation in early childhood. You must have recognized that this was so: in the beginning, we had a kind of defensive attitude on the question, which receded towards the end. And who would know better than you that it is anxiety that causes defenses?

We have been so uneasy, especially since the Bowlby research, that I have often been attacked by some of my colleagues here, who asked me why I had not dared to admit in the first place that the early mother-child "separation" is in itself a pathogenic factor, and why I had not used my influence sufficiently for the suspension of this practice. (As a matter of fact, there are psychiatrists and clinical psychologists in this country who used to advise members of the kibbutz who were in need of psychological help to quit the kibbutz.)

As psychiatrists and psychologists, we should above all respect patterns of living. I completely agree with what Fritz Redl said in his Oranim lecture, i.e., that a situation is not *in itself* pathogenic, and that one has to do the utmost to deal with it. We should avoid the concept of "natural" pathogenesis, and learn instead to take advantage, in any situation, of its mental help resources. After this conference, my friends in the educational field will be less defensive; they will therefore be able to find more and better ways to the solution of our problems. That we do have problems, there would be no use denying.

I have come to realize that some of the problems that lie at the heart of our concern are also very much at the core of your interest, especially where the second and third years are concerned. We are aware that this age group has been rather neglected in kibbutz educational practice and thinking. We tried in our subgroup to formulate some theoretical points, particularly about the integration and unification potentialities of the ego in early childhood. Since we did not overdo the theorizing, I think this discussion was beneficial.

There are quite a number of observations and anecdotes dealing with this age group of two to three years; unfortunately, we have not yet undertaken the task of collecting data scientifically on this very important period, which contains the first steps in the child's social life. It is a big challenge to us for the near future.

We have received some useful hints from you for research. So far, we have been too much involved to tackle acute problems; we have not yet reached that stage in which we would at last settle down in order to carry on proper and extensive research. What we will have to do first is to formulate and define accurate questions that can lead us, by methodologically proper ways, to the precise answers. We are thus much more in need of your *professional* aid than of any other kind.

I had hoped that we would have more discussions on group problems, especially since there are so many people here who have done so much research, thinking, and writing about group phenomena. We have come across some very interesting group phenomena here.

MORDECHAI SEGAL: May I address our friends from abroad as "chaverim?" In our kibbutz language, "chaverim" means "partners to a cause." This week, we have come to regard you as intellectual — and more than intellectual — partners to our cause. For the Israeli participants, it has been a deeply moving and inspiring experience. We truly admire the great amount of "in-feeling" and "in-thinking" into our life situation that you have achieved.

For you, this has no doubt been a chance to gain some interesting firsthand information; secondly, to find how you can apply this to your own situation; thirdly, to try to assist us if you can. For us, it has meant above all a fulfillment of our wish to be known. We do want to be known; in fact, we have something of a missionary spirit in us, as you must surely have felt. We have certainly been eager to impress our truths upon such a group of sensitive and developed minds as have participated in this Conference. But we also wanted to explain ourselves to ourselves, by way of our own formulations — and, even more so, of course, by way of your attempts at interpretation.

What have we achieved? (Not what have *you* achieved, but *what have we achieved together?*) It may have been the discovery that the kibbutz, although a recent movement and one that is very much planned, is still a rather varied interplay of theory and action. It isn't simply a "free" movement. As in every movement, there is much variation, not only from one kibbutz to another, but also from one children's home to another, even within the same kibbutz. This is a pattern of variation that springs from the diverse origins of the members of the kibbutzim, and the differences in our human experiences before we came to the kibbutz, as well as within the kibbutz. In a way, it would be correct to say that the middle-class Jewish population in the larger cities of the United States, which some of you probably know intimately, is much more homogeneous, as far as its child-raising practices and ideals are concerned, than the kibbutz. That may sound like a paradox, but it is true.

It is truly an achievement that you have been able to see this wide variety of practices and ideas against the common background of the kibbutz. We can't be dealt with in a piecemeal, mosaic sort of way; our practices could not ever be truly understood in that way. All the aspects of our practice are linked together: the setting up of ideals, the ideal-creating function, and the planning of educational practices, right down to the very finest items; and then, the confronting of our plans with reality — with the reaction of real people, real parents, real children, in real situations — and the correcting of our plans accordingly.

As far as our ideals are concerned, they are at bottom historically determined; but insofar as we are going to go on thinking about them, and putting them to the test, we are also able to look at them theoretically. This dual approach is characteristic of our population. Many of our convinced people do leave the kibbutz after a while, yet they do not leave its ideal. There are others, of course, who take leave of our ideals without taking leave of the kibbutz. The rest of us — not all the rest of us, perhaps, but the sort of kibbutz audience you have come to know here — stays on in the kibbutz with these ideals, yet still goes on thinking about them all the time.

Two fundamental questions have been raised about our life

and education here. First, should we go on with our "worship of manual labor?" Well, for us, frankly, this the "the Jewish question." We are not very happy — in fact, we are really troubled — by the fact that the largest part of the Jewish population during the Diaspora gave up manual labor altogether.

The other question has been brought up in connection with out attempts to create an ideal setting. It is the question of our being, not only a closed kibbutz system, but also a responsible minority in the country as a whole. Well, we feel we are a responsible minority; we are considered that by the general population. (It was noted earlier in the Conference that about 10 per cent of us work outside the kibbutz.) Still, there remains the question of the proportion between these two functions of ours: the creative kibbutz function *per se,* and the function of responsibility to Israeli life in general. There may be contradictions between the two in actual practice.

This is a question which we must work out for ourselves, and you can't very well help us settle it, although any suggestions would be valuable. You have helped us to see our planning ideas more clearly; you have encouraged us in the direction of fostering more *constancy* in our educational work — constancy of educators, prolonged contact of metaplot and teachers with children, and so on — and also in the idea that it is good to have diffused contact, diffused influence, diffused control of a child's life and education, during infancy as well as during adolescence, and also in the intermediate period.

It has been a very valuable lesson for us that you speak a psychological language and a pedagogical language that have grown out of your life situations, and that we have to translate your ideas into our own language. In that way, we will form a new language, remembering that languages differ from one another, not only in the basic meaning of words, or in their secondary connotations and associational power, but also in grammar and structure. This will be a very difficult task for us to achieve in the near future, but if we can rely on such able and well-meaning friends as you are, and can keep the contacts — the very precious contacts — that we have established here, then I am sure that we will achieve it.

SHIMON STERN: I should like to point out two features of the kibbutz, which we should keep in mind whenever we study it, or try to understand it.

At the opening of our Institute, we discussed the kibbutz in general; it took some time, I'm sure, for some of the participants to recognize that there are differences among the three movements. Later on, I think you all realized that one could truly speak of the "personality" of each kibbutz, since every kibbutz has its own characteristics. This is not the moment to go into the reasons for this, but in any case, it is very important to keep it in mind, because you can arrive at true generalizations only so long as you take into account these differences.

Secondly, the kibbutz is still a developing and quite dynamic sort of society. I know, from my own experience, that within my kibbutz, we made mistakes whenever we forgot this. A member of one of the oldest kibbutzim told me something that happened during the very first years, when (it's so easy to say that today!) "nobody really knew what a kibbutz would be," yet all the people who then lived in the kibbutz were convinced that *they* knew.

There were then about fifteen members, all living together in an old cowshed. After a few weeks or so, certain connections — certain feelings of the kind that exist in every human society — arose between one *chaver* and another *chaver*. One day, one of these *chaverim* brought in a mat and marked off a certain corner of the cowshed. There followed a fierce discussion, in the assembly of the fifteen members, as to whether this could be tolerated — on kibbutz principles. You smile, and I'm sure you even know what the decision was. Anyhow, this shows us that the people who discussed it then were very sincere — *and* very narrow — in their discussion. I think we are often in a somewhat similar position when we discuss kibbutz questions nowadays.

It's very hard for us to distinguish clearly between the basic principles of the kibbutz and changing appearances, changing approaches. In my opinion, you cannot understand many of the things that have gone on in a kibbutz, or that are going on now, without keeping that problem in mind. We have heard, for instance, about "the family point of view." I think we make a mistake when we say, as has been said here, that the family trends

that are showing up now, or other such changes that are going
on in the daily life of a family, may bring about "the end of the
kibbutz." We should free ourselves, of course, from the habit of
making comparisons between our families and the so-called
"normal" family of the urban West. On the other hand, we
should remain free to consider changes that can still take place;
then, I'm sure, we will find the right direction.

I want to conclude by telling you what I felt when you gave
your reports on your visits to the kibbutzim. I remember that
several times people spoke of the kibbutz as a real paradise. That
shocked me; at least it confused my conception of paradise. But
as I thought it over, I realized that every paradise must look
quite different, depending on whether you see it from the outside
or from the inside. It was really paradise, I think, to sit together
with people who showed so much and such quick understanding
— a very precious personal experience, that has left me with many
things to think about.

MRS. WINSOR: Although I shall speak as an educator, some of
my remarks may not be what educators might expect to hear,
when the psychopedagogical process is under discussion. Having
gone over my notes, I find, interestingly enough, that questions I
posed for myself only a few days ago sound now as though someone else had written them. I see among them many of the straw
men that we have so successfully demolished here. Perhaps this
has been my way of learning, once again, that even though we
may speak the same tongue, we can still build a great many straw
men: ideas we discuss at great length, only to find that they are
unreal, irrelevant, or unserviceable.

The first of these was our notion of the parental deprivation
that your children must be suffering, as compared with ours. After
a day at the kibbutz, we found that this notion did not really
have the validity we thought it had; in reading the literature, we
had shaped a construct and assumed that it was a reality. Our
questions on this subject are still there; now they have become
deepened, however, both in their meaning and in our hope of
arriving at answers.

We have accepted your basic premise, namely, that the major
purpose of kibbutz education is the preservation of the kibbutz

way of life. This was also something of a straw man, in so far as all education, the whole world over, is for the purpose of preserving or advancing the way of life that that particular society has chosen. The real difference here is that yours is a very small society within a larger society, while we think of our educational system as serving the total national community. Even that difference breaks down, however, because in our country every school system, every school, has its own structure and its own definition of how it is to achieve its goals.

Once we accept your basic premise, however, there are still techniques to be discussed. Otherwise there would be no purpose in any meeting of this nature: if one way is the only way, then thinking — even questioning — becomes fruitless. What we are talking about, within this basic framework of premises — about which we may or may not have differences — is the true function of education.

In our society, we also think of the school as having both the possibility and the responsibility for making an impact upon personality development. My own small institution is supported by government grants to study such problems as: "The Psychological Impact of the School Experience," and "The Role of the School in Promoting Mental Health." I say this only to remind you that we do not consider the school to be something apart from the problem of personality development, or mental health. When we talk about education or teaching, we, too, have in mind a larger role than the transmission of knowledge from one generation to another. While this idea is accepted quite widely in theory, in practice it remains more of an ideal than a reality in my country. Nevertheless, with such a basic concept, one continues to ask questions — even though sometimes humbly, because of one's limited experience in the situation.

First, then, some questions about your kindergartens as a common experience for children from three through seven. One can easily conceive of a child *learning productively* as a member of such a group; but then one asks, in the light of our understanding of the meaning of play, What use has been made of *children's play* as a learning experience? I am not now talking of play therapy, nor of play as relief from work. I have been reading that you think of the child, even at this early age, as *doing work* — making the bed, helping the metapelet — *after which* he plays. Has this not lost sight of an important personality developmental process — namely, that the child's play can really be regarded as *his work in the world?*

This leads us to a consideration of some techniques of education that might well be included among your basic approaches. One of these has to do with how the teacher is trained to understand *her* role, in helping a child to learn through clarifying the confusions of his world as he plays. This means such matters as how the groups are constituted, what materials you give the children to play with, what you use out of the environment, and how you draw learning and knowledge from what you use — how, in short, you make the child's environment his text, because that *is* his only text at this time.

If you regard the young child as learning in the main through his play and his sensory, kinaesthetic experiences, from the ages of three to five — and then, from five onwards, learning rather through vicarious experiences, as he is introduced to the world of symbols — then the role of the teacher changes markedly.

At this initial stage of introducing the child to his symbolic world, the teacher takes on a new role — in some ways an intellectually quite demanding role. Up to this point in the child's life it was all right to say that, for the child, things may be as we adults see them, or they may be as the child sees and interprets them.

But an aleph is an aleph, just as an "A" is an "A" for us; there are no two ways about it. Numbers also have their own rights and their own discipline, so that the child is being asked, as he meets his symbolic world, to move along an essentially *dictated* path. A question now emerges as to the meaning of the "togetherness" in the children's home, including as it does the threes through sevens. Can you provide the variety of experiences desirable for those different years, without rather carefully differentiating the patterns of learning and living?

Might one not question, for example, what you have done in the matter of toys for your children? I sometimes say that we, in our Western culture, first take out of a loaf of bread the major ingredients for good health, and then try to put them back in the form of "added vitamins." Often, the toys we offer our children are just that sort of attempt to put back into the environment what has been removed so completely from their primary experience.

You don't need to do that; you have the primary experiences right at hand, in very significant ways. In my very brief visits, I saw so many instances, directly available, of the materials that *we have to provide* for our children, who live in the very effete world of our cities, remote from contact with the world of primary experiences. Why should you too try to put into your already rich world what seems so good in our comparatively denuded world? This raises some basic questions, I think, about how one educates the young child in a rich world like yours.

As a schoolteacher, I must also look at the middle years of childhood, and then there arise other questions. For example, we too had the idea of a "project method" in education; we became very enthusiastic about the idea that learning should emerge from an entity of experience. We have since learned that we need to be more sophisticated about what we mean by "an entity of the learning experience." There is a wholeness of learning experience in such disciplines as mathematics, or science, or history, which have sequences and beauties of their own. In the learning lives of many children, these whole entities of knowledge can play significant roles.

During these middle years of child life, there is a tremendous opportunity for the development of value-structures. Has enough thought been given to comparative culture studies, if I may use so ponderous a term in talking about nine- and ten-year-olds? Or has there been such an intense involvement in the child's own kibbutz, and the riches it has to offer, that there has been a *narrowing* of the socio-educational experience? In these years, the child is given to questioning; he thinks of this questioning as a process of discovery rather than as a personal revolt. Does the kibbutz curriculum offer him adequate opportunity for simply becoming acquainted with the wide social-cultural world?

At Caesarea, for example, my mind simply buzzed with curriculum opportunities — not only because of the wonder of such an archeological find but, for example: what were the values of the people who built it? who did the building? for whom? What does all this mean in terms of understanding the culture of those times? What comparisons can be made with our times and culture? The world here is so rich that it really does make one's mind buzz, you see. I turn now to the high school curriculum, where there is a grave need for the differentiation of "subject matter" (along with the training of specialists needed to teach these different subject-matter areas). Can you afford to deny your children, particularly during their adolescent years, the dignity of struggling to master those disciplines that have tough content? Can you provide sufficient differentiation to meet their needs as adolescents, as well as their needs as adults, in the kibbutz or outside? Can you do all this in your small secondary schools? (Everywhere else, we are becoming aware of the increasing need for regional secondary schools.)

This conference, incidentally, has led me to a renewed and deepened concern for the training experiences of our own child-care staffs, not only in institutions, but in nursery schools. Thus, in one sense, at least, this has been, very deeply, a learning experience for me, too. We have truly communicated — which is why it has been so hard and so very, very rewarding.

MISS WITMER: I came to this Institute as a representative of the United States Children's Bureau, which, throughout its history, has been interested in child development. I too have been greatly interested in that field, in both its psychological and sociological aspects, so that both for the Bureau and for me this conference has been very important. The Bureau, however, has had an additional and very specific reason for interest in this conference. As you well know, the problem of providing adequate care for children while their mothers are at work outside the home faces our country increasingly. Just this year, the federal government is starting to help the states financially to set up and operate day-care centers for working mothers.

Two aspects of day care especially concern us. On the one hand, there is the long-standing question of how best to provide care for children when the mothers are away from home. On the other, there is the question of whether day-care programs can help to bring about cultural change in the lowest economic segment of our society.

For many years, it has probably been functional to our society to have a "lower class." While such a class was not deliberately created, there were advantages to the society as a whole in the fact that many members were accustomed to the tough, strenuous kind of life that went with the unskilled work that had to be done. Now, however, the functional utility of that group of people, and of that way of life, is diminishing greatly. Hence, it becomes ever more important to find a means of helping these people and their children to develop the aspirations and the abilities that will fit them for participation in middle-class society.

Some of us (and we are by no means the only people interested in this) see day care as one such means. These culturally deprived children come to the centers at an early age, and spend long hours there, five or six days a week. It would therefore seem that a well-designed program of activities might supplement their home experiences in such a way that these children would be much better prepared than they usually are for utilizing what the schools later have to offer them. This would be especially true if work carried on concurrently with the parents could enable them to bring *their* child-rearing methods more or less into line with those used in the centers.

This conception of shared child-rearing through day-care centers has made us think that we may have much to learn from the kibbutzim that can be applied back home. Especially, your experience might tell us whether it is wise to so divide the child-rearing job. On these points, I feel that I have learned a great deal. Part of what I have learned is something I should have known in the first place. I should have recognized that the child-rearing practices of the kibbutzim, and the institutional arrangements that underlie those practices, are part of an organic whole. Therefore, it would be too much to expect that we could find in your child-care arrangements a model that could be copied literally by our very different society.

To be more specific, I've been making a list of some of the elements in the kibbutz social picture as a whole that are different from ours — elements that account in part for the success of your child-care arrangements and that might have to be approximated, if those arrangements were to be successfully adopted by a different society.

Chief on this list are the values and customs of the kibbutz itself, from which, in a sense, all the other points on my list flow. In the kibbutzim — by contrast with our complex society — parents have much the same values, customs, ways of life as are represented in the shared child-rearing plan. There is a child-centeredness about the kibbutz, and a predominantly affectionate atmosphere. I have not deluded myself into thinking that every individual is all-loving but, relatively speaking, there seems to be a greater concern for children and a more freely expressed love of children than generally exists in our society. Also, the roles of the nurse and of the educator appear to be clearly defined and readily accepted by most parents. Lastly, there is the practical fact that the parents live and work very near the children's centers, so that they can come to the centers and the children can go out from the centers at will. All this is very different from what we would be likely to meet with in a day-care center in a large city in the United States.

Accordingly, I go away feeling that if we were to try to apply literally what we have learned here, we would have to make a great many changes, some of them beyond our present power to make. This doesn't mean that I feel there is nothing we can use from your experiences in shared child-rearing. Particularly, I feel that in spite of cultural differences, your success in maintaining affectionate parent-child relations and a sense of family, even though many parental functions are assumed by others, has important implications for all forms of foster care. To try to tell you in what other ways your experience can help us is beyond my time limit now. I conclude by offering you my own and my government's thanks for your teaching.

MENAHEM GERSON: It is really difficult to part from a group of people who are so gifted, straightforward, and warmhearted. There is the custom of bringing up a vote of thanks; in this case it is not merely a custom, it is really heartfelt.

Now I'm going to disclose one fault of the kibbutz that you haven't yet found out by yourselves. You see, we never thank our own people, it's all taken for granted. I would like to tell you that the burden of preparing this Conference, from this side, has been shouldered by Gideon Lewin. It would be easy to point out the mistakes that were made, but the only way to be quite sure not to make mistakes is by not doing anything. I am glad that Mr. Lewin did not choose to take the "safe" way.

About the business of this Conference, I am not going to try even to talk. In Israel, everything is brought under historic perspective. Let me say only that, during the last two thousand years, we have not had such an opportunity for consultation as we had here, this past week.

A word about the future. We can't come forward, unfortunately, with an organized research program. We have sat together and we have seen the problems; but we can't propose a program now. I hope, I am certain, that this won't be our last word, that we will achieve something.

It would be a pity if all connections between us were to cease in the near future. I can see two things that may be valuable for ensuring contact. One was the proposal made by one of the participants that we here should put out a bulletin, or something like that, telling you people what is going on here, what has happened recently in education, research, etc.

You are also cordially invited to revisit us. When you do come here, please feel free to announce your visit; otherwise, we may be working on the Shabbat when you come, and you will just have to take your place as potential members of our "living paradise." You have shown such great progress in Hebrew that some of you have even learned that the plural of "metapelet" is "metaplot" — so may I be allowed to say, instead of "farewell," the Hebrew "lehitraot," which is much nicer, because it means "We'll see you again."

GIDEON LEWIN: Summarizing an Institute like this is really an impossible task. Three things, however, now seem quite important to me.

There has emerged a tremendous responsibility for scientists and for teachers of psychology to translate their scientific concepts into a practical framework for teachers. It is a very difficult task to make a popularization of scientific concepts; but our metaplot and our nursery teachers want these concepts explained to them.

The most important thing for me has been that I have had to reconsider, to learn anew, and to understand more deeply many concepts and scientific problems.

I certainly hope that our proceedings will be published, for they would undoubtedly constitute a most valuable document on the subject of kibbutz education. We have been dreaming of an Institute like this since 1951, when I first met Dr. Neubauer, at a time when he also met with our great teacher, Shmuel Gross.

I think that we should plan for another Conference; that we should keep in contact. I'm not able, at any rate, to put my thanks in words, since whatever we would say would fall short. Just thank you very much.

DR. NEUBAUER: This review of the major issues discussed during the Institute should not be regarded as a summary. I shall not attempt to comment on all the events, nor will I make any effort to avoid the expression of my own views. I would rather follow the general spirit of the Institute, in adding my uncensored thoughts, based on my own interests and judgment, and on the various propositions I have been led to consider. I thus assume the editor's privilege of having the last word — with a warning to the reader, once again, that what follows is not a summary statement, arrived at by consensus.

In the Introduction, I presented some of the propositions and questions that we brought with us to this conference. How did we fare? To what degree were we able to find answers?

One thing is quite clear: we succeeded in avoiding the drawing of conclusions on the basis of a simple question-and-answer method. Our Israeli colleagues did not just place their problems before us, and then ask for specific solutions; nor did the visitors, at any time during the discussion, offer "directions," for we were all too well aware that the task of translating our comments into meaningful statements applicable to kibbutz life must rest with the members of the kibbutz. We recognized that the collective is a social structure in which the social conditions and the values and aims of life affect every aspect of the human condition, and that we had come with experiences quite different from those present in kibbutz society.

Aware of these differences, we were indeed hesitant to put forth "final" formulations. Our agreements, based as they were on community of experience, did not therefore signify approval; nor did our concern with certain aspects of the child's life in the kibbutz imply adverse criticism. Both areas — of agreement and of concern — will need further scientific investigation before we are able to come to definitive conclusions. Nevertheless, we sometimes gained impressions of such strength that we were able to speak with conviction; at other times, our impressions led to the posing of new questions as the means of finding our way through our hesitations and lack of knowledge.

In spite of the fact that the literature had led many of us to expect that we would discover deprivation in the young child of the kibbutz, we did not find evidence to confirm these anticipations. On the contrary, we were quite impressed by the strength of the family influence on the children's development, and by this unique example of how family life can not only be maintained unimpaired, but can even be integrated — to its own advantage — into a system of collective child care. *The geographic distance between parental quarters and children's home is a wholly inadequate measure of the quality of the emotional relationships between parent and child.*

Parental influence can be carried effectively into the children's home: nurturing, sensory and intellectual stimulation, and continuity of relationship can be provided, under kibbutz conditions, and properly coordinated with the care given by the metapelet. Individual pathology can be examined within the system in which it is operative, and by which it is either minimized or accentuated. Thus, this form of communal child care is, in itself, of extraordinary significance: it can be understood only within the totality of kibbutz life; its individual parts cannot be exported and used under different circumstances, without careful thought and examination.

It is a basic tenet of each viable society to improve itself. It would be shortsighted for anyone to assume that the kibbutz will not do so too, within its own structure.

While we had the opportunity to review, in some detail, certain phases of development, we were able to get a less clear picture of other developmental periods. Thus, we would have wished for more information about the separation-individuation stage, for some of us felt that less attention was given to the child between the ages of two and three than during infancy.

We spent much time on the adolescent. Alerted by the crisis of adolescence in our own society, and conscious of the specific vulnerability of that age level — in which an accumulation of childhood experiences becomes crystallized, so as to set the pattern of the child's individuality and to integrate it into the social fabric — we raised many questions about kibbutz adolescence: Is there sufficient opportunity for individual fermentation in the group life? Is there a "moratorium" granted, if one is needed? Are deviations from the norm permitted? Is the group pressure too great?

It is interesting to note that the concerns we have regarding that age group in our own society are usually of an opposite character. There, we are troubled rather by the *absence* of group influences, group responsibilities, and group ideas — a situation which does not make it possible for our adolescent to anchor his individual emotionality to clear social goals. (Not that our adolescents are without their own type of *conformity;* but that the *balance* of the individual and his society needs to be redefined for each new generation — which presents a constant challenge. Close examination of the period of adolescence may provide the clearest picture of how well one is succeeding in striking that balance.)

Similar questions arose in connection with the role of the sexes: the position of women and their fulfillment in kibbutz life; the extent of their equality in relation to their special role as mothers; their participation, as equal members with the males, in all facets of adult kibbutz life.

The contribution of the educator, as well as that of the metapelet, was frequently discussed. It was felt that the kibbutz has a unique opportunity to enrich its educational contribution by instituting a mode of teaching based on the individual experiences of the child, and making advantageous use of his natural surroundings. The maturity and the deep sense of responsibility so invariably present among those we met represented the most positive assurances for the achievement of such a strengthening of the present curriculum.

As was pointed out in the Introduction, some of us came to this Institute hoping to find help in answering problems of child care for some of our own groups of children. There are many children in our society who are altogether without normal family care, and we need to develop community facilities for them. What would the kibbutz child-rearing program offer us, from which we might feasibly draw up our own master plan in the service of these children? To be sure, one must be cautious about adopting techniques and facilities that have been developed to serve one given social unit, and then attempting to apply them within a totally different social system.

Those who look to the kibbutz for the answers to problems of institutional care will quickly find themselves forced to revise their concepts of kibbutz life, for it has not developed an institutionalized child-care program at all. There are quite significant differences between child-rearing in an institution and a collective child-rearing plan, in which the parents and the child-rearing person collaborate. The kibbutz has shown that this latter collaboration is possible, and what we might learn from it is just how *we* can achieve it.

The kibbutz never set out to offer substitute care — that is, a plan whereby the community would *take over* the child-rearing functions; on the contrary, its goal was to develop a *collective* care program. This in itself is of decisive importance, since it eliminates at once the "traditional" dichotomy of "family care or community care." The intensity of the mother's participation, and the stability of the metapelet's involvement; the long-term programming, continuity of contact and stability of the social structure — all these provide the essential ingredients for a more successful, new form of communal care.

There are many circumstances in our society — such as a prolonged physical illness — in which the young child may have to live outside the home; the kibbutz clearly illustrates how parental involvement can be maintained, in order to provide adequate contact and stimulation. Day-care programs which we have established out of necessity for the working mother have many problems in common with those of the kibbutz's "children's houses."

The Institute spent little time on the question of how the metapelet is selected: the individual qualities that are felt to be requisite for an effective child-care person, and the degree of training regarded as necessary for her functioning well with children of various ages. She is not a "professional person," in our sense of that term; she comes from the same milieu as the parents, and shares their aspirations and values. This last fact has been quite significant for us in considering both her willingness and her ability to share with the parents the care of the child.

The introduction of the "group" early in the child's life has been in the foreground of interest for many of us. One question has had to do with the use of the group to provide stimulation under circumstances in which it might not otherwise be given by the adult. Such a question naturally points towards the group as a substitute for inadequate adult-child interaction, or as an additional source for imitation, stimulation and experimentation within that same framework. To what degree, and in what form, can a group provide such experiences? How can it be used to further development under otherwise minimal conditions?

We know the value of continuity and stability in family life; we do not yet know enough about the effects of belonging to a continuous group as an essential experience in the development of a sense of social responsibility, or of the ability to integrate into a larger unit, nor are we yet prepared to estimate the efficacy of the group as a means of mitigating adolescent confusion. Groups, as we know them, are quite unstable; they come into being, most often, late in the child's life — for many, not until they enter military service, an experience which we have found many to be altogether unprepared to deal with. The role of the group, therefore, in the general conditions of life, and under special circumstances for reparative mental health purposes, raises many basic questions.

I would like now to deal with some of the clinical issues. There was no opportunity to discuss a comprehensive mental health program for the kibbutz, although some of us are of the opinion that each collective constitutes an unusually structured unit, which would readily lend itself to the programming of "total care." How does the clinician view his task in relation to the total population for which he has assumed responsibility? Is there a general evaluation of the development of all the children? What is regarded as pathology, and in need of additional clinical service? What are the criteria for the moment of referral? What are the socio-tonic and the socio-alien conditions? To what degree can community resources be drawn upon for the correction of maladjustment; has there been any change in the pattern of treatment, as compared with our own service programs?

Data were presented which indicated that the proportion of kibbutz children suffering from some emotional disorder is about the same as that among children outside the kibbutz. Such statistics must be studied carefully. Do they imply that even though one society is basically different from another, the difference between their impact on health is negligible? Or is it possible that pathology is more readily detected within the kibbutz — which would indicate that our comparative data are really misleading? However that may be, further child population studies along these lines would be very meaningful, and we can only hope that they will continue to be produced.

Some time was spent in an examination of the finding that many of the children's emotional disorders are family-bound, as indeed they generally are in other societies. This led to a consideration of the necessity for dealing with references to "mother" and "father" at a different level of interpretation from that which is true of our society. While we are used to associating these concepts with single persons, under the circumstances of collective child-rearing, the image of "mother" may refer to a composite, made up of various fused relationships. The question then arose of how child-rearing practices can be developed of such a nature that these fusion processes are maintained and fragmentation avoided. In dealing with these questions, we found many possibilities for study relevant to our theory, as well as to our practice.

The significant progress that has been made in the understanding of the separation-individuation phase by some investigators in the United States prompted inquiries regarding this stage of development under kibbutz conditions. The step from the home to the nursery very often constitutes the first move away from home. Separation, prior to this, is achieved *in the presence of a mother figure,* thus permitting the child both to leave and to return, back to the primary object. How does this take place in relation to metapelet and mother? How is separation regarded by the kibbutz child between the ages of two and three, particularly since "belonging" is here also connected with the group?

These separation-individuation processes could be carefully explored in a kibbutz and would undoubtedly yield very significant data. Does separation anxiety occur in the same form in a kibbutz, and does it have similar dynamic meaning? It the freer expression of aggression against one object rendered more possible by the fact that another object is readily available? What is the distribution of aggression and dependency under such circumstances?

This leads to the whole question of the psychosexual development of the kibbutz child. Data were presented which indicated that over a long period of time, there has been a significant absence of homosexuality. I shall not offer a detailed discussion of the various explanations that could be offered for this. I have not as yet come across any convincing propositions based on a careful delineation of those factors contributing to the formation of sexual identity among kibbutz children. The presence or absence of a specific form of psychopathology does not of itself provide sufficient insight into the developmental picture. Any study of this sort must therefore go beyond symptom formation and seek to bring to light its underlying dynamic forces. These must, in the end, be measured within the context of life in the collectives: the frequency of the divorce rate, remarriage, the role of the woman, etc.

Actually, any study of child development should be based, first of all, on a clearer understanding of those factors that contribute to family stability or instability. With the growing concern about rapidly rising divorce rates in our country, particularly among the younger people, a study of families in the kibbutz could shed light on our common concern in this area. In the absence of economic considerations which may otherwise bind a woman to her marriage, and in the absence of concern about the children's welfare in case of divorce, those factors that contribute to family stability can be more easily isolated. Selectivity, sexual compatibility, the faculty of overcoming misunderstandings and conflicts, etc., can thus be revealed. The reactions of children to their parents' divorce can be compared with similar experiences here.

I have mentioned a few of the issues which were outstanding to me, in the light of my own professional interests. The basically different character of the kibbutz offers uniquely rich possibilities for research activities; beyond this, the existence of a real striving for *new conditions of life* demands from all of us the study of differences, in order that we may all broaden our own views.

The Kibbutz and Communal Education

SHMUEL GOLAN AND ZVI LAVI

T HE KIBBUTZ movement in Israel is nearing its fiftieth anniversary. It was preceded by numerous experiments in communal life. Although at first the kibbutz regarded itself as connected with those experiments, its actual character and its direction of development have been determined not by the early communes but rather by the conditions of life in Israel. The ideology of communal life — of the kibbutz as a collectivist unit — emerged and took shape during the course of decades; these communal ideals have filled, and still fill, an important function in the kibbutz movement and in the education of the younger generation.

In the initial period, it was necessary, in coping with the difficult conditions then prevailing in the country, to depend on solidarity, maximum mutual aid, and the integration of new immigrants into a life of hard physical labor. These were the principal determinants of the first stages of communal life in Israel, which from the start has been rooted in the reality of this country.

The kibbutz has also been an important factor in the absorption of Jewish immigrants into Israel; it has made a decisive contribution to the emergence of a class of farmers and workers in this country; it is, in fact, bound up with all the social and political processes in Israel. In all these respects, it has had to be guided chiefly by its own experience.

The earliest period in the history of the kibbutz movement was the most difficult one. There is no resemblance between the flourishing kibbutz settlements of our time and the groping, primitive attempts that sprang up in this country before the First World War. Conditions of life in those days were harsh. The earliest kibbutz members had not had any experience with either economic management or the regulation of social life, and certainly not with child education under communal conditions.

The surrounding population showed a complete distrust of such "social experiments." Serious-minded persons, especially in economic circles, did not believe that a farm in which the work of the individual was *not* based on the profit motive had any chance for survival. They could not imagine that members of a commune would work devotedly and responsibly, purely out of their attachment to the farm and to kibbutz property, and without wages. But the kibbutz proved to be justified in its view that members would carry out their duties, *even when the economic motivation was not direct and personal.*

The kibbutzim have succeeded economically: they have built splendid farms, and have become a major supplier of the country's agricultural demands. They have absorbed a large number of additional members, including the second kibbutz generation. Today, the kibbutz movement comprises 220 flourishing, firmly established settlements in all parts of the country, with an aggregate population of approximately 100,000, i.e., about 6 per cent of the country's total population. The qualitative significance of the kibbutz movement — in the fields of economy, culture and politics — is undoubtedly many times greater.

Along with the kibbutz movement there grew and developed its educational enterprise — communal education. The first child that made his appearance in Degania (the oldest kvutzah, established in 1912) confronted the kvutzah members with problems they had not foreseen. The work and social status of women, the character of the family as a whole, were put to a severe test. Actual educational problems arose later, when it appeared that the traditional ways of family education were not adequate to the communal life-pattern.

Thus, stage by stage, amid gropings, retreats, and sometimes painful struggles, the educational ventures of the kibbutz movement took form. Even today, communal education has not yet solved all its problems; in day-to-day practice there are still differences, sometimes rather serious ones, between the main trends in the kibbutz movement. But at least we may speak today of common outlines of communal education.

I. The Kibbutz Community

Education in the kibbutz, or "communal education," is a direct function of the kibbutz community, and is intended to ensure its continuance. In order to understand its content and structure, therefore, it is necessary to understand the nature of the kibbutz community, its ideological, social and economic principles.

The kibbutz, as a producers' and consumers' commune, concerns itself with furnishing all the requirements of its members; it therefore constitutes an *independent economic and social unit.* The kibbutz derives its livelihood from a mixed farm with its various branches, or from a combined agricultural and industrial undertaking; the kibbutz economy is mechanized, with high technological and professional standards — a prerequisite for its economic viability. Out of its income, the kibbutz supplies the requirements of its members; its surpluses are used for development and the establishment of new branches of production.

The kibbutz is based on the *principle of self-labor*: there is no place in it for hired labor, any more than there is for private ownership of the means of production. Every member works according to his ability, and is supplied according to his needs — within the limits of the economic ability of the kibbutz. This ability advances with the growth of the kibbutz: at first the kibbutz was nothing but a "commune of paupers," who worked under difficult pioneering conditions; in the course of time, its standard of living has risen steadily.

The members of the commune work at fixed workplaces, in production or service (communal kitchen, laundry, etc.) . A member may change his work from time to time; he usually acquires specialist skills in a number of occupations. The kibbutz concerns itself with the vocational training of its members, especially the holders of key jobs in the management of the farm. Each economic branch is operated by its permanent personnel, who elect one of their members "coordinator-manager." Over the course of time, kibbutz economy has evolved a considerable occupational differentiation, which opens up to the individual member a wide and varied range of possibilities for specialized work.

The kibbutz, as a consumers' commune, supplies all the requirements of its members: food, clothing, housing, small personal effects, medical aid, education, recreation, and culture. A small sum of money is allowed for the strictly personal expenses of each member — such as visits to town, gifts, photography, and other hobbies. Various buildings and institutional arrangements, on the other hand, are designed for communal use: the dining-hall, children's houses, school, communal clothes-storeroom, sports and infirmary, laundry, cultural center and library, cinema, sports grounds, etc. The kibbutz also maintains full social insurance (old age, sickness, invalidism, widowhood, orphanhood, etc.)

The housing standard has been determined by the degree of economic development. During the first years, the members lived in provisional quarters: tents, huts, and other temporary structures. But as the kibbutz grows, each family (this is also true for the unmarried member) is allotted one-and-a-half rooms in a building, with a bathroom, kitchenette, terrace, and garden. (It should be remembered that the children do not live in with their parents, but are in special children's houses.) Even in a well-established kibbutz, there are still differences in housing, for example, between the rooms provided for younger and older members.

A member's annual leave is usually spent in one of several special recreation centers, at the expense of the kibbutz. Clothing and shoes are issued to each member according to his choice, in conformity with a certain norm. The kibbutz also supplies the furniture of the rooms (mostly according to the personal taste of the member) , books, radio, etc.

THE STRUCTURE OF THE KIBBUTZ: The kibbutz is a democratic community based on the equal rights and duties of its members, and on full equality of rights between the sexes. Decisions are taken by majority vote, after joint clarification of the issues involved. General meetings, at which matters requiring decision are discussed, are held once or twice a week. The general meeting, as the supreme body of the kibbutz, sets up the various institutions responsible (each in its particular sphere) for the practical work, which is carried on in accordance with the directives of the kibbutz. The meeting elects holders of various offices, who are responsible to it and report to it on their activities.

One of the institutions is the *secretariat,* which coordinates all economic and social matters (it is sometimes separated into two units: a social secretariat and a farm committee); it consists of full-time members (the social secretary, the treasurer, the farm manager) and of members who serve on the secretariat in addition to their ordinary work. The office-holders are replaced every two or three years. The secretariat refers matters requiring clarification and decision to the general meeting, and all its activities are conducted in accordance with the directives of that supreme body.

At the general meetings, committees are elected, the more important of these being the *farming committee,* the *work committee,* the *member's committee,* and the *education committee.* Other committees are set up to deal with culture, health, political activity, and sports. Finally, there is a *newspaper board* which issues, fortnightly, an internal newspaper of the kibbutz.

Like every other society, an old established kibbutz includes different *age-groups.* In the course of time, it has achieved a natural age-scale, comprising three successive generations: the founders; individuals and groups that have joined the kibbutz in the course of its development; and the children of the latter. A kibbutz starts, as a rule, as a group of seventy to eighty young people. After some thirty years have passed, it has grown to a population of approximately 750 (in some cases, over a thousand). The kibbutz consists almost entirely of families (the family is a distinct, but not self-contained, basic social unit). Economic cares have shifted from the family to the community; there is thus no economic dependence between spouses, and children are not directly dependent upon their parents.

Women in the kibbutz have attained a status of full equality. They are entitled to employment in all branches of the farm, although, for objective reasons (the great number of children), they work mainly in the service branches, which by their size have become public industries (kitchen, dining-hall, laundry, etc.), or else in communal education (child care, teaching). This change in the woman's occupation, away from the traditional practice of restriction to the private household, has been made possible by communal education, according to whose principles and procedures the children, from the day of birth, are brought up in babies' houses, children's houses, and schools.

Social and cultural life in the kibbutz is intense and rich in content. Relations among members are based on personal acquaintance and mutual responsibility. They meet at work and during meals, at weekly meetings, celebrations, social gatherings and political and scientific lectures, and they visit one another in their rooms. Meetings of work teams in each branch and of the various committees are fairly frequent. All this helps to imbue the members of the kibbutz with a deep, organic sense of comradeship.

II. Education in the Kibbutz

Communal education comprises all spheres of the children's lives: physical culture and health care, study, character formation, etc. It permits supervision of the child's development from the day of his birth, and timely intervention in case of any disturbances. It obviates many of the difficulties typical of family education, such as conflicts between the child and his parents. At the same time, communal education does not attempt to bypass the strong emotional bonds between the child and members of his family, but rather lays the foundations for the development of harmonious relations between them.

Communal education, at one and the same time, fosters the emotional attachment of children to their family and to the kibbutz community; it tries, from earliest childhood, to eliminate conflicts between the requirements of the individual and those of the group. The life of the child of tender age revolves round two centers — the children's house and the parents' room — which in the child's emotional experience form but one center. As the child grows up, the importance of a third center increases — that of the kibbutz community, the farm, and the rich and variegated reality of its life.

Education in each kibbutz is conducted in accordance with general principles laid down by the institutions of that kibbutz.

The responsibility for their application rests upon the local education committee — the education workers and representatives of the kibbutz. Educators in the kibbutz can be classified into three groups, according to the age levels among which they work: (1) the staff of women in the nurseries; (2) the entire staff of the "young children's society" (elementary school system), including teachers, educators, and matrons, and (3) the educators and teachers in the secondary school. The education staff meets once a week to clarify routine problems, to coordinate the activities of the various groups of children, and to plan programs for advanced study by the teachers and educators.

Educators and teachers receive their professional training in a special institution run jointly by three national federations of kibbutzim. This institution (the "Kibbutz Seminar") maintains departments for the training of nurses and matrons for all age-groups, kindergarteners, teachers for various levels. The Seminar also maintains three institutes: for physical education, musical education, and the visual arts. A child guidance clinic is connected with the Seminar.

Educational activities in the Kibbutz Movements are directed by the Education Department, which contains separate sections for the different age groups. Functionaries of these sections visit kibbutzim to supervise the work and to advise on the educational problems of the age group in question. A special subdepartment publishes textbooks, pedagogical and psychological literature and translations. The Education Department also issues a quarterly for general educational problems and psychology.

APPENDIX B

From Collective Education towards Education in Collectivism

J. RON POLANI

I. The Beginnings

In an address delivered in 1918, on "Education and the Working Woman," the late J. Bussel expressed his ideas on the communal education of the child in the kvutzah. Not yet a father himself, he nevertheless understood the feelings of the mothers of those days, who were working by day and standing guard by night, and especially those mothers who shared his vision of a way of life. In the midst of their striving towards a life of purpose and equality by the side of their laboring men, their minds were troubled and confused: what was the relationship between the obligations of the mother toward his child, and the duty to work for the community as a whole? The suffering of those mothers did not escape Bussel. Its basic causes lay in the lack not only of minimal hygienic conditions but also of maternal emotional satisfaction.

His ideas on the relationship between family and community in communal life are read to this day. Here is an excerpt:

> "This idea [i.e., of communal child care] encounters disapproval in our midst. The main reason is the tendency to turn the child into a personal possession, an image of his father and mother. We who are against domination wish to dominate our children.
>
> "Our life is based on the commune, yet here we contradict this principle. To assume a child to be private property . . . where will this lead us?"

What implications does the mutual responsibility implicit in communal life have for the structure of the family and the relationship between parents and children, and for educational theories as such? Who could have foreseen the implications in those days? (Even today we feel that generations must pass before adequate theories will have been evolved and finally crystallized.)

At the Women Workers' Convention in 1915, the problem of the working mother in the kvutzah had already been raised, and opinions voiced both for and against communal child care. At the Convention in 1918, however, the discussion was lifted to a higher level. "It was the first time that the question of communal child care had been placed before a public forum. . . . The importance of this Convention," writes Haya Tiaraeli, "lay in its moral strength and in its pointing the way to the future . . . No actual decisions were taken but as a result of the Convention experiments in communal child care were begun."

Here is a description of the start of child-raising "partnerships": "My child is two years old, and I am expecting a second child. Now another mother had joined the group and I rejoice. Conditions for child-rearing should become easier. When the second mother bore her child, I suggested that one of us take care of both our children and my suggestion was accepted — only temporarily, as it turned out." Such instances of mothers forming partnerships for the care of their children did not remain isolated; but they were short-lived, like the partnership between two mothers at Degania:

> "This arrangement was arrived at without the consent of any official body, and without the intervention of any of the members of the kvutzah. Typical is the reaction of one of them, on being told about it: he heaved a sigh of relief and said: 'Happily you have arranged this between yourselves.' Just as this unofficial institution was created, so it also broke up after some weeks — by itself . . . "

(Partnerships of this kind may have also occurred among women workers outside the collective settlements. But in the kvutzah they contained those elements which were to evolve, a short time later, into communal education.)

The first and foremost reason for this development was the desire of working women in those days to achieve equal status with the men. Even the single female worker found it harder than a man to get work in agriculture — the ambition of the "conquerors of manual labor," in those days. To a mother with a child, this aspiration was simply out of the question. Her fate was sealed; she was, in effect, condemned to spend the rest of her life as a housewife, in the limited circle of her family. In the high-spirited atmosphere of the joy of freedom — which was widespread in the country, almost as a compensation for the stark austerity then prevailing in living conditions — such a fate held no attraction for her.

The austerity of the life of the "conquerors of labor" was even less than the dangers to life and limb of the "watchmen standing guard"; but what part in all this could a woman fulfill? The manual work of the agricultural laborer, which involved the use of the short-handled hoe, was hard and back-breaking. The watchman's lot — did that not mean patrolling at night with a loaded rifle, lonely and ever ready? Could such tasks be undertaken by a woman at all? And what if she was with child, or the mother of an infant?

It seemed obvious then that the work should be divided according to the traditions of the old world. The "breadwinner" would do the earning and safeguarding for the whole family, while the wife would keep house for him, do the cooking and laundry, and care for the children. What sense was there in talking about "equal worth and status," when there was no possibility of putting it into practice?

Despite this, "to earn a living as domestic help in a farmer's house in the village, when such work was available, was regarded as a disgrace by the conscientious working woman. Better to starve than to serve in a farmer's household! How great was the joy when a light task of sewing could be exchanged for hard field labor!"

The struggle was not easy. As to what went on in the workers' movement of that period, and even the kvutzah circles, we have convincing evidence: ". . . even among those members who shared our opinions, there were some who saw a struggle against 'natural boundaries,' as it were, in our fierce desire to work in the fields and to do the hardest agricultural labor."

In the kvutzah, women members had to struggle against the prospect of continually working in the kitchen.

"We did not want it, we rebelled against it . . . When asked about work, we would answer: 'Anything but the kitchen.'

"In the actual days of settling on the land, the women members remained detached from the land and tied to house and kitchen. Enraged and bewildered, they saw a breach forming in their common front with the men."

In this struggle for equality, it is obvious that the women's status was weakened when she became a mother. Here is one of the mothers speaking:

"It is considered right for me to devote my whole time to looking after my child. I fought against this idea with all my power. . . . I realized that as a result of it I would have to withdraw from the public life of the kvutzah. . . . I said: I shall take on myself an additional burden; perhaps my child and my maternal feelings will suffer from it, but I am determined to take part in the work and in the social life of the kvutzah."

The anxiety felt by these mothers for the health and even the existence of their children played a big part in their demand for communal child care. The story of one of them is characteristic: "We were all ignorant of the traditional ways of child care our mothers used to practice. The few mothers in our district were bewildered by the climate and the hard conditions." In the words of another mother: "Which of us did not feel helpless with the little squalling creature who was all yours and so much in need of you; and yet, while you were prepared to make every sacrifice for him, you could not devote your whole self to him since you also had to remain a working woman and keep your place in the group. . . . For me there was no doubt whatsoever: 'No parents' collective can exist without educating its children communally.' "

At the 1918 Convention, where the first mothers gathered for consultations, the distress which had mounted in their hearts for years was poured out. It was then that J. Bussel said: "Only in the kvutzah can the woman find support in liberating herself. The kvutzah must not be a home which limits your scope; from it you must be able to view the whole world. . . . Children are an asset of the community as a whole, and it is in this spirit that they should be educated."

For the mothers of the collective settlements, this Convention was a crossroads: those who were in accord with the idea of communal child care would continue to live in the kvutzah; for those not in harmony with the idea — the *Moshav*. Thus it was confirmed that to live in the kvutzah meant to accept communal child care as one of its principles.

Five years had passed since the 1918 Convention. The Kibbutz Movement had enjoyed a period of prosperity during those years. There were now 1600 members in twelve collective settlements, including 190 children. There were also thirty-four nuclei for future settlements, whose 3000 members lived a collective life.

In 1923, a meeting was held, at which not one voice was raised against communal education. As some expressed themselves: "There is no other way in the kvutzah but communal education." In workers' circles generally, at that time, it had not yet become an accepted fact that suitable conditions could be provided for the existence of the family in the kvutzah. The birth rate in the kvutzah was limited not only by serious economic difficulties, but also by the fact that, on the birth of a child, parents often left the kvutzah. A deep anxiety for the future of the kvutzah was expressed, as follows: "In the established Kvutzoth there are hardly any families. Our Kvutzoth are mainly groups of single young men and women. . . . A community without children lacks responsibility; our feeling of responsibility will grow with the children in our midst."

This became the fundamental guideline, now accepted by all — i.e., that the family is the basic unit of kibbutz society, just as the basis of the family in the kvutzah, as everywhere else, is its children. This conception has remained undisputed.

On the other hand, at this meeting four decades ago, there were already differences of opinion expressed, which exist to this day. These differences revolve around the optimal proximity between mother and child within the educational framework of the kvutzah. This was the viewpoint of one of the speakers: "Life in the kvutzah stifles the woman's soul. . . . She has neither a complete home life nor a complete family life." Where did the acceptable solution to this problem lie?

There were those who argued: "The natural basic instincts of the mother should not be subdued . . . Surely a mother's time belongs to her child . . . We must not deprive a child of its family. . . ." Against these there were others who contended: "It is not by traditional upbringing that we shall educate our children towards collectivism. We shall not better ourselves by giving in to 'natural instincts.' The care of our children must be communal, by day and by night, without any exceptions." This was the conclusion that finally emerged: "The fundamental basis of the children's house must be a maximum amount of contact between child and parents."

Already, at this meeting in the 1920's, it was evident that certain significant experiences had been gained during the few short years of communal child care. The need for trained educational workers was stressed, as was the need for "children's nurses who persevere in their job." There was even a debate about the measure of indulgence the child was getting in communal child care: against the opinion that "nothing must be allowed to stint the physical and emotional development of the child, not even the urgent needs of the farm," it was contended that "an attitude of idolatry towards our children exists in our midst. The children too must feel the economic straits of their parents. Shall the parents suffer deprivations, whilst their children shout: 'Give, give!' or are we to do the shouting for them? No, this will not do!" This meeting pointed towards those basic changes that would be required if the early partnerships in child care were finally to lead to education for collectivism.

Clearly, communal education was not based on an "outside" pattern. It is well understood that "the kvutzah is a typical creation of this country, its source being day-to-day reality." This can be said just as truthfully of communal education.

Where, then, are we to search for the source of the inspiration that gave birth to the idea of communal education in the Kibbutz Movement? With regard to the appearance of the kvutzah in agricultural settlements it has been well said: "The first kvutzah did not spring up by people coming and deciding, 'We wish to settle on the land and we shall do it in this particular way.' How did it come about then? There was *the dream of the commune, the dream of collective life, a life of friendship and equality, the socialist idea. . . .*"

It was this same dream of the commune which, after the first children were born in the kvutzah, tried to find its expression in education, although in as yet undefined forms. If it had not been for that dream, who can tell whether the strength of the decisive factors would have sufficed to bring about those changes that were required?

Many years have passed since that meeting, and most of the educational structures in the kvutzah and kibbutz have now assumed a more or less permanent form. The chief element is undoubtedly the children's house, as the center for the development of the child in collective life. It is agreed that the child's emotional stability requires not only an unchanging educational staff, but also a relatively unbroken sojourn in the children's house, with a minimum of transfers from one children's house to another.

We see the *age group* as the suitable educational unit for the children's house (each age group should at the same time have close and regular contact with adjacent age groups, whether younger or older). All of the child's needs are fully met in his age group, in which the children's community is guided by the principles of mutual responsibility and maximum consideration for the individual. To achieve those aims, the number of children in each age group must be limited. The lower the age group, the smaller that number should be.

The relationship between child and educator is based on the principle of independent conduct; it has two hallmarks: (1) The child is well aware of his responsibility, in every one of his reactions to educational demands. (2) Out of mutual love and honor, the child identifies himself with the educator and his aims. Public opinion in the children's community, shaped by the example of the adult community with its atmosphere of freedom, is also a decisive factor in the relationship between children and their educators.

This system provides a unity of teaching and education — the aim of every educational method whose purpose is the shaping of the child's personality. On this basis new ways of teaching are being discovered and have begun to flourish in communal education. It is our hope that our system of communal education will continue to be shaped by objective ideas and based on stable foundations, while still striving forward on the highest scientific level.

With the children's house as the center for all educational activities, the educator (nurse or teacher) becomes the instrument of the kvutzah. It is her task to carry out a multiplicity of activities on its behalf. Here, at an early age, the foundations are laid for collective living, and the child's tendencies are furthered in that direction. This requires a fundamental revision of our conception of on whom the responsibility for the educational achievements of each child should rest. It must not be placed with the parents, as it is, traditionally, in society outside the kibbutz. Instead, it is entrusted to responsible educators for every age group and every educational framework.

Indeed, in the *Jubilee Book* of the Teacher's Union (1903-1953), all the contributors, speaking on behalf of the various streams in the Kibbutz Movement, were united in this view:

> "Communal education lays the full responsibility for the complete education of every child on the educator. . . . In so doing, it stresses the fact that the educator's work is not considered as a service to the parents but as the means for preparing the younger generation to continue the work of their fathers."

On joining collective life, which recognizes no private property, the family loses its status as an economic unit; it remains, however, a social unit, in the love of the parents for their children. In a *voluntary* collective society, there is no *basic* contradiction between the ideology of the community and that of the parents. Nevertheless, we must face the fact that problems of education have sometimes caused much tension between parents and the community as a whole.

On the one hand, according to our ideology, parents must recognize the right of the community to determine the educational activities of all children in the kvutzah, including their own. On the other hand, their deep emotional ties with their children cannot but rouse the desire in parents to have a hand in deciding the educational fate of their children. Communal education alleviates this tension by giving parents guarantees in the following respects:

1. Arrangements must not be detrimental to the physical or emotional welfare of the child.
2. The healthy instinct of the family towards the child ("parental gratification") must not be frustrated.
3. The wholeness of the family must not be violated.

Parents are also guaranteed the opportunity to contribute all they can to their children's education. They are, in fact, "coopted" in the following fields:

1. To provide a healthy family atmosphere in their daily contact with the children during leisure hours — an atmosphere in which there is neither neglect nor overindulgence.
2. To help their children, but only with the approval of the educator chiefly responsible for the child's progress.
3. Maximum participation in the activities of the children's house.
4. Furthering high standards in all spheres of life in the kvutzah, thereby providing a living example to be followed by the younger generation, as it prepares to carry forward the collective idea.

These prerogatives of the family in communal education do not contradict, rather they complement, the basic principles of the kvutzah — mutual responsibility and equal status between fellow men. In order to realize these principles in the educational field, there must be a division of tasks. By doing all in their power to further these moral values in the lives of the adult members of the kvutzah, parents will be assisting the educators, whose task it is to convey these values to the younger generation. All this can be put into practice in a planned community, founded on a maximum of cooperation.

Communal education is clearly worthy of being described as "an experiment which has not failed" (M. Buber). Nevertheless, it is still too early to say that it has won full recognition from the family in the kvutzah or kibbutz. Every new pattern of life brings

with it certain social changes. Even when these have been accepted
by all, the deeply rooted emotions of those directly affected do not
permit the automatic assimilation of these changes. The reappraisal of the division of educational tasks, for example, has encountered family traditions that are not easily overcome.

The most fundamental emotional changes in the establishment of collective life — in which we strive towards an "equality
in freedom" for every person in the family and in the parents' relationship to their children — must be made by the women. Once
assimilated to the kvutzah, no woman can doubt that the present
form of communal education is capable of fulfilling all the child's
needs. Nevertheless, this striving towards "equality in freedom"
has grown weaker, it seems, or perhaps even lost its importance
altogether, for a considerable percentage of women in the kvutzah
and the kibbutz. Instead of facing the problem and struggling to
overcome their weakness, they tend to give in and to romanticize
the family. In every additional freedom that the framework of
communal education affords them, they see instead an infringe-
ment upon their motherly rights.

Communal education will contribute its part to the strengthening of the mother's spirit, whenever her loyalty to the kvutzah
is put to the test, only by perfecting its means and methods, while
still adhering closely to the principles of collective life. With this
aim in mind, communal education must strengthen its roots by
the sort of research work that has been lacking up to now. This
research must deal, first and foremost, with two basic problems:

1. Are there any characteristic lines of development of the
   child in the kvutzah, and what are they?
2. Are there any characteristic lines of relationship between
   parents and children, and what are they?

Psychologists and sociologists who have visited this country
have undertaken such research work. And, in the circles of our
movement, beginnings have also been made in this respect. Recently the first chapter of *Research on Collective Settlement* was
published. This research, which is being carried out by the Department of Sociology of the Hebrew University, is based on a
cross-section of twelve kvutzoth. The first chapter deals with the

question of sleeping arrangements for children. In it, answers to the following questions were taken into account:

1. What is your attitude to the demand that children sleep in the parents' room?
2. Are you in favor of this; if so, for which age groups?
3. Why?

The arguments presented in replies to the question: "What are the advantages and disadvantages of communal education?" were also taken into account. Here are some of the conclusions arrived at: "Examination of these arguments has brought to light the weak ideological basis upon which communal education rests — a weakness more pronounced in women than in men. The satisfaction of the woman with the present sleeping arrangements (i.e., dormitory) is closely connected with the satisfaction she gains from her work and her desire to persevere in her job. Women who hold public office in the kvutzah are less 'family conscious' than are men in this position, and far less 'family conscious' than women who do not hold office in the community."

What can the results of this or any similar kind of research mean for us, after they have been examined and either finally verified or amended on one point or another? If the process of emotional change is a very slow one, surely many generations will have to pass before that generation at last arises, born in the kvutzah, to whom collective life with all its implications will be a system with which their conscience is in full harmony. In order to hasten this process, we must, on the one hand, teach the Kvut- zoth ideology from infancy on and, on the other hand, improve the means for its realization. Both these tasks are likely to bene- fit from research, which may show us where that path lies which will lead us to success, so that we may transform collectivism in education into education in collectivism.

I shall conclude with words similar to those of J. Bussel. In a discussion on the relative merits of collective or individual farm- ing, he said: "If there really are modes of life in which there is more freedom than in the kvutzah, we must accept them joy- fully." In the same strain: If there are modes of life in which a woman can find "equality in freedom" more completely than in the kvutzah, we must accept them joyfuly. It seems to me that sooner or later, however, our women will realize that they will not find it outside the collective community. When they have become acclimatized to this mode of collective community life, they will lay claim to it and make it their own. Communal education will help them towards this aim.

On Learning Processes

MORDECHAI SEGAL

I. Integral Patterns

COMPLEX AND PROJECT: During the last half century, the desire for integration of learning has turned many against the common-school curriculum, split as it is in accordance with the splitting of the sciences. Some form of integrated study has been recognized as desirable, at least for the early school grades.

Two main forms have crystallized in recent decades: the *complex* in Europe, and the *project* in America. As the terms themselves suggest, the complex lays its stress on *wholeness*, the project on *aim*.

The *complex* method cuts out of the life-picture a cluster of phenomena, which cling together as a pattern, and brings this "whole" into the classroom. There is the danger that study will remain secluded within this static cut-out pattern, and thus sink into *contemplation*. What is missing is the *vector of motion*: the impulse to wish and to do. As a consequence, the direct interest of the learners, both as individuals and as a collective, is likely also to be missing.

The *project* method chooses a close and well-defined aim with which to generate doing and learning. A justifiable apprehension arises that in *this* case, the channels may remain narrow, that such scattered aims will not rise to further integration, and study will soon sink into "practicism." What is missing here is an encompassing *principle of construction*; learners are thus denied the rich spiritual pleasure of grasping the world in its fullness and oneness.

Nevertheless, both methods are to be viewed as healthy — even if incomplete — revolts against the splitting of the world and its patterns into *elements,* that had been fostered by the schools of Europe and America for the previous century and a half. This had been of course not the accidental product of one individual's error (Pestalozzi's) ; the atomization of learning was rather the natural outcome of the general nineteenth-century decay of economic, social, and cultural organisms.

Both the *complex* and the *project* represent a revolt, not a revolution: the one *contemplates without doing,* the other *does without contemplating.* Education in Israel, quite naturally has not found either method satisfactory. We have instituted here a revolution in the ways of living — the gist of which is *creation through learning* — neither the extreme of Olympic contemplation, nor that of fractionated activity. The schools of this Israeli revolution have striven, therefore, to develop a method of learning that contains *both wholeness and movement.*

The correction has been attempted in three different directions. One was to keep the complex without giving up the project, on the assumption that since each of the two methods possesses what the other lacks, the joint use of both will produce the desired balance. A second way, looking towards greater unity, has drawn out the complex so as to make it resemble the project, by adding to it goals of doing, and enlarged the project to make it resemble the complex, by grouping around it material not directly connected with its doing goals. Both procedures are represented in numerous *study units.* The third way, which has developed in some kibbutz schools, elaborates a different form of integration — the *"process"* — a dynamic learning pattern with new points of departure and arrival.

WHAT IS "PROCESS" LEARNING? The term "process" denotes a method which runs roughly parallel to the life processes and adheres to them at a series of points. The adhesion is mainly *practical* in character during the first stage (ages seven to ten) ; *study-like* in the second stage (ages ten to fifteen) , and *inquiring* in the third stage (ages fifteen to eighteen) . Needless to say, none of these three ways of adhesion is exclusive for any one stage, and the transition from state to stage is extremely gradual.

What are the life processes to which these learning processes are meant to adhere?

The *first stage* is concerned with processes going on in the child's home and in the near vicinity: seasonal changes in living and inanimate nature; work performance in the various fields, factories, and services; the sequence of social occurrences in the school society, as well as in the child's own and in neighboring communities.

Second-stage learning will add to the above: physical, chemical, and biological processes, *such as may be discovered only by theoretical study and experimentation*; the full span of kibbutzim economic and social goings-on; contemporary life and happenings in Israel and abroad; historical developments of economy, society, and culture among our own and other peoples.

The *third stage* will add: acquaintance with processes in science and social thought, especially as *directed towards some selected fundamental problems*; taking a position on questions of actual social and political life; practical and theoretical entry into some area of work and of *creative activity*.

The full realization of such a "learning process" has more than one significance. As far as *method* is concerned, it means the organizing of a series of adhesion points with life processes: so many acts of work, excursion, study, experimentation, etc. From the more general standpoint of *intellectual effort,* the outstanding phenomenon would be the opportunity to draw many spontaneous impressions into the array of thinking. The basic role of the "adhesion points" is then revealed as: first, to defeat the danger of an anarchically scattered outlook, which threatens to take hold of the schoolchild as soon as the primeval, naive, and synthetic outlook of infancy and kindergarten has been shattered; secondly, to develop the child's grasp of reality along well-defined lines of viewing and thinking.

This brings us to the ideological connotations of process learning as a *training in reality-viewing* — that is, the development of the ability to discern *developmental connections and dynamic tendencies in phenomena,* as well as to perceive the flowing together of reality processes into a unity within plurality.

Out of all this springs the psychic meaning: the child becomes *affectively involved and personally related,* up to the limits of identification, with persons, phenomena, processes, principles that are alive and active in his material and spiritual vicinity.

The whole balance finally becomes meaningful in terms of personality building. Learning processes tend to merge with processes of orientation among the paths of life; *self-control and control of surroundings, self-expression and self-realization.*

II. Modes of Learning

Man acts out his life in three modes: the mode of the *artist*, which is also the mode of perception of any man, in moments of psychic overflow; the mode of the *scientist*, which is also that of any man overpowered by curiosity; the mode of the *man of industry* — of all men in their creative functioning.

Artists, scientists, men of industry — it is only the contemporary splitting of culture that has led the particular tendencies of each of these to exaggeration, and turned them into *one-sided* "specialists." For innumerable generations, such specialists were rare: every man bore within himself some synthesis of the three fundamental modes.

This same broad synthesis of contemplative, analytical, and active tendencies is still to be found in the personality of every child. And a new integration of culture in the future — the dream of socialism — will lead to the emergence of a new human type, which will again synthesize within itself these three approaches, but on a higher level. Education will assist in the birth of this new man, to the extent that it itself comprises and interconnects art, inquiry, and doing.

Vital Art. At the basis of art lies the naive synthetic *viewing* of the child. This is worthy of cultivation; certainly, disillusionment with it should not be hastened. The child's free-time wanderings within and about his community; planned excursions to places of interest; steady, fresh contacts with the art products of our own and past generations — all these will nurture his intuition with the sights of the world. His reactions will take the form of free creation in all fields of art. It is the child's needs and drives that will generate this creation, but the breadth of its perception and the wealth of its images will depend on the amount and character of its world-viewing.

Free artistic creation, which is strong in the kindergarten, gradually weakens while the child is at school. One reason for this lies within the child himself. The kindergarten period is one of psychic storms: the many distresses of the four- and five-year-old, unable to be alleviated in reality, burst into artistic solution. The eight- and ten-year-old, on the contrary, experiences a balancing process, with many real and satisfying achievements.

Still, this does not explain the situation fully. Not everything has been solved, even during a balanced latency, and is there not a new psychic storm lurking for the child in preadolescence, which will be just as surely in need of artistic expression?

The customary artistic drought of our children has other and stronger reasons, stemming from the nature of school and of learning. The schoolchild is group-addicted: the group rule is his rule. If the school does not create an interest in and appreciation for art creation within its walls, the child will lack a chief motive for such activity. The conservative school, while it may not ignore individual creativity, nevertheless does not *warm up the social atmosphere* to the degree that is essential for a generally thriving artistic activity.

The planned appearance of art in the school curriculum, on the other hand, often defeats real creativity. Art is handled like any other subject of systematic study, squeezed in between bells, and taught with all the particularities of a school lesson. Or else it may appear not for its own sake, but as a sort of didactic housemaid, ordered about to assist, alleviate, or endear different studies. Either way, its essence is silenced.

School art will not come into its own until we perceive in it an *important path for the child* toward several aims: expression of inner stirrings, self-knowledge and personality integration, concentration of outside impressions, interaction with others, group adherence. When we do see it so, art will be constantly flowing through informal channels, *soaking in all of life and not enclosed within compartments.*

Inquiry and Study. Curiosity, leading to the examination of nearby items and experimentation with them, to the manipulation and taking apart of every object, to peering into every corner and crack — this curiosity is characteristic of the infant during the first three years of his life. Kindergarten and school raise such activity to higher rungs, aimed towards the *analytic orientation* to surrounding phenomena.

The young child's curiosity, and the activity generated by it, are vital to his development. He is compelled to take apart the patterns of his world and inquire into their structure, character, and properties, in order to incorporate himself into that world and place himself within every one of its vital patterns. It is our obligation to guard his largely spontaneous methods of reality inquiry. We should keep open, for example, a long daily period for *wandering* in and about the community. (Even our organized forms of systematic learning should remain close in spirit to the child's spontaneous forms.) Our child could learn his country, as well as his own community and region, through his legs and his eyes.

These wanderings, excursions, and observations occupy most of the child's time during the first school stage (ages seven to ten). Upon this foundation of concrete learning, theoretical study is built up during the second school stage (ages ten to fifteen). (Concrete learning will, of course, continue at the same time.) A series of larger study blocks, each one of a full year's duration, could be designed to lead to an elementary scientific orientation towards some of the chief factors of the material world and of the human economy — including such elements as water, weather, food, machines.

In each of these blocks, study would begin with a local factual inquiry, thereafter widening out to include the region, the country, the world. It would then continue with the investigation of physiochemical and biological data, and end with economic considerations, brought home once again to the nearby reality: the country, the region, the community. Clearly, this is not theory for its own sake, but *the sort of learning that will be needed by founders of communities and fosterers of culture.*

Midway between this series of studies in the exact sciences and social studies stands the unit "Man," of a single year's duration (at the age of thirteen). This is intended to present the workings of the human organism as a whole — stressing the functions of the brain, and the central nervous system and internal excretion systems; giving an elementary idea of psychical functioning and of the concept of psychophysical unity; explaining the sexual life of man, and raising the idea of personality. This detailed "know thyself," by its very nature, will not serve as mere information.

The social studies series is divided into two parts: *Peoples and Countries,* and *Jewish History.* Although the connections between our national existence and world developments need continual clarification, basically we do not go along with the idea of mingling these two studies. It would be wrong, of course, to consider great phenomena in world history under the rubric "Is it good for the Jews?"; but we are certainly not interested in letting Jewish history become drowned in the mighty stream of world history. The learner's attitude is, on the one hand, intimate and active, insofar as it is within the framework of his people's history that the Jewish individual can act directly, whereas, in world history, he can act only indirectly.

Continuous Doing. Both the integrative and the analytic mode of "taking in" the surrounding world generally lead the child into doing. His sense of action is acute, and his creative urge forceful and alert. Inquiring observation generates, even at the earliest ages, innumerable, sporadic and scattered doings. But school age is also the time for stable long-term enterprises. The school should therefore create its own bases for *continuous doings of all kinds,* which will also assist the child in the direction of adult doings.

This extensive doing, which will fill the days and years with rhythmic work processes and with the hum of constant growth and development, serves as the basis for the physical and mental self-realization of each individual child. It also provides a classic opportunity for the closer linking of the children's society: the common tending of homes, farms, shops has long been the basis for most other forms of human association; so also, at school, social ability will be forged and tested in daily work activity.

Such self-directed economic activity by the children and youth is not meant to preclude their gradually taking their place in the work of the *adult farm.* This process of joining is another important means for environmental learning, as well as for associating with a wider social circle; it also serves to strengthen self-confidence. The cow barn and the chicken coops, the shoemaker's workshop and the machine garage, the baby home and the sewing shop — all these are suitable for active participation by children above the age of nine; their tasks will be assigned to them through collective work-distribution conferences.

Enterprises of this kind are valuable, not only for the children, but also for the community in general. Sometimes, a permanent co-operation will arise between children and adults. The accumulated learning will not remain the privately owned and guarded ducats of each individual. They will be brought together into collective books and exhibits, representing all the extensive activities in art, inquiry, and doing. The individual effort will thus become a contribution to the collective. Group study brings together and correlates individual activities on the spot, whereas the book or the exhibit does the same thing in a permanent fashion.

At the third school stage (ages fifteen to eighteen), the youngsters will take a gradually increasing regular part in the work and social activity of the adult community. The principle of free choice, already stressed for art and inquiry, will of course also hold for work. The school should make it possible for every boy and girl at this age to choose his or her own — not too restricted — work area, to learn it thoroughly, in practice and in theory.

A THREEFOLD WAY: Needless to say, the three ways of learning — the creative, the inquiring, and the laboring — cannot exist in isolation from each other. Any separation is only a momentary convenience, so as to make things more easily surveyable, through the grouping and enumeration of details; in actual school life, they are permanently and irreversibly interrelated.

This is not a mere external linking. The welding together of all activities is brought about by the force and heat of one major movement — that of making a place in the surrounding culture. All the inquiries and the creations move towards that one big encompassing aim: *to join the culture; to understand it; to act, and take stands within it; to mount its horses, and gallop towards the future.*

This is a tendency natural to every growing child. The "natural" educational environments of old — the family home, the small community, the peer group — provided, as long as they were able, rich opportunities for the daily realization of this acculturational tendency. In our times, the public school has more and more replaced these now impoverished educational agencies. Woe to the school, if it shrinks from this tendency, which dominates in the long run all of child behavior; if it encircles the child with a battery of dry science extracts, literary catechisms, and art grammars; if it cuts out for the child some static pieces of reality, and trims them with flowers of literature and art; if it immerses the child into many momentary small tasks, answering to momentary stimulations, like so many unthreaded beads.

There is no other way for the school, if it wishes to exist as a living force, than to direct its life and activity fully on to the high road of the surrounding life and activity, to multiply the moments of contact and participation, and to let the children feel the hot breath of their own culture, as it struggles forward.

APPENDIX D

The Family in the Kibbutz

EMI HURWITZ

ANY SERIOUS APPROACH to the problems of the kvutzah must take into account the problems of the world around us. It would be a mistake to regard our problems as fundamentally unique; their solutions have much in common with those that must be arrived at by the world in general. Only in terms of the realization of these solutions does it become possible to speak of the *special* problems of the kvutzah. For example, the problem of the division of property is a general one. Since the kvutzah recognizes only public property, a special problem is created — the satisfaction of the needs of the individual. Similarly, while the problem of the working woman is a general one, the problem of the relationship between the existence of institutions for children and the procedure for putting children to bed is peculiar to the kvutzah.

The family has long been the basic unit of human society, but during that time, it has more than once changed its form. In our generation, this change is being accompanied by a deep crisis, which is perhaps most visibly expressed in an enormously increased rate of divorce. As a consequence, society is confronted on a wide scale with the phenomenon of children who must be brought up without a family framework.

Understanding the factors that have led to this is vital for us. The contemporary family, to begin with, *lacks stability,* from several points of view. It is not centered around a family enterprise (farm, business, workshop) ; instead, members of the family are often widely scattered, in accordance with their places of work. *The parents' home is no longer a center, nor even a meeting place, as it was in the past.*

The need to create both an economic and a social framework for themselves imposes upon the young couple the necessity of making their own decisions in all facets of living; they must, in effect, *create new life patterns*. Living independently of their families, they lack the economic and social security that mutual interdependence gave each member of the family in the past. Moreover, the traditions that formerly guided the family in managing the home, or in defining the tasks of the man and the woman, as well as the relationships involved in the education of their children — all these time-honored solutions have become negligible. The modern family thus lives in a condition of permanent tension, asking itself at every step how to behave, what to do, how to decide.

From birth to death, the traditional family meant, for all the generations that were part of it, a stable and continuing base. Today's family lacks all such continuity. The child — even one who enjoys stable family life — usually leaves home when he grows up, to open a new chapter in life, more often than not in a different place, a different profession, a different society. Everything to which he has been accustomed he leaves behind him.

On the other hand, the average life span is continually on the rise: from the beginning of this century to its midpoint, life expectancy grew by more than twenty years (from forty-four to sixty-six, on the average). After their children leave the parental home, the parents thus have ahead of them a new and what may be a rather long period of life. Although they enjoy a new freedom from previous burdens, they are also likely to be bereft of economic support. In any case, they are without a family.

There is no doubt that this fragmentation (lack of continuity within a single family group) explains to a certain extent the great increase in the number of divorces. From childhood on, there exists a lack of security, expressed in fears or in the exaggerated dependency of the child on his parents. At times, parents are even asked by their children whether they are going to be divorced. The child knows that such a thing can happen, and there is good reason for his feeling, when he senses that his own family may be resting on unstable foundations. The danger of the family's falling apart increases if it is based (as it often is) on

erotic attraction only, which contains neither a common background, nor common values, nor a common vision of the future.

Although the independence won by women in our time is a
tremendous achievement — for the women themselves and for all
humanity — it has also brought in its wake insecurity and tension,
and no small danger.

The most distinctive characteristic of the life of the modern
woman, apart from her having gained the right to marry a man
of her own choice, is that she works and supports herself. In her
relationship with her husband, she thus becomes an equal and
independent partner. (By the way, this economic independence
also plays its role in any decision to break up the family, in case
of a crisis.) Her work also permits her to marry at an early age;
at times it may be she who, by working, makes it possible for her
young husband to learn a profession.

The home has ceased to be the only center for her. She comes
into contact with many people outside of the home, and forms
many and varied social ties. Work serves as both an expression
and an extension of her personality. Contemporary woman must
therefore strike a balance between work and motherhood. This is
a new problem.

One solution is for the woman to stop working for a certain
period and instead devote herself to the care of her children and
family. On the surface, this is a simple and satisfactory arrangement; sometimes it does provide the way out. But often the
nature of the profession, or the need or desire to work, will not
allow this. It may mean giving up a calling for which the woman
has prepared herself for many years; furthermore, not every woman can find satisfaction in housework alone. The fact that she
has given up her work does not of itself make her into a good
mother. On the contrary, this act of relinquishing her personal
objectives often leads to a continually increasing dissatisfaction,
which may result in disturbed relations with her children and
her husband.

Another solution is to attempt to combine work with motherhood. While still continuing in her full- or part-time work, the
woman also takes care of the home and brings up the children.
Private and public institutions come to her aid here: kinder-

gartens, schools, day-care centers. Large factories sometimes maintain children's institutions of their own, where children are looked after while the mother is at work. This solution, however, inevitably leads to unrest and great tension, for the mother is torn between two tasks. While the tension is particularly great at times of illness or conflict in the family, the mother is always in danger of feeling that she is neglecting either her family or her job.

A third solution, once customary in several countries, has been to transfer the child during the work week to institutions set up for his education and care, returning him home on weekends and holidays only. This was found to be altogether unsatisfactory — particularly, with regard to the very young child.

Today, psychologists have generally come to accept the view that, up to the age of three, the child needs personal and intimate contact with his parents, and particularly with his mother. The tie between mother and child is an essential condition for the child's physical and emotional development. Children educated in institutions equipped with the best facilities are often retarded by comparison with children brought up by their mothers, even under conditions worse than those in the institutions. The child needs mother love no less than it needs mother's milk.

Children raised solely in institutions live all their lives under the threat of negative personality development. They have difficulty in their studies; they are likely to be asocial. In any event, they lack the ability to form proper interpersonal ties. The fear has been expressed that, when they themselves become fathers or mothers, they will reveal an inability to love which will be damaging to *their* children, so that no correction of their condition is possible, even in later generations.

This has led to far-reaching changes in the construction of educational institutions, the attitude of hospitals towards the mother, and the system of child adoption. Today provision is made for the adoption of homeless children *in infancy,* in order to ensure that measure of stability, and those firm personal ties with the father and mother, which are regarded as essential to the normal development of the child.

Another factor in the contemporary family is birth control. This is well known to every one, although we may not yet have grasped the meaning of the changes resultant in family structure and internal relationships. Parents can now choose the desirable time for childbirth and determine the number of children they wish to have. Contemporary man, now the lord of his impulses and instincts, does not always sense, however, that he may be thereby suppressing the most intense personal strivings for creation with which man is endowed, as well as the expression of ties of love in the life of the family.

What follows is tension, want of understanding, lack of faith; or else, estrangements, to the point of the break-up of family relations. Sometimes the parents recognize that their lost relationship cannot ever be regained; sometimes they seek to improve the situation by giving birth to still another child. These decisions generally have to be made by young and inexperienced people who are often without the inner balance they need, in order to be able to grasp fully what is involved in their decisions.

In any case, as the result of family planning, the number of children per family has become limited. The family now consists only of parents and a few children, who do not live, as very likely the previous generation did, under the same roof with grandparents, aunts and uncles; instead, a basically individualistic relationship is formed, child-centered and more tension-loaded. Fluctuations in the moods of the parents affect and influence the child more in the small family than they do in the large one, where the child is able to find refuge in one or another of many possible relationships.

Such problems also face the individual in the kibbutz, and we must determine to what extent they have found a solution here. In the beginning, the kvutzah lacked any adequate plan for the education and care of children; this was essentially a group of unmarried young people. In about 1918, Zvi Shatz said:

"The family of the past, or the kvutzah in our future life — that is the real and permanent refuge that will save the soul of man. . . . In the life of the kvutzah may be found the special atmosphere within which the characteristics of the new man can be formed. . . .

"The family is being destroyed. . . . But the eternal life

values will remain and only their form will change, because the need for a family environment is very deep and organic. . . . On the basis of spiritual, not blood ties, the family will be reborn — and in the form of small, modest work groups."

The appearance of the first families seemed to the kvutzah to be a disturbing event. Privacy became a new category in the collective, which apparently shook the kvutzah's organicity. This was well expressed by Smetterling in his article "The Family," which appeared in 1924:

> "Until today, the kibbutzim struggle with the family as with a difficult adversary. . . . As compared with love in general, the love of two people for each other is a matter of the most private choice. That is what separates couples from the rest of the members, and encloses them as an 'isle of the happy,' against whose shores beat the waves of collective living."

Tabenkin, on the other hand, at a meeting of the kibbutzim in 1923, had proclaimed the existence of the family as the necessary *precondition* for the existence of the collective:

> "In kibbutzim that have been established for some time, there are almost no families. With every new family, the problem arises: will it or will it not remain? The existence of the family in this form and with these relationships does not augur well for the future. The kvutzah, as it is today, becomes a goal connected *only with the time of youth*."

With the coming to maturity of the kvutzah, the family became rooted in the life and consciousness of its members. Nevertheless, the conflict between family and collective still continued in one or another form. For many years, when there was a housing shortage, the collective would require the family to admit a "third party" into its room, to the detriment of family life. The role of parents in cooperative education became generally accepted only after much deliberation and much experience, and until now the relationship between parents and the educational authorities is being constantly reshaped and revised.

Little by little, then, the family has gained a foothold in the life of the kvutzah and established its own pattern of existence. It is a far cry from the informal weddings of the first generation to the sumptuous weddings of today, from the modest "family room" to the *shikun* apartment for veteran members. Some justification has begun to appear for the apprehension originally expressed by the kvutzah towards the family. We often witness today the shutting up of the family within the confines of its room, the development of an exaggerated interest in improving the room, withdrawal from the life of the community, absence from general meetings, protests against cooperative education. . . . And an image has begun to take shape of the family as a "special-interest" group in the kvutzah, in such matters as the direction of their children's work and vocational training. To the same extent, the family's identification with the kibbutz family and its needs is weakened.

From my own observations, I would be inclined to assert that these dangers are in fact the necessary by-products of one of the most significant achievements of the kvutzah. Zvi Shatz expressed the hope that the kvutzah would become a substitute for the decaying traditional family. That hope is now being realized, although not in the form that he imagined. In the oldest Kvutzoth there live today three generations of kvutzah members; we have even seen the marriage of one of our granddaughters, at a time when both the grandparents are still active in the kvutzah. The multi-generation family has been woven, as was the traditional family, into a single web of life.

The parents' home has once again become a center and a meeting place; mutual obligations have been revived, have become a living force for the family. This is expressed in the care of grandchildren during the absence of parents for various reasons. (Grandmother, for example, may make it possible for the young mother to study and train for a vocation.) This mutual assistance and "standing in" for one another can prevent many serious crises from arising in the family; in cases of divorce, it can maintain the home, for the sake of the children. It removes the loneliness from old age and restores a human function and life content to the old.

All this may seem unrealistic to the members of a young settlement, but it is very real in a settlement that comprises various age-groups. In fact, only such a settlement can any longer really be regarded as the "normal" kibbutz. Here, at all events, we have succeeded in gathering a many-branched family into a single life enterprise, as the direct result of the building of the kibbutz, which is a life enterprise for all generations, and not primarily a one-family project.

The kibbutz includes agriculture, workshops and even industry. It has all the distinctive marks of a modern economic enterprise: professionalization, division of labor, planning, mechanization, rationalization, etc. It establishes educational and cultural institutions, to give scope to its sons and daughters. Its goal is continual development: within its framework, the young generation has a wide area of choice, so that only in rare cases are children forced to leave the life undertaking that their parents initiated.

Moreover, since the whole structure of the kibbutz rests upon the establishments of values and their realization, since it unites the different generations through the same ideal, it has the opportunity to create a tradition, and to establish those values and life patterns that are generally lacking in the modern family.

These are, of course, only the background conditions; as in every human undertaking, great efforts of will and much patience are necessary in order to translate possibility into fact. Although we can record some achievements, not a few of the possibilities still remain unfulfilled. While the family is no longer an economic unit, it is deeply integrated into the broad cooperative enterprise. Thus freed from day-to-day worries, it has been raised to a higher level of cultural relationships. In place of that separation which is so often the fate of the modern family, the kvutzah promotes family continuity and family cohesion.

Although, with regard to the continuity of the family, we have reached an outstanding and significant achievement, such is not the case with regard to the birth rate. There is no doubt that, from the biological point of view, the Kibbutz Movement is not maintaining itself. It must be admitted that life in the kibbutz has not, in the past, tended to encourage a high birth rate: economic difficulties and generally unstable conditions, among other things, led to the voluntary limiting of births. Since we have arrived at the normalization of life, however, and the establishment of a stable economic and social base, we can now encourage families with many children.

The earlier influence of economic factors on the birth rate should not, however, be exaggerated; the economic argument was, to a certain extent, a rationalization of hidden factors, among which rebellion against the accepted family relationships in the Jewish family played no small part. Women, particularly, were seeking a new role, with new content; giving birth to children and caring for them would encumber them, they thought, in their efforts to realize the new way of life. Neither of these factors is today of decisive importance for the young couple; they no longer determine the birth rate.

In our generation, there has emerged a danger of a certain mechanicalness in sexual relations, as a result of the development of contraceptive techniques. Education for a good sex life has thus become one of the central tasks in the education of the young today. We lack set patterns, in which respect there is no difference between us and the society that surrounds us. In particular, we lack any preparation of the girl for motherhood. That fact is not accidental: the society that equalized the status of women with that of men went to an extreme conclusion — that of oversimplification. It planned a single study curriculum for both boys and girls, restricting this to academic subjects, because it saw its main task to be that of preparing girls as well as boys for a career.

The women who participated in the establishment of the kvutzah were filled with rebellion against the traditional position of women in Jewish society, as the result of which they had lacked all those rights and duties that belonged to men. In this country, the woman sought a *new path,* to begin with, in work. While she was still unmarried, her aspirations to full equality presented no special problems to her or to society; when she became a mother, however, the need arose to find patterns by which she could combine work with motherhood. The solution found in the kvutzah for this combination of motherhood and career was based on the primary fact of the woman's *continuing to work.*

Since the kibbutz is both an economic and a social unit, the woman does not thereby cut herself off from her family. The *settlement is the natural surrounding of the child from his first day*. The woman can go to her child at any time, and when he grows older, the child is familiar with the mother's place of work, as well as with his father's occupation and place of work. These are not remote from the child, as is generally the case in the world at large, where the father may work a great distance from home, and at an occupation which is not at all understood by the small child. In the kibbutz, on the contrary, the father can dedicate himself to playing an important part in the upbringing of his small child.

In the kibbutz, then, the child can see both his parents, even when they are at work; he can understand the meaning of their activity. They are within his field of vision, so to speak, organically linked in the web of life and creativity within which he is growing. Atomization, the fate of man in the modern industrial world, does not exist among us.

There are questions that have no solution, apart from the balancing of those conflicts in the midst of which man must live. There is a permanent tension between freedom and equality, family life and community life, the individual and the family, etc.; success here depends upon man's ability to relinquish neither one nor the other, but rather to *live within the tension* and there find his balance. The tension within which the woman must live today is between personal independence and family life, motherhood and career.

Often the kibbutz member makes the mistake of regarding the demands of life as edicts issued by the kibbutz organization, forgetting that a man's work and his authority are both limited by the society he lives in, among other factors. There are kibbutz members who mistakenly look upon these limitations — the necessary conditions for all society — as something it is possible to dispense with. For example, the working mother generally regards the establishment of institutions for children and of kindergartens as an essential aid, which she would under no circumstances be willing to give up; the kibbutz mother sometimes tends to view the children's institutions mistakenly as "limitations" upon her motherhood. A woman outside the kibbutz does not always look for a scapegoat for the guilt feelings in her heart about her child; the kibbutz mother often lays the blame on the kibbutz for this weakness of hers. This leads to tension between her and the children's institutions, often resulting in her indifference and lack of participation in cooperative upbringing.

Despite its structural limitations, the kibbutz solution to the problem of combining motherhood with work seems to have proven satisfactory. Intensive contact is maintained between parents and offspring, in spite of the fact that both parents work. The integration of the parents into the social and economic life of the kibbutz assures the children's identification both with parents and with the kibbutz enterprise, and prepares the ground for organic growth. The mother works without extended interruptions, and can at the same time participate in community life. As has been already noted, the family has gradually gained a status for itself in the kibbutz. Correspondingly, the status of parents, and particularly the place of the mother, has been established in cooperative education.

As to the satisfaction of the woman worker in her work, the picture is not uniform. For the woman outside the kibbutz, it is enough to be able to support herself, to add to the family budget, to maintain economic independence. In the kibbutz, the woman achieves all these things by the mere fact of her belonging to the community, so that *satisfaction* in her work has become an *essential* need.

By contrast with the first women kibbutz members, women today have generally withdrawn from positions in agriculture, and become entrenched in services and in education. On the one hand, experience has taught us that not all work is suited to women — e. g. work with a tractor or with a mattock. On the other hand, women have had to contend with the fact that the men have tended to disparage either their work or their femininity when they have worked on some jobs. Similarly, criticism directed against a woman in charge of an agricultural branch used to be generally much sharper than the criticisms leveled against a man in the same position.

Although the path chosen by the woman pioneer may have

been too extreme and difficult, the present general retreat from work in the fields and in economic branches seems to me to be a matter for concern. The fact that women are being cut off from agricultural work impedes the identification of the adult woman and the young girl with the kibbutz economy and with the community in general, because it generally brings with it a weakening of the woman's social activity and a decline in her participation in the administrative apparatus. This can hardly be regarded as a process of "normalization." (The organizational talent of the woman in the kvutzah cannot be doubted. Mass-catering, the management of the clothing stores, the setting up of institutions for children — these are no narrower in their organizational and financial scope than other branches of economic activity.)

The loss is especially great in the education of the young girl, who is likely to accept family-bound existence as a matter of course. Since she cannot imagine her future in an agricultural branch, her relationship to creativity in general is likely to be impaired. Of course, we cannot ignore the fact that a diversified society needs a network of education and other services, which requires the work of women. But the overall change in relation to women's work in agriculture was a social result of their competition with the men, and of the unspoken concept of woman that society holds on to (and particularly the men in it) : "*You* can't aspire to be a father!"

Although the ideology ostensibly sings the praises of the pioneer woman — the woman who works in the fields and in outdoor jobs — men actually prefer women to have soft hands and to make their home life pleasant. Even the woman who has worked, or is now working, in the fields and in agricultural branches, often does not want her daughter to follow in her footsteps. The husband, one may be certain, does not want his wife to work in the fields: he fears that it would affect her attractiveness — even though, in his speeches at the general meeting and his articles in the news-sheet, he will still in all likelihood advocate "the path of pioneering" and much deplore the fact that "the girls have turned their backs on agriculture."

Actually, there is no necessary contradiction between agricultural work and feminine charm. In the early days of kibbutz life, it is true, women suppressed the instinct towards a feminine and attractive appearance, believing that too much attention to outward appearance was contrary to the principles of simplicity and pioneering. As a result, a feeling took shape that agricultural work leads to the loss of femininity. It is necessary, it seems to me, both to encourage a feminine style of dress and care of the body, and also to renew our efforts to bring women back to work in agricultural branches. We must, however, see to it that the encouragement of femininity is not carried away by the influence that comes to us from outside — mainly from America, by way of its films and literature.

Fashion and cosmetics have placed sexuality in the center of human experience; they have established "sex appeal" — that is, the art of being attractive to men — as the main aim of women from the age of thirteen to over sixty. This goal has become so deified that sacrifices are made to it, sacrifices of values and life experiences, money and time, interesting work and family life. In Israel, such idolatry has also had many adherents, although in our country this has been simply a matter of aping and assimilation, not as in America, where it is the direct product of the social structure. In the kibbutz, too, there are signs that this worship is making some advances. The first to be affected will be those who *do not identify* with the kibbutz and *are not rooted* in its life.

Our target should be for each woman to acquire her specific profession or calling — an agricultural service or educational profession. (We must add two professions to life of the kvutzah — professions for which women have particular capacities — i.e., social work and psychology. No modern society, even the kibbutz, can do without them.) A woman generally needs two professions, since she cannot be expected to work in agriculture at all periods of her life. She must sense the value of her work, she must be convinced of her usefulness both in agricultural work and in services and education.

Lack of participation in agricultural activity tends to impair the woman's identification with the kibbutz enterprise, thus weakening her status in society and in the family; the lack of professionalized levels in services and in child care leads to a lack of work satisfaction. If the woman does not find satisfaction in her work, she will have no desire for the life of a working mother. She will feel herself frustrated both in work and in motherhood; and the fruitful tension described above, between motherhood and work — the life portion of modern woman — will lose its positive content.

The Metapelet and the Daily Routine in the Infant Age Group

RIVKA ZVIKELSKY

OUR AIM IS TO provide the metapelet with full training in the care of the child — including his physical, emotional and educational care — from the day of his birth until his transfer into the kindergarten. In order to accomplish this, we must hold seminars, as well as practical and theoretical courses, for people working with this age group. Until such time as the metaplot have been fully trained, their work must be so arranged that in every children's house, a baby nurse will work hand in hand with an infant nurse. One will teach and train the other.

There is a problem of the transfer of nurses from one age group to another. Usually this is how it happens: a nurse who has done a good job with infants is transferred to the kindergarten; the kindergarten teacher, after a few years of experience, is given additional training and then takes up class teaching. But has it not become clear that the age groups up to the kindergarten level *need* those "successful" nurses who have been trained and who possess the particular talents required? Is being transferred to a higher age group considered a "rise in grade?" In the meantime, the infant groups are made to suffer from a lack of trained personnel; there is a marked deterioration in the educational work; at the same time, more working hands are needed to complete the daily tasks.

There is much to be said in favor of specialization in child care. A nurse who has worked in one children's house for many years, covering a certain limited period in the child's life, has become well-acquainted with the mode of life in that house and with the characteristics of the child at that age. She has learned how to organize her work; her duties have become easier for her, and more work is accomplished in a shorter time. The attachment of such a nurse to that house is therefore of major importance: she shapes its patterns, lays the foundations for its content, and continually makes improvements in its functioning. Thus positive traditions are formed, for the benefit of the children and for her own benefit. If, on the contrary, she were to wander from one age group to another, most of her abilities and her energy would be wasted.

By working regularly in one house with one age group, the nurse becomes able, when there is a manpower shortage in the settlement, to adapt herself to the demands of the community, and even to cut down the hours she spends in the children's house. Such a demand could not be made of nurses who were being continually transferred from one house to another, and were not sure of their continuity in any one of them.

The Daily Routine for Nurse and Child

"Daily routine" is not an abstract term; in dealing with it, we should consider a particular place in a particular children's community. To set a routine for a children's house, we must take into account such factors as climatic conditions, the house and yard, the distance to kitchen and to stores. We must know at what time of day parents finish their work, what type of settlement we are dealing with, etc. Thus, there is no single daily routine that is suitable for all settlements. All we can do is to develop guidelines upon which the construction of a daily routine should be based.

What sort of daily routine is beneficial for the young child? It must be one that will satisfy all his needs, without being too strict and burdensome. The child in these age groups (and later on, too) is entitled to a simple routine, with ample time to discover his own points of interest in his surroundings; there must also be warmth and harmony, so as to provide a background suitable for the development of his emotional stability. In this framework, the child's elementary needs will be cared for — bathing and sleeping at the correct times, and meals suitable to his appetite and his digestive requirements. The daily routine should not entail such early rising that the child has to be roused from his sleep. On the other hand, no routine should allow the child to stay in bed longer than is necessary, simply because there is no one to get him up.

The daily routine must permit the nurse ample time to devote herself to the child. She should not be rushed in feeding or washing him; she should be free to spend time with him both indoors and outdoors, to answer his questions, and so on. If a child wants to help us clean the house, we must be patient, give him a floor cloth, and guide him in its use. "Disturbances" of that sort must be taken into account when we are arranging the daily routine.

We should allow — and this is very important — a few "extra" minutes for each chore, taking into consideration that we are dealing with toddlers. Herein lies the solution to our main problem — which is how to arrange an unhurried daily routine that will permit us to be "educators" as well as "working hands." If we are constantly rushing, we shall not succeed in creating a homelike atmosphere. We shall have no leisure to consider the child's education, for our contact with him will be superficial and sporadic. The outstanding symptom of such conditions is a state of tension. We must organize things in the children's houses in such a way that they will not be burdensome to the nurse, and still less so to the child.

How can this be accomplished? There are some who see the solution in the allocation of additional staff; but they are mistaken. We must fix norms, and calculate the number of working hours required in each house, according to the abilities of the average nurse, not the exceptional one.

We have, accordingly, laid down this rule: two nurses will be used to take care of eight infants. Occasionally, two nurses may look after ten children, but this must be regarded as an exception, which takes into account the nurses themselves, the children, and the local circumstances. It is important to limit the number of staff working in children's houses, not only for economic reasons but also on educational grounds. With a smaller staff, there is more cooperation, a more uniform attitude toward work, and more tranquility.

The decisive thing is efficient organization. Every nurse must know exactly what her tasks are, as well as those of her co-worker, in order to avoid overlapping. There is no need for both of them to participate in all activities; it is certainly not feasible for two nurses to be occupied working inside the house, whilst the children outdoors are left without supervision. There should be harmony between them in outlook, attitude and care for the children; at the same time, a division of duties is imperative.

I recall a case where four nurses were working with thirteen children in one house. Tension was rife. After we had discussed the situation, it was decided to cut the staff in that house down to three. This was sharply opposed by the nurses; following a short trial period, however, the work went smoothly. In the mornings, only two nurses came to get the children up, instead of three, as before. The children were dressed in a calmer atmosphere, and became more independent. They assisted in dressing themselves, feeling that their help was really needed. It had been customary for two nurses to give the children their supper, and for the third nurse to dress them to go to their parents' room. The problem arose of how to manage this with only two nurses. The solution was to give one group their supper a quarter of an hour earlier. One nurse ate with them and prepared them for their parents, while the other nurse was otherwise occupied with the rest, who were dealt with similarly, a little later on. This arrangement not only saved working hands, but also resulted in an important educational accomplishment — the creation of a tranquil atmosphere for children and staff.

Two nurses working with eight children are likely to live a simple, homelike life without tension. They can manage all the work in the house, give the children the necessary care and education, and create a home in which a warm atmosphere prevails, providing a background for experiences that will later be a source of happy childhood memories.

To accomplish such an aim, we must shake off some accepted traditions, examining objectively the organizational possibilities in each place according to its specific circumstances, the age group, its make-up and every child in it. Sometimes we hear stock answers such as, "This is our custom," "Our work cannot be arranged in any other way," etc. — the kind of attitude that springs from traditions (sometimes of very recent origin). Though traditions are generally regarded as cultural achievements, habits should not be idealized simply on the grounds that they have become traditions. What is required is constructive criticism and scientific grounding, as well as knowledge of the experience of others in this field. Whenever a change is considered necessary, and its benefits seem obvious, we should have the boldness to implement it. Many different methods of organization may have to be tried, until the one suitable for a particular case has been found.

Some years ago, discussions were held on the daily routine in summer and winter. The doctors maintained that in winter, the children should benefit from the ultraviolet rays of the sun during the midday hours. The nurses, however, would not agree to a change in the sleeping hours, which had been customarily assigned to that time of day. They argued, "The infant will not be able to stay awake until then. He will fall asleep outside." Despite their opposition, the method was implemented for a trial period, during which they became convinced that it was indeed beneficial for the child, and a suitable change of routine was worked out. Now it is customary for the children to spend the after-dinner hour in winter outside. They play in the sunshine, and then they are washed and put to bed, whereupon they fall asleep immediately. Thus a solution was found at the same time for some of the difficulties that had been common at bedtime.

We must show flexibility in our daily routine. A child should not be transferred from one activity to another simply because "the clock says so." A few minutes must be devoted to preparing the child for the shift. When the time has come for being washed or for meals, the child should not be torn away from his play. Such treatment harms the child and does not instill in him trust in the adult, his educator. It is imperative for the nurse to have the time and the patience to wait until the child has overcome his reluctance to leave whatever he is occupied with, and goes to do willingly what is required of him.

The child's concentration, when it has been aroused by his curiosity, is very important to us. To further his interest and his powers of observation, we must let him linger during a walk and *examine whatever arouses his curiosity*, we must let him *fully absorb his impressions*. On no account should the child be hurried along by the demands of the daily routine. If we follow the sort of strict routine that obliges us to take the children home at fixed times, we are liable to interrupt cruelly the child's impressions and experiences.

Now and then, for example, we take the children for an outing by horse and cart. This is a rich emotional experience for them, filling them with curiosity and the desire to learn and gather new experiences. But, alas, our strict routine follows us relentlessly: suddenly we must turn and rush back. Tension rises; the fear of "We shall not manage in time, we shall be late for bathing and bedtime" persecutes us. The benefit of the morning's outing has been lost.

Occasionally, a child is not ready to eat or sleep when routine demands it. Must he *always* eat and sleep at prescribed times, with *no exceptions* to the rule? Is it impossible to find a way by which a child may now and then do these things *when he is ready and willing,* and not have that considered a sin?

Our principle must be flexibility: let us have a fixed framework, but let it be pliable. Let us create this framework after a thorough examination of the child's needs in every age group, taking into account the possibilities and conditions at our disposal. Regular periods must be allowed for the nurse to perform her *educational* duties, that is, to devote herself exclusively to the children, both indoors and outdoors, and not to be occupied otherwise.

The *center* of the children's house is the child. In our daily contact with the child, we must show *both flexibility and consistency.*

BIBLIOGRAPHY

Bentwich, N.: "The Collective Settlements of Israel." In *A New Way of Life*. London: Shindler and Golomb, 1949.

Bettelheim, B.: "Does Communal Education Work? The Case of the Kibbutz." *Commentary*, February, 1962.

Diamond, S.: "Kibbutz and Shtetl: The History of an Idea." *Social Problems*, Fall 1957, *5*:68-79.

————: "The Kibbutz: Utopia in Crisis." *Dissent*, Fall 1957, *5*:132-40.

Faigin, H.: "Social Behavior of Young Children in the Kibbutz." *Journal of Abnormal and Social Psychology*, 1958, *56*:117-29.

Golan, S.: "Collective Education in the Kibbutz." *American Journal of Orthopsychiatry*, July 1958, *28*:549-56.

————: "Collective Education in the Kibbutz." *Psychiatry*, May 1959, *22*:167-77.

Gruneberg, R.: "Education in the Kibbutz." In *A New Way of Life*. London: Shindler and Golomb, 1949.

Hartog, A. E.: "The Kibbutz as an Economic Unit." *Jewish Communal Settlements in Palestine*, Fall 1945, *3*:21-30.

————: "The Kibbutz as a Social Unit." *Jewish Communal Settlements in Palestine*, Fall 1945, *3*:10-20.

Infield, H.: "The Daily Work Schedule in the Kvutza." In *Cooperative Living in Palestine*. New York: Dryden, 1944.

Irvine, E. E.: "Observations on the Aims and Methods of Child Rearing in Communal Settlements in Israel." *Human Relations*, #3, 1952, *5*:247-75.

Kaffman, M.: "Inquiry into the Behavior of 403 Kibbutz Children." *American Journal of Psychiatry*, February 1961, *117*:No. 8.

————: "Children of the Kibbutz. Clinical Observations." In *Current Psychiatric Therapies*, Vol. III. New York: Grune & Stratton, 1963.

Karpe, R.: "Behavior Research in Collective Settlements in Israel." *American Journal of Orthopsychiatry*, July 1958, *28*:547-48.

Lader, L.: "Family Life in the Kibbutz." In *A New Way of Life.* London: Shindler and Golomb, 1949.

————: "The Road from Buchenwald." *New Republic,* September 20, 1948, *119:*16-19.

Lucas, E.: "Family Life in the Kibbutz." In *A New Way of Life.* London: Shindler and Golomb, 1949.

Luria, Z., Goldwasser, M., Goldwasser, A.: "Response to Transgression in Stories by Israeli Children." *Child Development,* June 1963.

Mohr, G. J.: "A Discussion on Behavior Research in Collectives in Israel." *American Journal of Orthopsychiatry,* 1958, *28:*584-86.

Nagler, S.: "Clinical Observations on Kibbutz Children." *Israel Ann. Psychiatry,* 1963, *1:*201-216.

Orni, E.: "Kvutsa and Kibbutz." In *Forms of Settlement.* World Zionist Organization, 1955.

Rabin, A. I.: "Culture Components as a Significant Factor in Child Development": Symposium 1960—*Kibbutz Adolescents.* Discussion A. I. Rabin's "Kibbutz Adolescents" by Abel, Theodore M. and Diaz-Guerrero, Rogelio. *American Journal of Orthopsychiatry,* July 1961, *XXI:*No. 3.

————: "Attitude of Kibbutz Children to Family and Parents." *American Journal of Orthopsychiatry,* January 1959, *29:* 172-179.

————: "The Israeli Kibbutz (Collective Settlement) as a Laboratory for Testing Psychodynamic Hypotheses." *Psychological Record,* 1957, *7:*111-115.

————: "Kibbutz Children: Research Findings to Date." *Children,* 1958, *5:*179-84.

————: "Personality Maturity of Kibbutz and Non-Kibbutz Children as Reflected in Rorschach Findings." *Journal of Projective Techniques,* 1957, *21:*48-53.

————: "Some Psychosexual Differences Between Kibbutz and Non-Kibbutz Israeli Boys." *Journal of Projective Techniques,* 1958, *22:* 328-32.

Rapaport, D.: "Die Kibbutz-Erziehung und ihre Bedeutung fur die Entwicklungpsychologie." ("Education in the Kibbutz and its Significance for Educational Psychology") *Psyche,* Heidelberg, #6, 1959, *12:*353-66.

————: "The Study of Kibbutz Education and its Bearing on The Theory of Development." *American Journal of Orthopsychiatry,* July 1958, *28:*587-97.

Rettig, S. & Pasamanick, B.: "Some observations on the moral ideology of first and second generation collective and non-collective settlers in Israel." *Social Problems,* 1963, *11:*165-178.

Rosenfeld, E.: "The American Social Scientist in Israel: A Case of Role Conflict." *American Journal of Orthopsychiatry.* July 1958, *28:*563-71.

————: "Institutional Changes in the Kibbutz." *Social Problems,* 1957, *2:*110-36.

Roshwald, M.: "Social Class Structure in a Fluctuating Community: A Study of an Aspect of the Jewish Community in Israel." *British Journal of Sociology,* 1955, *6:*61-70.

Schwartz, R. D.: "Democracy and Collectivism in the Kibbutz." *Social Problems,* 1957, *5:*137-47.

————: "Some Problems of Research in Israeli Settlements." *American Journal of Orthopsychiatry,* July 1958, *28:*572-76.

Spiro, M. E.: "Is the Family Universal?—The Israeli Case." *American Anthropologist,* October 1954, *56:*839-46.

————: *Kibbutz: Venture in Utopia.* Harvard University Press, 1956.

————: "Education in a Communal Village in Israel." *American Journal of Orothopsychiatry,* April 1955, *25:*283-92.

Tauber, E.: *Molding Society to Man.* New York. Bloch Publishing Co., 1955 (5716).

Viteles, H.: "Cooperative Agricultural Settlements in Israel." *Sociology and Social Research,* Jan.-Feb. 1955, *39:*171-76.

Weingarten, M.: *Life in a Kibbutz.* New York: The Reconstructionist Press, 1955.

Winograd, M.: "The Development of the Young Child in a Collective Settlement." *American Journal of Orthopsychiatry,* July 1958, *28:* 557-62.

Wolman, B.: "The Social Development of Israeli Youth." *Jewish Social Studies,* 1949, *11:*283-306.

INDEX OF PARTICIPANTS*

---

*This index is designed to facilitate the reader's finding a specific contribution by any participant. Numerals in **boldface type** indicate *prepared* papers or remarks.

INDEX OF SUBJECTS

repeating and believing in, 207-208
transmission of, 53, 208
Verbalization of ideals, and "life atmosphere," 226
Vocational training, 15

W

Weaning, 106-107
Westermarck, F., 27
Womanpower, 246
Women
  as "minority" in kibbutz, 239
  equalization of opportunities for, 4
  in manual and professional work, 240
  "kitchen-children" role of, 243
  training of, 22
Women Workers' Convention, 331
Women's work
  fields for (kibbutz), 263
  professional opportunities in, (U.S.), 244
Work, satisfaction as necessary to, 361

Y

Youth movement, 243